The Marshall Cavendish
ILLUSTRATED ENCYCLOPEDIA OF
PLANTS
AND
EARTH SCIENCES

The Marshall Cavendish
ILLUSTRATED ENCYCLOPEDIA OF
PLANTS
AND
EARTH SCIENCES

VOLUME EIGHT

EDITOR-IN-CHIEF
Professor David M. Moore

SPECIALIST SUBJECT EDITORS
Professor V. H. Heywood
Botany
Professor A. Hallam
Earth Sciences
Dr S. R. Chant
Botany

ADVISORY EDITORS
Professor W. T. Stearn
Flowering Plants
Dr I. B. K. Richardson
Flowering Plants
Dr Peter Raven
Plant Ecology
Professor Lincoln Constance
Special Consultant

EDITORIAL DIRECTOR
Dr Graham Bateman

Marshall Cavendish
New York · London · Sydney

CONTENTS

Reference Edition Published 1990

Published by:
Marshall Cavendish Corporation
2415 Jerusalem Avenue
Bellmore N.Y. 11710

AN EQUINOX BOOK

Planned and produced by:
Equinox (Oxford) Ltd
Littlegate House
St. Ebbe's Street
Oxford OX1 1SQ
England

Copyright © Equinox (Oxford) Ltd 1988

Library of Congress Cataloging-in-Publication Data
The Encyclopedia of plants and earth sciences.
  Bibliography: p.
  Includes index.
  1. Botany—Dictionaries. 2. Botany, Economic—Dictionaries.
3. Crops—Dictionaries. 4. Angiosperms-Dictionaries. 5. Earth
sciences—Dictionaries. 6. Ecology—Dictionaries. I. Marshall
Cavendish Corporation.
QK7.E53 1988 580'.3'21 87-23927

ISBN 0-86307-901-6 (Set)
ISBN 0-86307-909-1 (Vol 8)

Previous page
*Satellite picture of the Red Sea and Gulf of Aden (see
  p.1000).*

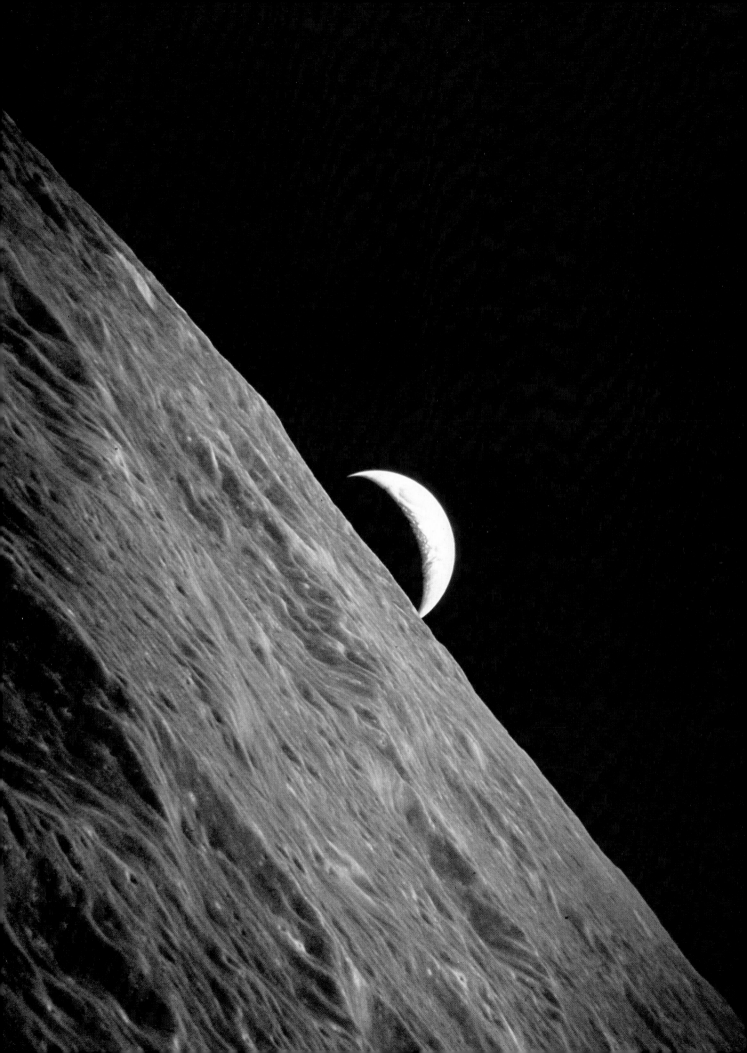

EARTH SCIENCES
Introduction

Everyone has looked from the window of a car or train and seen a mountainside or the meandering course of a river and wondered how it came to be there. Everyone has encountered in the course of a country walk an unusual rock or a cave and wondered about its past history. Some have indulged their wonder further than this by spending an occasional weekend searching for fossils or reading a book on the evolution of the landscape. Some have gone still further to become professional geologists.

Geology has long been a subject of interest to the layman: indeed, contributions made by amateurs to our understanding of the Earth's history have been of great significance during the last two centuries, and there are still many fields of geology in which the amateur can play a major part. And the science of geology itself is currently enjoying a renaissance as new ideas are coming to the fore and old ideas are being discarded.

There are many features of Volumes 8 and 9 that would have been drastically different – perhaps even excluded – had the encyclopedia been published only a few years ago. This is the result of two "revolutions". The first is the elucidation of the process known as plate tectonics. Perhaps as much as fifty per cent of these Volumes relates in some way to this all-important concept, which provides answers to problems posed by paleontologists, stratigraphers and geophysicists for decades. A single example is provided by the unique series of maps in Volume 9 showing the distribution of the Earth's landmasses at various stages during the geological past. The second of these "revolutions" has come about through our exploration of the nearby planets: space probes have given us our first fascinating clues to the geologies of the Moon, Mercury, Venus, Mars and the outer planets.

Because an understanding of the Earth depends on an appreciation of the fruits of recent research, the authors of the articles have been selected from those actively pursuing such research. They have been conscious that technical terminology is unavoidable in the literature of any scientific discipline, but have ensured that specialist terms are thoroughly explained in everyday language, either *in situ* or, where a term occurs frequently, in the glossary. For both these reasons, the editors have been able to include much that has appeared before only in learned journals. Chemical formulae and, occasionally, mathematical notation have been used but in all cases the less scientifically oriented reader will find no difficulty in following the argument simply by reading the surrounding text.

Although each article is self-contained, in cases where a topic mentioned is dealt with more fully in another article this is indicated by a star (*) immediately before the name of that article. Such cross-references, together with the many shorter entries and comprehensive index (Volume 10), permit rapid access to the information contained within this section.

Earthrise seen from lunar orbit.

The Earth and its Neighbors

Planet Earth

Over 4.6 billion years ago, a tenuous, rotating cloud of dust and gas drifting through interstellar space began to contract. The contraction was caused by gravitational attraction between different parts of the cloud with – perhaps – a little push from the explosion of a supernova or the light of surrounding stars. As the cloud contracted, the temperature and pressure near its center increased. A nuclear reaction, fusing hydrogen atoms into helium, was triggered by the high temperature and pressure, and so, close to the center of the cloud, the Sun began to shine. Meanwhile the dust and gas further from the center of the cloud were coalescing to form the planets – among which, of course, was the planet Earth.

This is the nebular hypothesis for the origin of the Solar System, the contracting cloud of dust and gas being termed the solar nebula. In its most general form, the nebular hypothesis is several centuries old, but only very recently have the processes which could have occurred within the nebula been studied in sufficient detail to tell us something of the origin of the Earth.

There are several important features of the Solar System which must be explained by any hypothesis of its origin. First is the regularity of the motion of the planets about the Sun. All the planets, with the exception of Pluto, revolve around the Sun in nearly circular orbits which lie close to a common plane. They also revolve around the Sun in the same direction as the Sun itself rotates. Furthermore, nearly all of the moons of the various planets revolve around the planets in the same direction that the planets rotate – and *that* is in the same direction as the Sun rotates. Although the Sun contains 99.9% of the mass of the Solar System, it possesses only 2% of the rotational energy, or angular momentum. Distinctive chemical differences also exist among the planets of the Solar System. The innermost planets – Mercury, Venus, Earth and Mars – are composed primarily of compounds of iron, magnesium, and silicon: these planets, known as the terrestrial planets, are small and of high density. The outer or Jovian

The nebula M42 in the sword of Orion, one of the largest in the Galaxy. In this nebula, discovered in 1610, astronomers believe that new stars are forming. The cloud of interstellar dust and gas glows because of the cluster of very young, hot stars embedded in its center. The blue color is due mostly to light emitted by ionized oxygen, the red to the presence of hydrogen.

planets – Jupiter, Saturn, Uranus, and Neptune – are large and of low density. Jupiter and Saturn are composed primarily of hydrogen and helium and have an overall chemical composition close to that of the Sun. Uranus and Neptune have a higher density than Jupiter and Saturn and probably consist of carbon, nitrogen and oxygen combined with hydrogen to form solid methane, ammonia, and ice. Pluto's nature is little known.

The nebular hypothesis provides an acceptable explanation for many of the regularities of motion noted above. A rotating cloud of dust and gas will eventually take the form of a disc whose plane is perpendicular to its axis of rotation. Hence, as planetary bodies coalesce from the nebula, they will revolve about the Sun in the same direction and in coplanar, approximately circular orbits. Much more difficult to explain is the observed distribution of rotational energy: unless significant forces act between different parts of the nebula, the rotational energy of each part will be preserved as the nebula contracts, and so most of the rotational energy should reside with the Sun.

Since early theories could offer no explanation of the forces required to redistribute rotational energy, the nebular hypothesis was abandoned in favor of catastrophic theories. These proposed that the close approach to the Sun of another star or perhaps a comet pulled a stream of hot gas from the Sun which on cooling condensed to form the planets. It is now recognized that such a theory provides no better an explanation than does the nebular hypothesis. (The catastrophic theories have the additional difficulty that the hot gases pulled from the Sun would disperse into space before cooling sufficiently to condense.)

The nebular hypothesis regained credibility when several mechanisms were suggested to redistribute angular momentum within the contracting nebula. It has been proposed that large turbulent eddies would form in the nebula causing viscous forces that could be responsible for the redistribution of angular momentum. Another possibility is the interaction of ionized gas in the nebula with the magnetic field generated within the Sun: differential rotation between the Sun's magnetic field and the ionized gas would introduce forces that would tend to make the gas rotate more rapidly.

Astronomers now believe that stars like

our Sun can be observed forming today within our own galaxy. In addition, studies of certain of the closer stars have revealed perturbations in their motion that seem almost certainly to be due to the gravitational effects of planets that are orbiting them: indeed, if the nebular hypothesis is correct, as we believe, then planetary systems should be a very common thing. On the other hand, if the Solar System were formed by a catastrophic event such as the near collision of two stars, this would be an exceedingly rare event, and so planetary systems like our own would be very limited in number. Therefore, understanding how the Solar System formed is important not only to our understanding of the origin of the Earth but also to our understanding of our own place within the universe.

In addition to explaining regularities of motion of the Solar System, the nebular hypothesis must also account for the differences in chemical composition between the terrestrial and the Jovian planets – and also differences occurring within these two groups. It is generally accepted that the composition of the nebula was the same as that of the Sun. It is then necessary to explain how the terrestrial planets have been almost completely depleted in hydrogen and helium, which together make up 99% of the Sun. A reasonable explanation is that temperature varied with position in the cooling nebula. The center, near the Sun, was hot, the edges cooler, perhaps only a few degrees above absolute zero. The chemical compounds that condense as solids from a gas depend on temperature. In that region of the nebula occupied by the terrestrial planets, the temperature was never low enough for hydrogen, helium, and other inert gases to condense, but in the outer regions complete condensation occurred so that Jupiter and Saturn reflect the composition of the nebula.

Gases in the vicinity of the terrestrial planets must have been dispersed from the Solar System, and several mechanisms by which this could have occurred have been suggested. The same magnetic forces on ionized gas in the nebula as were suggested to explain the redistribution of angular momentum could also have pushed ionized gases out of the inner region of the nebula. Again, there is a possibility that, as nuclear reactions began within the Sun, large amounts of mass were lost: the wind set up by this mass loss could have swept the inner region of the nebula clear of uncondensed gases.

The planets formed from the condensed matter of the nebula. Dust grains forming within the cooling nebula collided and adhered to each other, gradually accumulating to form small planetary bodies which themselves collided to form larger bodies. The present planets of the Solar System and the moons which orbit them represent the end stage of this accumulation process. An alternative theory is that the planets could have formed by the direct condensation of gases from the nebula onto the surfaces of growing protoplanets.

These two processes would have each implied a very different form for the early planets: the physical accumulation of dust and planetesimals would result in chemically homogeneous planets, while direct condensation of gases onto planetary cores would give rise to an onion-like layer structure, the composition of successive layers being determined by the sequence in which various solids condensed as the nebula cooled. Refractory oxides of calcium and aluminum would have condensed first, followed by metallic iron-nickel, then the magnesium silicate mineral enstatite and, at still lower temperature, water would condense in the form of ice. As each compound condensed it would be buried in the forming protoplanet and would have no further chance to react with the gases remaining in the nebula. If the solids condensed as small grains of dust, chemical equilibrium could be maintained and continued reaction between the dust and gases would be possible as the nebula cooled.

One line of evidence to distinguish between these two processes comes from ★meteorites. Meteorites are fragments from the breakup of earlier planetary bodies in the Solar System – perhaps from the asteroid belt between Mars and Jupiter. Various types of meteorites have been identified. The major division is into "irons", composed primarily of an alloy of iron-nickel, and "stones", composed primarily of silicate minerals such as the enstatite we have already mentioned.

Meteorites show differing degrees of previous involvement with planetary bodies. One type, the carbonaceous chondrites, are rich in volatile materials and highly homogeneous, suggesting that they have at no time been a part of a planetary body: these meteorites also have elemental abundances very similar to that of the Sun. It is therefore natural to regard the carbonaceous chondrites as samples of the primitive nebular condensate. Since they contain abundant serpentine and troilite, they lend strong support to the equilibrium-condensation hypothesis.

Using an equilibrium-condensation model, reasonable temperatures can be ascribed to the formation of the various planetary bodies in the Solar System according to their distance from the Sun; but it is still hard to explain the loss of hydrogen and helium from Uranus and Neptune. It is important to realize that any model for the formation of the planets from a condensing

nebula is based on limited data and that our ideas on such matters are likely to change as exploration of the Solar System continues.

More specifically, let us consider the conditions under which the Earth would have formed as predicted by such models. In addition to hydrogen, helium and other inert gases, it seems likely that water did not directly condense out of the nebula to form a part of the primitive Earth. This means that the water presently at the surface of the Earth was originally contained in hydrous silicate minerals, like serpentine, amphibole and mica. These minerals lose their water above a temperature of about 450°F (230°C) so that a relatively cool origin for the Earth is indicated. Since the gravitational energy released by infalling planetesimals is large, enough to raise the temperature of the whole Earth by over 18,000 F° (10,000 C°), accumulation must have been slow enough to allow most of this energy to be radiated into space.

As the Earth grew in size by the further accumulation of planetesimals, its interior was heated by the decay of radioactive isotopes. The long-lived isotopes of uranium, thorium and potassium continue to be an important heat source within the Earth today, but other short-lived isotopes could have been important early in its history.

Chemical differentiation of the Earth also occurred. Metallic iron compounds, being heavier than silicates, sank towards the center of the Earth to form what we now recognize as the core: the silicates formed the outer shell, or mantle, of the Earth. As heating continued, some melting of the silicate mantle probably occurred and the less dense liquid fraction rose to the surface to form a primitive crust. As this occurred, water would also have been liberated from the constituents of the mantle to form the oceans.

In the geological record, nothing remains of this early period of the Earth's evolution. The oldest known surface rocks are about 3.7 billion years old, nearly a billion years younger than the formation of the Earth. Although we have no evidence, it seems likely that at this time large-scale convection currents were established in the Earth's solid mantle. These currents carried heat from the interior to the surface and aided in the chemical differentiation described above: such convection currents are thought to be important to many of the geological processes occurring at the surface of the Earth today, and have played a dominant role in establishing the structure of the present-day Earth. They provide the genesis of the process known as ★plate tectonics.

Structure of the Earth. The radius of the Earth is determined by astronomical measurements to be 3950mi (6371km), and the mass can be determined, from the value of gravity measured at the surface, as 60×10^{20} tons (about 5.976×10^{27}g). These values combine to give a mean density for the Earth of 356lb/ft³ (5.2g/cm³).

To study the internal structure of the

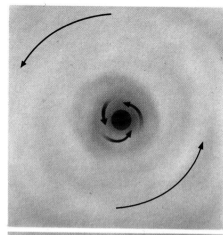

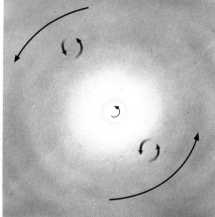

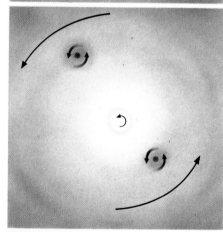

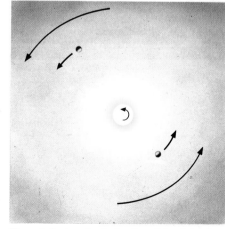

The nebular hypothesis for the origin of the Solar System. As a swirling mass of interstellar gas contracts, the Sun begins to shine: eddies in the outer regions give rise to planets.

Earth in detail, indirect methods must be used since only the upper few kilometres are accessible to direct examination. The Earth's deep interior is studied primarily by seismic methods (see *geophysics).

By studying in the laboratory the velocity of propagation of seismic waves through various representative materials, the relationship between density and seismic velocity can be determined. Observed seismic velocities then allow the variation of density with depth in the Earth to be determined. On the basis of density, the Earth is divided into three major zones: the crust, the mantle and the core. In addition to determining density, seismic-wave velocity places important constraints on the chemical composition of each zone.

The Earth's Crust. The crust is the thin, low-density outermost layer of the Earth. It is separated from the underlying mantle by an abrupt increase in seismic velocity and density termed the Mohorovičić Discontinuity, or Moho. Across the Moho seismic velocity increases from about 14,500mph (6.5km/s) in the crust to 17,850mph (8km/s) in the mantle, and this indicates a density change from 190lb/ft³ (3g/cm³) to 210lb/ft³ (3.3g/cm³). Defined in this way, the crust represents less than 1% of the Earth by volume and less than 0.5% by mass.

Two distinctly different types of crust are recognized: oceanic and continental.

The crust beneath the oceans, comprising 70% of the surface of the Earth, is by far the simpler. It has a fairly uniform thickness of around 3mi (5km) and is composed of *gabbro and *basalt, rocks made up primarily of feldspar, quartz and pyroxene and produced by partial melting of the underlying mantle in the process called seafloor spreading (see *ocean floor; *plate tectonics). All the present oceanic crust has been created within the last two hundred million years. Beneath a superficial layer, called layer 1, of sediments that collect on the ocean bottom, the crust has two distinct layers, layers 2 and 3. The 11,000mph (5km/s) seismic velocity of layer 2 is consistent with it being either highly compacted sediments or a mixture of sediments and basalt: results of deep-sea drilling suggest that it is the latter. Layer 3, with a seismic velocity of 14,500mph (6.5km/s), is probably composed of gabbro, the deep-seated equivalent of basalt.

The continental crust is more complicated in having a more variable thickness and a less well defined structure. In areas which have not undergone recent deformation or mountain-building, continental crust has a thickness of about 22mi (35km), while beneath mountain belts it can be as much as 30mi (50km). In some areas an upper and lower crust can be identified on the basis of a change in seismic velocity and density: this is called the Conrad Discontinuity and occurs at depths of 9–12mi (15–20km). In other areas, the Conrad Discontinuity cannot be observed and density increases more uniformly through the crust.

The upper part of the continental crust is accessible for detailed study, drill holes having penetrated to a depth of 5mi (8km) or so. It has an average density of 180lb/ft³ (2.8g/cm³) and, beneath a superficial layer of sediments, is composed of a granite-like rock type called *granodiorite whose most common minerals are feldspar, quartz, hornblende, and pyroxene. It differs from the gabbro of oceanic crust in being much richer in silicon and poorer in iron and magnesium. The continental crust also contains relatively high concentrations of the incompatible elements, so named because they do not fit into the structure of minerals making up the mantle: the heat-producing elements, *uranium, *thorium and *potassium, are among these incompatible elements, so that the upper continental crust has a high heat productivity compared with other parts of the Earth. This is of very great importance for understanding the flow of heat from the Earth's interior.

The lower continental crust is of higher density, about 190lb/ft³ (3g/cm³), and its composition is a matter of controversy. The similarity of density and seismic velocity suggests that it may have a composition much like oceanic crust; but density and seismic velocity depend not only on chemical compositions but also on the minerals which make up the rock. At high pressures, a phase transformation can occur in which the minerals feldspar and pyroxene react to form garnet and quartz, and this results in the transformation of gabbro into a rock type called *eclogite, which has a very high density (220lb/ft³ (3.4g/cm³)) and seismic velocity primarily due to the presence of *garnet. Laboratory studies suggest that gabbro, although stable in the oceanic crust, would transform to eclogite in the higher-pressure environment of the lower continental crust; and this would exclude the possibility that lower continental crust is similar in composition to oceanic crust. The lower continental crust must be richer in silicon – that is, more like the rock of the upper continental crust. Hopefully, further laboratory study and better seismic data can resolve this uncertainty.

Although oceanic crust is produced by partial melting of the mantle, the origin of continental crust is much more complex. The older view is that most continental crust was produced early in the Earth's history by differentiation of the primitive Earth. We now believe that continental crust may be produced more uniformly with time and that the area of the continents is still growing at the present day. Continental crust is probably not produced by direct partial melting of the mantle, but by remelting oceanic crust.

The Mantle. Beneath the Moho, the mantle extends to a depth of 1800mi (2900km). It is characterized by seismic velocities and densities which generally increase with depth. Based on its density distribution, the mantle has been divided into three parts: the upper mantle, which

extends to a depth of 250mi (400km); the transition zone, which extends from 250 to about 430mi (400–700km); and the lower mantle. Most of the volume and mass of the Earth – approximately 83% and 67% respectively – are contained within the mantle. It is not simply because it makes up so large a part of our planet that study of the mantle is important: the processes that operate within it are responsible for crustal plate movement (see * plate tectonics).

The upper mantle has a density of about 210lb/ft³ (3.3g/cm³) and a P-wave (seismic pressure-wave) velocity of about 17,850mph (8km/s). This density is consistent with it having the composition of *peridotite, a rock composed of the minerals olivine and pyroxene with small amounts of garnet. These minerals are all magnesium-iron silicates, with the exception of garnet which also contains aluminum. Our knowledge of the composition of the upper mantle is supplemented by information from other sources. Basalt, mentioned in connection with oceanic crust, is a very abundant volcanic rock type in the crust – indeed, it is so abundant and widespread that it must be produced by partial melting of the upper mantle. Therefore, by comparing the composition of rocks produced by partial melting of representative source materials to natural basalts, additional constraints on upper mantle composition have been derived. Volcanic eruptions also transport to the surface of the Earth fragments of rock that appear to have been unaltered by their transport in volcanic liquids. These fragments, called xenoliths, come from depths as great as 125mi (200km). Although the details remain controversial, all of these sources suggest an upper mantle composed of peridotite with a ratio of iron to magnesium of about one to ten.

In detail, the seismic-velocity structure of the upper mantle is complex. Under oceanic and some continental areas, the velocity of seismic waves decreases with depth in the uppermost 60mi (100km). This variation gives rise to a zone of low velocity about 60mi thick at the base of which seismic velocity again increases with depth. In the low-velocity zone, seismic waves are also more strongly attenuated than in the rest of the mantle. Lateral inhomogeneity also exists in the upper mantle since a low-velocity zone is not detected under some continental areas.

In the transition zone several abrupt increases of seismic velocity with depth are observed. The first of these occurs at a depth of about 250mi (400km) and corresponds to a phase transition in which the molecular structure of *olivine, under increased pressure, changes to a denser form called *spinel: unlike the case of the velocity discontinuity at the crust/mantle boundary, such a phase transition does not involve differences in chemical composition but only a spatial rearrangement of the atoms in the silicate structure. A further distinct velocity increase, again probably

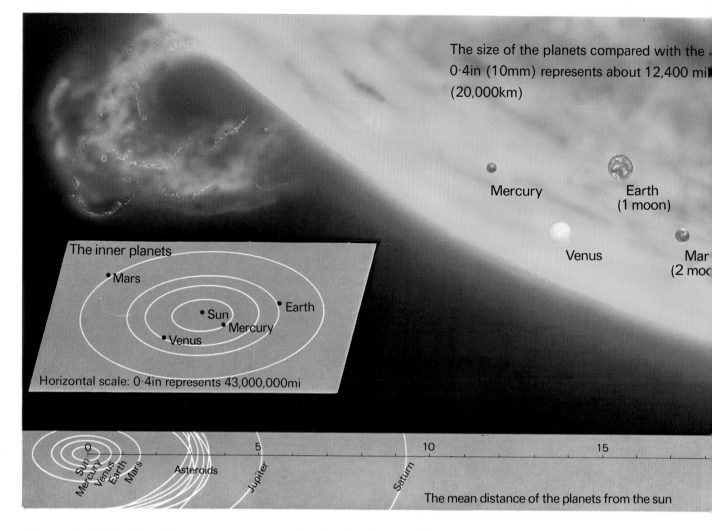

The size of the planets compared with the
0·4in (10mm) represents about 12,400 mi
(20,000km)

Mercury   Earth
             (1 moon)

Venus   Mar
             (2 mod

The inner planets

• Mars

• Sun
• Mercury   • Earth

• Venus

Horizontal scale: 0·4in represents 43,000,000mi

Sun
Mercury
Venus
Earth
Mars
Asteroids   Jupiter   Saturn

0   5   10   15

The mean distance of the planets from the sun

The scale of the Solar System. The nearest star, α Centauri, is about 25,501 thousand million mi (41,040 thousand million km) from the Sun: to the scale of the lower part of this diagram it would be some 1.9mi (3km) distant from the Sun.

caused by a phase transition, occurs at a depth of about 400mi (650km). This could correspond to the breakdown of silicate minerals into their component oxides. For example, olivine (Mg_2SiO_4) breaks down into periclase (MgO) and stishovite (SiO_2) with about a 10% increase in density. Such a phase transition would seem to account for the density increase in the lower transition zone. However, density is also sensitive to the relative proportions of iron and magnesium, so that part of the density increase could be due to an increase in iron relative to magnesium, although this does not seem to be required by the available seismic data. As in the upper mantle, there is evidence of lateral inhomogeneity in that the 400mi velocity discontinuity is not observed under all areas of the Earth's surface. The reasons for this are not clear and may be related only to the difficulty of observing the velocity discontinuity in seismic data which are influenced by shallower crustal inhomogeneities.

In the lower mantle, seismic velocity and density increase uniformly with depth all the way to the core-mantle boundary. The data are consistent with a composition of mixed oxides having the same bulk composition as the upper mantle, density increasing primarily due to the compression caused by increasing pressure with depth. Again, some compositional variations could occur, but this has not yet been shown.

The class of ★meteorites called chondrites has also influenced our thinking on the overall composition of the mantle. These meteorites, comprising 90% of the stony meteorites, are thought to have evolved from primordial condensate in the interior of small protoplanets perhaps broken up by collisions early in the evolution of the Solar System. The mineralogy of the chondrites – 46% olivine, 25% pyroxene, 11% feldspar, and 12% iron-nickel – is consistent with what we know of the mantle from other sources, the only difference being the metallic iron-nickel, which segregated from the mantle to form the core.

The Core of the Earth. The core extends from the base of the mantle to the center of the Earth, and contains 16% of the volume and 32% of the mass of the Earth. It is metallic.

The core is in two parts. The outer core does not transmit shear waves and so must be liquid; the inner core, having a radius of 755mi (1220km), is solid and is thought to be composed of an iron-nickel alloy similar to that found in meteorites. It has a density in the range of 510–770lb/ft³ (8–12g/cm³),

which is consistent with the measured density of iron-nickel extrapolated to the pressures of over 4 million atmospheres found in the core: when combined with crust- and mantle-densities, our figures for the core give the correct average density for the Earth as a whole.

The composition of the outer core is controversial. It has a density too low to be a pure iron-nickel melt, so some lighter element must be mixed in with the iron-nickel. The element silicon has been considered most likely, though sulfur has been suggested as another possibility. This difference could be significant since, if sulfur is the light element in the outer core, the formation of compounds of potassium and sulfur could mean that a significant fraction of the Earth's potassium is in the core. Since radioactive potassium is an important heat-producing element, this could seriously influence our ideas about temperatures within the Earth.

Internal Temperatures. We know the Earth's internal temperatures only approximately. Once again, the most direct information is available for shallow depths – the crust and uppermost mantle. Many measurements of heat-flow from the interior have been made at the Earth's surface, the temperature within the upper half mile or so being measured in drill holes. If the physical properties and heat

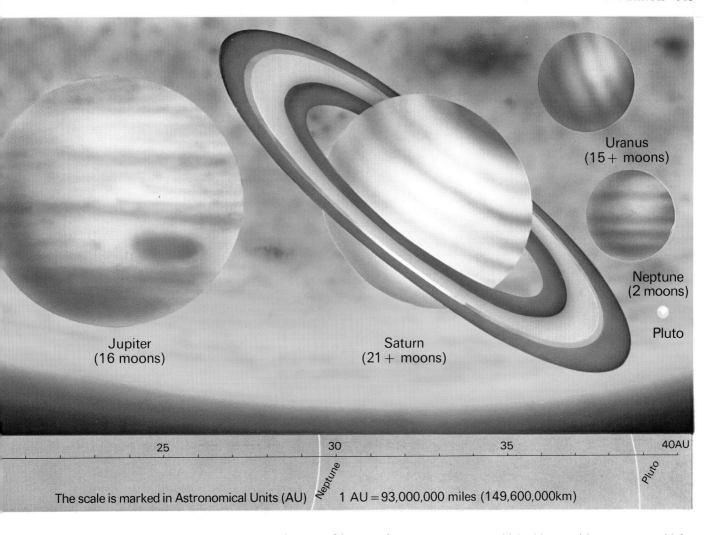

Uranus
(15 + moons)

Neptune
(2 moons)

Pluto

Jupiter
(16 moons)

Saturn
(21 + moons)

25   30   35   40AU

Neptune   Pluto

The scale is marked in Astronomical Units (AU)   1 AU = 93,000,000 miles (149,600,000km)

productivity of crustal rock can be measured or inferred, the observed temperature can be extrapolated to greater depth. As measured in this way, temperature in continental areas rises by about 87F° for each mile of depth (30C°/km). This is an average, since measured values range from 29F°/mi (10C°/km) in some areas to over 290F°/mi (100C°/km) in others.

In interpreting the observed heat-flow, it is helpful to recognize several sources of heat. One source, already mentioned, is the high concentration of heat-producing isotopes in the crust. A second source is the heat of formation of the crust: since crustal rock is produced by melting it forms at a high temperature and cools with time. A third source is the heat supplied to the crust and upper mantle from deeper within the Earth. The relative importances of these different sources of heat differ between oceanic and continental areas. Oceanic crust is younger, thinner, and has lower concentrations of heat-producing elements than has continental crust. In oceanic areas almost all the heat-flow can be attributed to cooling of the crust and underlying mantle. In continental areas heat production by radioactive decay and heat supplied from the interior of the Earth are of approximately equal magnitude: in older continental crust, the remaining heat of formation is small. In both oceanic and continental

areas, the rate of increase in temperature with depth decreases significantly with increasing depth.

The xenoliths carried to the surface of the Earth in volcanic liquids provide information on temperatures to depths of about 125mi (200km). From laboratory studies of the composition of various coexisting minerals over a range of temperatures and pressures, the pressure and temperature conditions under which the minerals composing the xenoliths formed can be determined. Temperatures determined in this way agree with extrapolations of surface heat-flow measurements in predicting a temperature of 1800°F (1000°C) at a depth of 95mi (150km).

In the deeper mantle, temperature can be estimated only by indirect methods. The electrical conductivity of mantle rock is sensitively related to temperature: using measurements of the temporal variation of natural magnetic fields, conductivity can be determined as a function of depth, and temperature can then be inferred from conductivity. Unfortunately, conductivity also depends on other variables such as composition, and so this method does not give very accurate results. The phase transitions discussed earlier, particularly that of olivine transforming to a spinel structure, occur at a particular temperature which depends on pressure. Therefore, the depth

at which this transition occurs could be used to measure temperature at that depth. Again uncertainty arises because the depth at which the phase transition occurs is not known accurately and because the temperature at which the phase transition occurs depends on composition.

Seismic data indicate that the mantle is solid, so that the melting temperature is nowhere exceeded: melting temperature then provides an upper limit on temperatures in the mantle. Extrapolating measured melting temperatures to the high-pressure conditions of the deep mantle indicates an upper limit on melting temperature of about 9000°F (5000°C) at the core/mantle boundary. The complex structure of the upper mantle may be related to incipient melting. One explanation of the low-velocity zone is the partial melting of silicate minerals in the presence of small amounts of water and carbon dioxide. If this is correct, then temperatures within the low-velocity zone must be about 2000°F (1100°C).

Thus our knowledge of temperatures within the Earth, particularly in the deep interior, is very meager. It is an area of study in which much more information is needed if we are to fully understand the present structure of the Earth and how this structure may have evolved through time.

EMP

The Moon

On July 20, 1969, men from Earth stood for the first time on the surface of an almost unknown planetary body, the Moon.

The successful landing of Apollo 11 at Tranquillity Base marked the culmination of over ten years of unmanned lunar exploration by remote-controlled orbiting, hard-landing and soft-landing spacecraft from the USA and the USSR. It also signalled the beginning of an extensive scientific study of the rocks and minerals, the interior, and the surface environment of the Moon; the new science of lunar geology.

About a hundred and fifty scientists from laboratories throughout the world were selected to conduct a wide range of geological, chemical, physical and biological tests on the rocks returned to Earth, and to design measuring instruments for the astronauts to place on critical areas of the Moon's surface. These scientific studies have led to a host of new discoveries, not only about the Moon but also about its relationship to the Earth and to other planets. Most dramatic of all was the discovery that the Moon was born at the same time as the Earth, about 4600 million years ago.

Such studies will continue for many more years, as each discovery poses new problems to be solved. For example, only recently has it been discovered that lunar crystals contain a fission-track record of particles from the Sun that have bombar-

Apollo-17 astronaut Schmitt collects rocks from the moon's boulder-strewn, dusty surface.

ded the Moon for thousands of millions of years. The Earth's atmosphere has prevented such particles, cosmic rays, from leaving such a record here of variations in the Sun's activity through time. Another recent discovery is that the surface of *Mercury seems much like that of the Moon, and that Moon-like craters are abundant also on *Mars. It will be decades before these planets can be visited by Man, but by then the Moon should be well understood.

The first astronauts to land on the Moon, Armstrong and Aldrin, collected 48lb (22kg) of rocks. Since then, another five

Apollo lunar missions have taken place, the last of the series being the Apollo 17 landing on December 11 1972.. The total rock collected amounts of 845lb (382kg) plus 4.6oz (0.13kg) from the two unmanned Russian Luna missions. At the Lunar Receiving Laboratory in Houston, USA, are catalogued 35,600 small pieces of the Moon.

The first aim of the researchers has been to discover whether any forms of life exist or have existed on the Moon. The most sophisticated methods of biological analysis currently possible have failed to reveal even the most primitive life-forms or their molecular precursors. Secondly, the composition of the Moon and its evolutionary history needed to be known, and particularly the nature of the processes that have pocked its surface with the huge craters visible through terrestrial telescopes. Thirdly, we needed to know more about how the Moon originated, since it is the satellite of our planet and since it is the closest of the 55 or so known moons in the Solar System. Some people thought that we also needed to know whether precious minerals existed on the Moon, but geologists already knew that the processes that operate on Earth to concentrate minerals of economic importance were unlikely to have operated on the Moon; also, economics tells us that even diamonds would be barely worth collecting in any abundance from a world 240,000mi (385,000km) from Earth. After all, the short Apollo program alone cost around $25,000 million (£14,000 million).

General Physical Properties. Our satellite is about a quarter of the Earth's size and one eightieth of its mass. Hence its gravity is only a sixth of Earth's; and so the Moon was unable to retain its original gases, such as water vapor and oxygen, to form an atmosphere and oceans.

The average density of the Moon is only 215lb/ft³ (3.34g/cm³) compared with Earth's 356lb/ft³ (5.52g/cm³), so it cannot have a dense metallic core of any appreciable size. In fact, its density is similar to that of the Earth's mantle and higher than that of the Earth's crust. The pressure at the center is about 50kb and the temperature about 2200°F (1200°C), compared with 300kb and 7600°F (4200°C) for the Earth.

The Moon spins on its axis once a month (Earth time), so most parts of its surface are heated and illuminated by the Sun's rays for around 15 days, and then are in cold darkness for the next 15 days or so. The temperature changes between lunar day and night are extreme by Earth standards, because the Moon's atmosphere, being virtually a vacuum, provides little protection from the direct heat of the Sun, and little insulation from the ultracold of space. Temperature ranges from 230°F (110°C) at the height of the lunar day to −275°F (−170°C) in the lunar night are typical, and result in *erosion of rock to dust through cracking by thermal expansion and contraction. The only other erosional agent is the solar wind, the constant stream of protons from the Sun, which has given melted, glassy skins to the rocks.

The Moon moves round the Earth in an elliptical path, so that it is illuminated to varying degrees by the Sun as viewed from Earth. This path, like the axial spin, also takes a month, and from our point of view the Moon varies within the month from being fully illuminated (full moon), through partial (crescent moon) to non-illumination (new moon). A feature arising from the mechanics of this coupled Earth-Moon system, where each body exerts a pull on the other, is the tidal effect. As noted above, the Moon spins round its axis at the same rate as it rotates round the Earth. The result is that the Moon always presents approximately the same face to the Earth.

Before leaving the subject of the Moon's illumination it may be mentioned that "moonlight" is simply a reflection of sunlight from the Moon's surface. But the degree of reflection, the albedo, varies across the face of the Moon so that some areas appear light, and other areas dark. The early astronomers, starting with Galileo who, in 1610, first used a telescope to observe lunar surface features, called the dark areas "*maria*" (singular *mare*), because they looked like seas, and the light areas "*terrae*", or lands.

We now know that the "land" areas (or highlands) are the primitive Moon's crust, and that the maria are meteorite-excavated basins filled with dark-colored volcanic lavas. But, more than that, we now know the chemical compositions, ages, and evolutionary history of those huge rock masses.

Surface Features. The near face of the Moon, as observed by the naked eye or through a telescope, consists of whitish and blackish areas nowadays referred to as the highlands and the maria, respectively. In contrast, the far side is composed almost entirely of highlands with only a few small maria. This asymmetry is also a characteristic of Mars and Mercury and the reasons for it are not yet understood.

The highlands once seemed to resemble terrestrial mountain belts and were named accordingly. The topography is not rugged by terrestrial standards but the Apennines range, for example, is 400mi (650km) long and includes about 3000 prominent peaks with gentle slopes, the highest being Leibnitz at 20,000ft (6km) above base level. It is now known that these mountain ranges were not produced by the mountain-building processes we know on Earth, but are simply huge piles of rock debris encircling the craters and maria basins. The debris consists of jumbled boulders and rock dust thrown from craters as they were formed by the impact of giant meteorites. The heat generated by the impacts resulted in some rock melting, so that the debris is usually welded into *breccias.

The maria prominent on the near face are really huge craters now filled with volcanic *lavas. The largest, Mare Imbrium, is 775mi (1250km) in diameter.

There must have been a deluge of huge meteorites early in the Moon's history, Mare Tranquillitatis being excavated early on. It was followed by 16 more until the culmination of Mare Imbrium and Mare Orientale about 3900 million years ago. During the next 700 million years, these basins were filled with volcanic lava. Meteorites have continued to bombard the Moon's surface, so that the older lava-filled basins are more damaged than the younger ones: a glance at a photograph of the Moon shows clearly the younger darker areas as being less scarred than are the older. Close-up photographs of any part of the lunar surface show an abundance of small pits, indicating meteoritic and micro-meteoritic bombardment of virtually every part of the surface, including the lava flows. As a result, the surface sampled by the astronauts is a boulder- and dust-strewn terrain. The debris blanket is given the name "regolith" and is, on average, 50ft (15m) thick.

Outside the 17 lava-filled basins, over 300,000 craters are significant enough to have been named. Two prominent examples are Tycho and Copernicus, each about 55mi (90km) in diameter. They are prominent because each is surrounded by a ray system consisting of streaks of light-colored rock radiating from the crater. The streaks are of highland-rock debris, excavated so recently that the rays have not yet been darkened either by the glassy skins resulting from long periods of cosmic-ray bombardment or by a covering of volcanic lava. These craters are about 900 millions years old, which is young by Moon-activity standards.

Most craters possess central peaks and this feature, together with measurements of depth/diameter ratios, indicates that they were produced by impacts rather than by volcanic processes. However, some volcanic features on the Moon have a few associated craters of a non-impact origin. These features, known as rilles, are shallow, often sinuous, valleys that cut across the maria. They are commonly more than 3mi (5km) wide and may be hundreds of kilometres long. Once they were thought to be ancient river channels but such water bodies are now discounted and the rilles are more closely comparable with lava channels such as those in Idaho and Iceland. There, where the lava has flowed through subterranean tubes, later collapse of the upper skin has given rise to rille features. The Hyginus rille on the Moon is peppered along its length with small craters, which must be due to circular collapse-depressions of volcanic origin.

The surface features of the Moon can thus be attributed to only two major processes: impacts of meteorites from outside the Moon (exogenic), and *vulcanicity induced by melting of the interior of the Moon (endogenic). We should therefore expect to find only two rock groups, meteorite debris and crystallized Moon lavas. Although this is broadly true, the samples returned to Earth are much more complex.

Meteorite debris amounts to only about 2 %
of the sampled regolith, which suggests that
the huge crater-producing meteorites were
mostly vaporized on impact. Volcanic lavas
of various ages are abundant amongst the
rock samples, but so also are pale-colored
rocks from the highlands that yield evidence of such ancient ages that they have
been recognized as broken-up primitive
lunar crust. The most complex of all are the
breccias, made up of rock fragments representative of numerous cratering events
throughout the Moon's history.

Moon Rocks and Minerals. From each
landing site the Apollo astronauts hammered fragments from large boulders, collected a host of smaller rocks and scooped
samples of the regolith gravel and dust. Yet
it could be argued that the sampled population is too small to provide sure knowledge of the composition of the Moon in its
entirety. This criticism would be valid also
for Earth. But, firstly, the Moon is fairly
simple in its variety of rock units; secondly,
continued meteorite impacting has redistributed rock debris around the Moon's
surface with great ease due to the low force

Crater Schmidt on the western edge of the Mare
Tranquillitatis is some 7mi (4.5km) across.

Looking into Tsiolkovsky crater on the far side of the
Moon. A lava pool has flooded the adjacent valleys
and encircled the central mountain peak. This crater-
strewn terrain contrasts strongly with the comparative evenness of the lunar maria.

of gravity; thirdly, analyzing instruments operated by the third astronaut of each mission during numerous orbits of the Moon's surface were carried by the later Apollo Command Modules: the measurements were crude but could be refined by comparison with the properties of the collected rocks.

A typical example of a scooped sample is not a dust or soil, but consists of variously sized fragments of rock. Such samples were separated into hundreds of individual fragments, and each fragment analyzed for its mineral and chemical composition. Such properties as isotopic ages, cosmic-ray damage, magnetism or density, were also measured; while a few samples were treated at high temperatures and pressures in order to establish the conditions under which they were formed. Although such fragment samples contained a host of different rock types redistributed from distant parts of the Moon, every set of landing-site samples had a characteristic unique to that site, indicating that the local bedrock had contributed most of the material of which they are composed. This was important because, for example, it permitted the dating of each visited maria lava site. The fragment samples were supplemented by larger pieces of rock, 2.5in (10cm) or so across, from which pieces could be separated for various analytical programmes, and the whole data then correlated. This large-rock sampling was unique to the manned Apollo missions, and could not be achieved on the unmanned Luna missions.

The volcanic lavas were soon shown to be of basalts similar to those erupted from Earth volcanoes: they were molten around 2200°F (1200°C). They vary from an older group, rich in *titanium-bearing minerals, to a younger group low in these minerals. All consist predominantly of the minerals *plagioclase, *pyroxene, and variable amounts of *ilmenite. Other common minerals are *olivine and *cristobalite. Important accessory minerals include metallic iron-nickel, which indicates crystallization under strongly reducing conditions in the absence of an oxygen atmosphere. Earth minerals notably absent are those, such as *hematite or *mica, containing ferric iron or hydroxyl (OH) ions that require the presence of free oxygen or water. In all, about forty mineral species have been recognized and analyzed from various types of basalt. These include minerals not found on Earth, occurring as tiny crystals that can be analyzed only by use of a special instrument, the electron microprobe. One such mineral, named armalcolite (for Armstrong, Aldrin and Collins), is a titanium-rich iron oxide. Another, named tranquillityite, is rich in zirconium, uranium and rare earth elements. At least five other minerals related to tranquillityite have since been discovered. Patches of granitic glass occur alongside these rare minerals, as the last material to solidify within the basalts.

The light-colored rocks from the high-

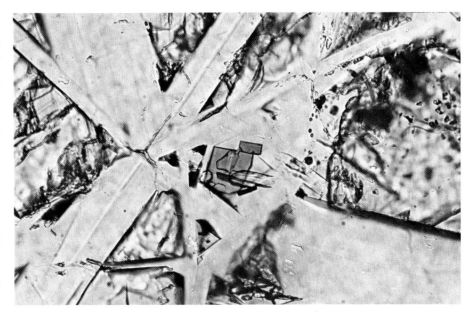
A color photomicrograph of tranquillityite, a mineral discovered only on the Moon.

lands are very different from the dark maria basalts. They are rich in plagioclase feldspar, and their average density (2.9) is much lower than that of the basalts (3.4). Several fragments are of pure feldspar (anorthosite), but the bulk composition of the highlands is believed to be that of a pyroxene-bearing, gabbroic anorthosite. These rocks are older than the maria basalts, and have been deformed by meteorite impacting. Because the feldspar is white, they impart the pale color to the highlands as seen from Earth.

Most of the highlands rocks forming the mountain belts that encircle the basalt basins are layers of breccia comprising welded rock fragments. Rock fragments in the breccia, and loose in the regolith, have sometimes been converted to glass beads by impact melting. Although the fragments are chiefly of gabbroic anorthosite and anorthosite, some are of feldspathic basalt, of plutonic rocks rich in olivine and pyroxene (dunite and norite), and more rarely of granitic rocks. The story here is a complex but intriguing one. The breccias are revealing to us the relics of an original lunar crust that formed and was reconstituted several times during violent meteoritic bombardment in the period 4600–3900 million years ago.

Isotopic Ages and Chemical Properties. All the known *elements have been sought in the Moon rocks, and their relative abundances used both to trace the Moon's evolution and for comparison with the Earth's geochemical processes.

The measurements of certain isotopic ratios provide an accurate means of determining the ages of rocks. In particular, the ratio of strontium-87 (produced by radioactive decay of rubidium-87) to common strontium-86 is of value in lunar chronology. The age of the Moon has thus been shown to be about 4600 million years (expressed as 4.6AE, where 1 aeon = 10^9 years). This is the age attributed to the Earth and other planets. The ages of major

impact basins range from 4.6 to 3.9AE. The volcanic lavas were erupted from about 3.8AE to 3.15AE. Since then, the Moon has been a "dead" planetary body, except for continued meteorite cratering, including the Copernicus rayed crater at about 0.9AE.

The Moon's basalt lavas originated by partial melting of the Moon's upper mantle of *peridotite, through heat produced by radioactive decay of elements such as uranium, thorium and potassium. Such heating took about 700 million years to develop to the point of rock melting, followed by a further 700 million years during which the heat-producing elements were transported in the lavas to the Moon's surface. The lava compositions thus reflect the composition of the upper mantle from which they were derived by partial melting.

The surprise in the basalt compositions is that when they are compared with Earth basalts, or with average Solar-System compositions as derived from meteorite analyses, they are found to be depleted in certain chemical elements – broadly, the volatile elements such as sodium and chlorine, and those elements that accompany iron and sulfur, such as nickel, cobalt, platinum and zinc. They are enriched in refractory elements such as uranium, titanium and the rare earths.

The low oxidation states result in some low-valency elements such as divalent europium, which can then enter feldspar minerals in abundance. Using this feature, geochemists have shown that the Moon's feldspathic crust (rich in europium) formed as a low-density, complementary crystal fraction to the underlying basalt source layers (low in europium).

Physical Measurements. One of the Apollo Command Module instruments measured gravity profiles and explained the mass concentrations in the maria basins as due to deep, solidified lava lakes in old crater basins. The existence of such mass anomalies for over 3000 million years im-

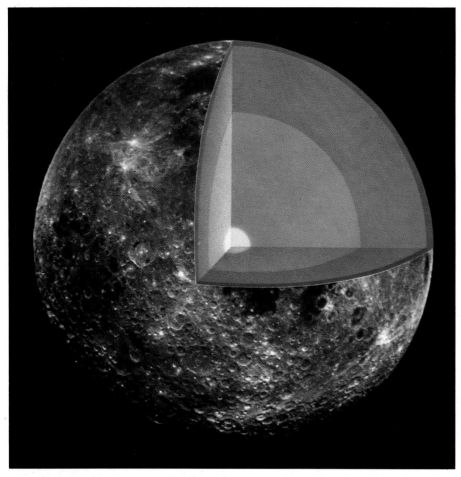

A section through the moon. Central is an irregularly shaped asthenosphere, with a radius of about 700mi (about 1100km), which may contain a core. Above this is the mantle, with a radius around 1000mi (about 1680km), and the crust, which is some 37mi (60km) thick. The surface crust is of two types: primitive anorthositic lunar crust and more recent basalt lavas.

plies a thick, rigid lithosphere. The X-ray spectrometer mapped aluminum:silicon ratios and delineated the extent of· the aluminous highlands. The gamma-ray spectrometer mapped the distribution of radioactive, heat-producing elements.

Instruments placed on the surface at each landing site measured moonquakes, heat-flow from the interior, cosmic-ray compositions and magnetic field. The strength of the magnetic field is now about one-thousandth of that of the Earth, but the lavas show that 3500 million years ago they crystallized in a stronger magnetic field, around 1/20th of the Earth's. One reason could be that the Moon's metallic core was liquid, so working rather like a dynamo, whereas now it is solid.

The seismometers measured the travel speeds of natural and artificially induced moonquake vibrations, and thus the internal structure of the Moon. There is a distinct boundary between the crust and the upper mantle, and a deeper, semi-liquid "asthenosphere" that incorporates a zone that is possibly a metallic core. The main difference from Earth is that the Moon's rigid "lithosphere" is now very thick, (about 370mi (600km)), which explains the absence of orogeny and young volcanism.

Origin and Evolution of the Moon. About 4600 million years ago, the Earth and

Moon formed as planetary bodies. The Moon is too ancient to have been drawn from the Earth, except while both were forming; and even this is unlikely because of the bulk chemical differences. Alternatively, the Moon could have been captured by the Earth, but if so it should have a primitive composition related to Solar-System compositions, whereas it is in fact strongly differentiated in terms of several chemical elements.

Most probably, the Moon formed from a dense atmosphere, generated by the high temperatures of solid-particle accretion at the surface of the proto-Earth. This atmosphere then condensed to give a ring of small, solid objects around the Earth, like Saturn's rings. As the objects (planetesimals) collided and grew, so the Moon formed. It lost the volatile elements to outer space, and probably the metal-associated elements to its interior.

Shortly after formation, the outer 370mi (600km) or so of the Moon melted through accretional energy. Feldspar crystals of low density floated to give a light-colored, aluminous crust about 37.5mi (60km) thick. Denser minerals such as olivine and pyroxene sank from the molten liquid. Between 4.6AE and 3.9AE, the crust was pulverized by meteorites, and feldspathic lavas were generated as impact melts. Large basins

such as Mare Imbrium developed, probably due to impacting by those large planetesimals that were still circling the Earth. Around 3.8AE ago, radioactive heating of the denser mineral layers underlying the crust gave rise to partial-melt liquids which flooded the maria as basalt lava flows. About 3.2AE ago, volcanic activity ceased but, because of the absence of an atmosphere, meteorites continued to bombard the Moon's surface – as they still do.

Conclusions. We now know a great deal about a part of our Solar System outside the Earth. On Earth, it is not possible to examine parts of the primitive crust, because Precambrian rocks older than about 3000 million years occur only as isolated patches of one-time sedimentary and igneous rocks that have suffered several stages of metamorphic deformation and recrystallization. In contrast, the Moon's surface is covered by the feldspathic crust that crystallized at the very beginning of the Moon's formation, together with still-fresh lavas that formed as long ago as 3800 million years. When we look at the Moon, we are looking at a sort of cinematic "still", preserved throughout the ages, of a planet in its early stages of evolution. Because it was small by Earth standards, and therefore could not retain water and other volatile components, and because it was initially richer in elements such as aluminum, it has a feldspathic crust that is probably not a safe guide to what the Earth's primitive crust was like – but the crust of Mercury, for example, may turn out to be more like that of the Moon.

A small accident of size prevented the Moon from retaining water and oxygen, and therefore from providing an environment in which life could develop and evolve. For 4600 million years, our nearest neighbor and relative has moved with us through space but has been unaffected by the dramatic developments of Earth history.

At least, that was so until 1969.

That was the year in which Man had evolved to the level at which he could move from Earth to another planetary body for the first time. He had opened a new gate of knowledge, not only by walking upon the Moon, but also by beginning to find answers to its ancient mysteries.   GMB

Mercury

Almost all of our knowledge regarding the geology of Mercury was acquired in a matter of hours, on March 29 1974, when the Mariner 10 spacecraft swept by the innermost planet of our Solar System. The photographs it took revealed a cratered surface very similar to that of the *Moon. Additional information, acquired as Mariner 10 circled the Sun and twice more passed close to Mercury, further confirmed the Moon-like appearance.

Mercury's average distance from the Sun is 35.9 million mi (57.9 million km). At closest approach to the Earth, Mercury is

Mariner-10 photograph of Mercury, taken on September 21 1974, showing typical craters formed by the impact of meteorites, and a compressional ridge extending from upper left to lower right which is more than 185mi (300km) long.

about 50 million mi (80 million km) distant from us. Its diameter is 3025mi (4880km), slightly less than half that of the Earth. Its average density is $348lb/ft^3$ ($5.4g/cm^3$), approximately the same as the Earth's.

Mercury rotates relatively slowly, in about 58.7 days, and its period of revolution about the Sun is 88 days. These periods couple in such a way that certain longitudes are more frequently directly beneath the Sun when the planet is at its closest approach (perihelion). For this reason, even though the spin axis is approximately vertical to the orbital plane, places on Mercury experience seasonal changes in the amount of light and heat they receive.

Approximately one hemisphere of the planet was photographed by Mariner 10. The dominant features are meteoritic craters which, in the absence of atmospheric *erosion, have retained many of their original impact features. Deposits of material ejected from the craters, secondary craters

and bright rays and haloes are well preserved. Because the Mercurian gravitational field is stronger than that of the Moon, secondary craters and ejecta deposits tend to occur closer to the primary crater. Wall slumping owing to the greater gravity has led to shallower crater depths.

The large craters display central peaks and rings, as do lunar craters. At still larger diameters, several basins have been observed. Most prominent is the Caloris basin, 900mi (1400km) across: associated ejecta deposits are widespread over an entire hemisphere.

There are on Mercury smooth plains materials which occur both between craters and superimposed over subjacent cratered terrain. These may record widespread volcanic flooding, perhaps at the same time as the flooding of the lunar maria. However, in the absence of clear morphological evidence for volcanic activity, this interpretation can be no more than speculative. Plains materials might also form by emplacement of partially molten material ejected from large craters and basins.

Lobate scarps, ranging in length from 12.5 to 300mi (20–500km) and in height from a thousand feet to 5mi, are visible in

Mariner 10 pictures. They are generally interpreted as compressional ridges, perhaps formed during an early stage of crustal shortening.

Photometric measurements carried out with the Mariner 10 imaging system suggest that Mercury is covered with a dark, fine-grained soil similar to the lunar regolith. Where the terrain is heavily cratered it is somewhat brighter than are the lunar highlands. The dark smooth plains have color and albedo suggesting basaltic composition.   TAM

Venus

Venus has 0.815 times the mass of the Earth, and the solid part of the planet has a radius of 3770mi (6070km). It rotates once every 243 days, but in a direction opposite to that of the other terrestrial planets: the lack of a magnetic field may be a consequence of the slow rotation.

In spite of space research, the composition of Venus' bright clouds – found up to 43mi (70km) above the surface – is unknown. The clouds preclude remote viewing of the surface, where the pressure

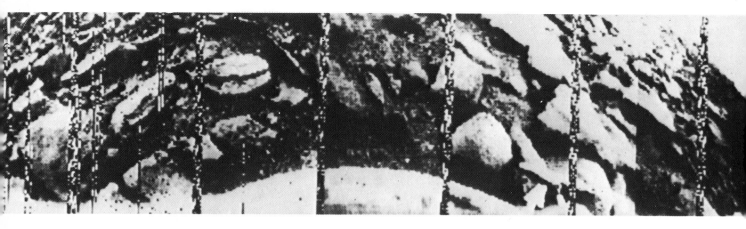

Panorama of the Venusian surface as seen on October 22 1975 from the Soviet soft-landing spacecraft Venera 9. Prior to the taking of this photograph it had been thought that Venus' surface would be sandy due to extreme erosion and weathering; but, as can be seen, angular rocks are in fact present. (The white arc at lower center is part of the spacecraft.)

can attain more than 90 atmospheres and the temperature is nearly everywhere around 900°F (480°C): this is too hot to support any known form of life. In addition, some 96% of the atmosphere is carbon dioxide; and the upper atmosphere also contains traces of the poisonous gas carbon monoxide and the corrosive agents hydrochloric acid and sulfuric acid. Perhaps only a few tenths of one per cent of the lower atmosphere (analyzed from the Soviet Veneras 4, 5 and 6) consists of molecular oxygen and water vapor.

It was widely conjectured (largely through interpretations of cloud motions observed using ultraviolet photography) that high winds wore down the rocks of Venus. However, using radar, US astronomers have demonstrated that Venus displays appreciable differences in surface altitude; and the surface panoramas transmitted back to Earth from the Soviet soft-landers Veneras 9 and 10 show a barren landscape that contains both angular and rounded rocks – proof that not all parts of the surface have been reduced by erosional processes to sand. GF

Mars

Among the planets, Mars has always been singled out for speculation: throughout the more than three centuries that it has been observed telescopically, many laymen and scientists have considered the planet to be populated by an alien civilization.

These ideas were fueled by alleged sightings of a network of "man-made" canals, a misconception whose origins lie, oddly, in a mistranslation. The Italian astronomer Giovanni Schiaparelli made a detailed study of the Martian disc in the years 1877–81, and announced that certain of the surface markings could only be interpreted as a network of straight lines, which he named "channels" – in Italian, canali.

Canali was translated into English as "canals", and the excitement began.

In the early part of the 20th century the hypothesis was taken to its ultimate extent by a US astronomer, Percival Lowell, who wrote several best-selling volumes which described in detail how Martian citizens were living on a planet that was becoming progressively more desert-like. In order to husband the dwindling supply of water, canals carried water from the polar caps to the equatorial regions, where the natives lived underground.

Results from several spacecraft which passed by Mars – Mariner 4 in 1965, Mariners 6 and 7 in 1969 – and one spacecraft which orbited Mars – Mariner 9 in 1971 – have demolished such theories and radically changed and enlarged our impressions. The old ideas of Martian canals and civilizations have turned out to be complete fiction. However, Mariner pictures reveal a spectacular landscape, complete with new puzzles which stubbornly resist solution.

The most up-to-date information currently available is that from the US Viking probes 1 and 2, which arrived on Mars in the summer of 1976. After achieving orbital trajectories, the orbiters deployed landers which descended to the surface slowed by parachutes and retrorockets. Shortly afterward began a flood of transmitted data, visual and otherwise, concerning the nature of the red planet. Perhaps the most provocative investigations – in both intent and results – were those seeking microscopic lifeforms in the soil. Analysis by the landers revealed no traces of organic material, and although some of the results have provoked stormy debate it seems unlikely that Mars can support even the most elementary micro-organisms.

General Properties. Moving outward from the Sun, Mars is the next planet encountered after Earth. At the time of closest approach (opposition) the two planets are separated by about 38 million miles (60 million kilometres). The diameter of Mars is 4180mi (6740km), about half that of the Earth. The average density is 251lb/ft³ (3.9g/cm³), compared with 356lb/ft³ (5.52g/cm³) for Earth.

Mars completes one rotation in approximately 24h 37min compared with 24h for

Earth. It takes 687 Earth days (670 Martian days) to complete one revolution about the Sun, so that a Martian year is approximately twice as long as a terrestrial year. Because the equator is at an angle of 24° to the orbital plane, different regions on the planet experience seasonal variations related to periodic changes in the amount of radiation they receive from the Sun. Polar caps of carbon dioxide (CO_2) ice grow and shrink each year.

The surface of Mars, viewed telescopically, shows irregular dark and bright markings of reddish hue. Photometric measurements suggest that the dark material is *basalt and that the reddish color is caused by *weathering of the basalt, resulting in the formation of hydrated iron-oxide minerals (e.g., *goethite). The configuration of dark and bright markings changes seasonally and annually, probably because of wind transport of bright, fine-grained sediment.

The atmosphere of Mars has one hundredth of the density of the Earth's. Carbon dioxide is the chief constituent, with nitrogen and argon making up most of the rest. About 0.3% water vapor is also present.

Physiographic Provinces. Most of what is known regarding the geology of Mars is based on interpretations of pictures acquired via Mariner 9. The first thing that strikes one is the difference between the terrains of the northern and southern hemispheres: cratered terrain appears in the south; smooth, undivided plains in the north. Global elevations show a similar distribution, relatively high in the south and low in the north. The cratered terrain is relatively old, preserving the record of heavy bombardment that occurred in the first few hundred million years of the planet's history. The smooth plains probably represent regions of thin crust that have been fractured from beneath and flooded with volcanic lava and wind-deposited sediments.

Other terrains include the cratered plains. These surfaces have crater densities intermediate between cratered terrain and smooth plains. The materials of cratered plains resemble terrestrial *plateau basalts, and may record volcanic activity that occurred about 3000 million years ago. Hummocky terrain may have formed – in part, at least – by the melting and flowing away of subsurface ground-ice with attendant collapse and *erosion of surface materials.

Distinctive landforms – layered deposits and etched plains – are found in both polar regions. These indicate that the erosional-depositional cycle near the poles differs from that in the equatorial region. The succession of strata in the layered deposits has been attributed to periodic changes in climate, this in turn related to systematic variations in Mars' orbital configuration due to gravitational interaction with other bodies.

Craters. Almost all Martian craters have been formed by meteoritic impact. Crater morphology changes with size: many small craters (0.6mi (1km) in diameter and less) are bowl-shaped, while progressively larger craters show flat floors, central peaks, central-peak rings, and multiple structural rings. The same features are displayed by lunar and Mercurian impact craters.

Erosion has removed the traces of most of the ejecta deposits, the material scattered around the craters by the impacts. Bright haloes and rays, observed around youthful lunar craters, are almost totally absent. Hummocky ejecta deposits have typically been stripped or eroded back to form a narrow annulus close to the crater's upraised rim.

Ages of planetary surfaces can in suitable cases be estimated by measuring the number of craters per unit area. Assuming that all craters are formed by impact, adopting a model for erosional modification and obliteration, and employing an independently determined frequency of impacting bodies, it is possible to calculate an age for surface materials.

Absolute calibration of the meteoroid flux (i.e., the "population" of meteoroids) in the vicinity of Mars is more difficult. Early investigators assumed that, because Mars was close to the asteroid belt, impact rates might be ten or twenty times as great as for the Moon; but current investigations suggest that flux rates are and have been similar throughout the inner Solar System. Accordingly, Mars has probably experienced an impact history not unlike those of Earth, Moon and Mercury. For all these bodies, initially high impact rates were associated with the terminal stages of planetary accretion and the sweeping up of interplanetary debris. During the first few million years after this, impact rates must have dropped off rapidly, finally reaching a rate that has remained more or less constant to the present.

As we have already noted, then, the cratered and mountainous terrains probably indicate the appearance of the planet as it was fairly early on in Martian history, though erosion has played a modifying role. The lightly-cratered smooth plains are comparatively recent developments.

Volcanoes, Canyons and Channels. More than twenty unambiguous volcanic constructional landforms have been identified in Mariner 9 pictures. Most are

This color picture of the Martian landscape was taken on July 21 1976, the day after Viking 1 landed on the planet: it is roughly noon, Martian time. Orange-red surface materials cover most of the surface, apparently forming a thin veneer over darker bedrock. The surface materials are thought to be limonite: such weathering products form on Earth in the presence of water and an oxidizing atmosphere. The reddish cast of the sky is probably due to scattering and reflection from reddish sediment suspended in the lower atmosphere. The view is southeast from the Viking craft.

characterized by a conical shape, presence of summit collapse calderas, roughly textured slopes, lava channels and ridges radiating down-slope from the central caldera, and lava-flow fronts in adjacent plains materials.

Olympus Mons, the largest Martian volcano and almost certainly the largest in the Solar System, is approximately 370mi (600km) in diameter and rises to a height of 16mi (26km) above its base. In shape and surface morphology it resembles terrestrial shield volcanoes; however, it is more than twice the size of the largest terrestrial shield volcano complex, that underlying the island of Hawaii. Martian volcanism has probably

occurred episodically throughout the planet's history. The Olympus Mons eruptions are among the most recent, probably occurring only a couple of hundred million years ago.

A giant system of canyons, the Valles Marineris, extends from (Martian) latitudes 20°W to 100°W, a distance of 2500mi (4000km). These canyons were probably formed by erosional widening of crustal fractures that are part of a radiating set of extensional faults resulting from crustal doming in the vicinity of the Olympus Mons volcanic province.

Numerous irregularly sinuous channels are to be found on Mars, chiefly in the

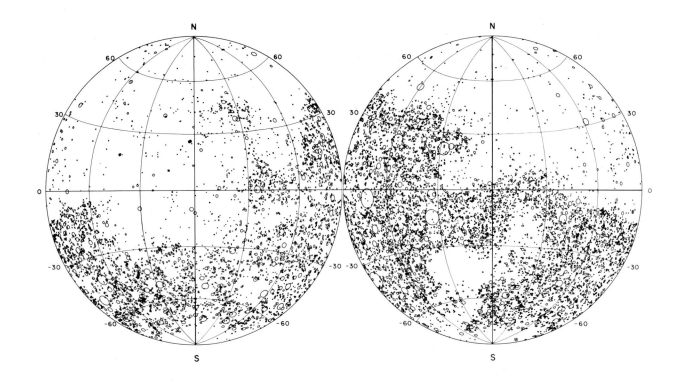

Polar Units
- Permanent ice
- Layered deposits
- Etched plains

Ancient Units
- Cratered terrain, undivided
- Mountainous terrain

Volcanic Units
- Volcanic constructs
- Volcanic plains
- Moderately cratered plains
- Cratered plains

Modified Units
- Hummocky terrain, chaotic
- Hummocky terrain, fretted
- Hummocky terrain, knobby
- Channel deposits
- Plains, undivided
- Grooved terrain

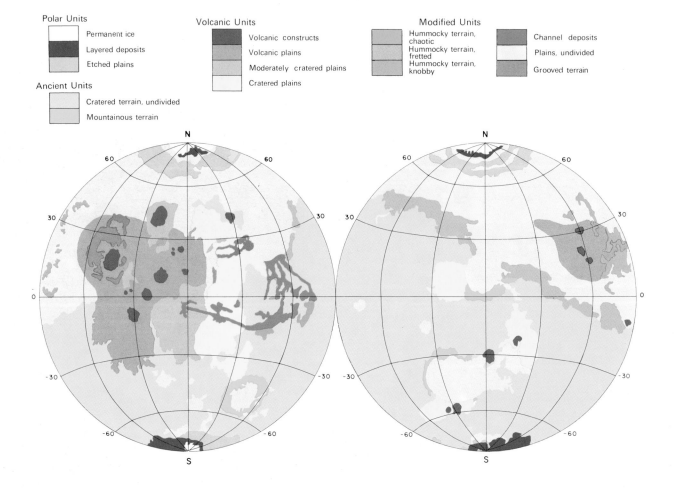

cratered terrain not far from the equator. The larger of these channels are several hundred kilometres long and tens of kilometres wide. Their origin is uncertain, but is generally believed to be related to surface flow of water during some former epoch – that is, they are the beds of Martian rivers of the past. (Under present tenuous atmospheric conditions liquid water would simply boil away.) Large amounts of water might have formed from a primitive atmosphere, have been stored in the soil as groundwater and ground-ice, and subsequently have been released through an artesian mechanism to form the observed channels.

Wind Deposits. Terrestrial observers have noted that, during some observing periods, the entire disc appears uniformly bright, with no dark surface markings visible. This condition has been attributed to global dust storms which occur most commonly during perihelion (closest approach to the Sun). The observed transport of sediment is somewhat unexpected, since wind velocities required to initiate movement are about six times as great as for Earth, due to the low Martian atmospheric density. The Mariner 9 spacecraft arrived at Mars during the height of one of these dust storms: during the craft's approach, only the highest (Olympus Mons) and brightest (polar caps) regions were visible.

Bright and dark streaks are visible in many Martian pictures, commonly occurring in association with small bowl-shaped craters. The orientation of the streaks is constant over large regions, but changes systematically with changing latitude. The streaks apparently form downwind of youthful craters, whose upraised rims perturb near-surface winds. High-speed winds cause turbulence in the lee of craters, and associated erosion leads to the exposure of dark bedrock. When wind speeds are lower, protected regions of deposition exist downwind of craters, and these are the bright streaks.

Some flat-floored craters have interior dark splotches, preferentially occurring on the downwind side (as determined by streak orientations). High-resolution pictures show that some of these dark splotches are transverse dune fields.

Some Martian landforms are due to wind erosion. These include irregularly-shaped, flat-floored deflation basins and cigar-shaped ridges of bedrock (yardangs).

Satellites. Mars has two small satellites, Phobos and Deimos. Both are densely cratered and irregularly shaped, lacking sufficient mass to yield a spherical "hydrostatic" shape. The maximum diameter of Phobos is about 17.5mi (28km),

Opposite, Above, a plot of all the craters of diameter greater than (9.3mi) 15km. The uneven distribution of these is clear evidence both of erosion of surface features by wind and wind-transported particles and of tectonic activity. *Below*, the physiographic provinces of Mars, the different units being described in the accompanying legend.

100 km

Olympus Mons, Mars, the largest volcano in the Solar System. The diameter of its base is about 370mi (600km); its height is about 16mi (26km).

A Mariner 9 photograph showing one of Mars' sinuous channels, thought to be possible valleys of vanished rivers.

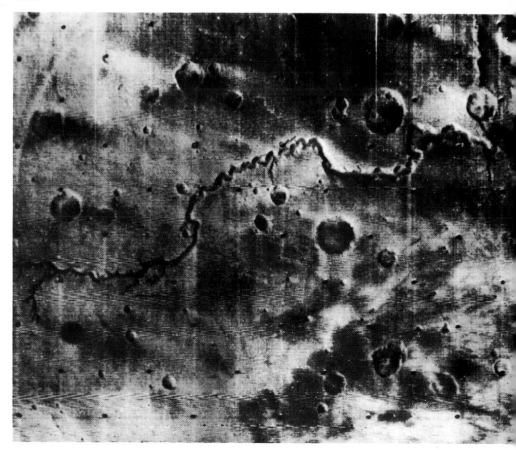

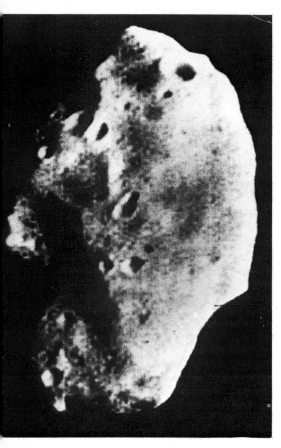

Phobos, the inner moon of Mars, from a distance of 3444mi (5540km). The profusion of craters suggests that Phobos is very old and of great structural strength.

while the maximum diameter of the smaller moon, Deimos, is just 10mi (16km). Both satellites have low albedo (reflectivity), and this dark appearance suggests a basaltic composition.

Phobos orbits Mars at a distance of 3780mi (6100km) every 7h 39min; while Deimos orbits at a distance of 12,400mi (20,000km) with a month of 30h 18min. Their orbits are very circular, and this has led some astronomers to suggest that the two moons, rather than being the captured asteroids that their appearance would imply, are the remains of a single, larger Martian satellite that was shattered by some unknown agent at some unknown point in the past.   TAM

Meteorites

On November 30 1954, Mrs E. H. Hodges of Sylacauga, Alabama, was resting on her sofa after lunch when a stone weighing about nine pounds crashed through the roof of the house, ricocheted off a radio, and struck her on the leg. This is the only authenticated instance of a person being hit by a meteorite, a rock from outer space captured by the Earth on its journey around the Sun.

Thousands, perhaps millions, of tons of extraterrestrial material enter the atmosphere each year. The fate of this material

and the extent to which we are aware of it depends entirely upon particle size. Minute dust-like fragments make up most of the total, and these sink unnoticed to mix with terrestrial dust, so that they are extremely difficult to identify and recover. Somewhat larger particles, sand-sized grains, offer sufficient air resistance to be briefly heated to incandescence by friction before being entirely destroyed in the upper atmosphere. We are aware of these as transient streaks in the night sky – meteors, or shooting stars.

Other, much rarer fragments, weighing upwards of a few grams, are large enough to partially survive their passage through the atmosphere: they are reduced in size by ablation, and may be fragmented by the violence of their deceleration from cosmic velocities. Those remnants that reach the Earth's surface are called meteorites. It has been estimated that the total number of meteorites falling to Earth each year is about 500, of which perhaps 150 would be expected to fall on land. The world's population is, however, so irregularly distributed, with vast areas of land almost devoid of habitation, that an average of only four "falls" (defined as recovered stones whose arrival has been observed) are in fact recorded each year. "Finds" – those meteorites found on the surface, perhaps after plowing, excavation or some such, but whose date of fall is not known – also contribute to the growing list of authentic meteorites, presently totalling around 2000.

Meteorites vary in weight from a few ounces or so to several tons, with a theoretical upper limit of about 100 tons. The largest known, the Hoba iron of Namibia (South West Africa), weighs about 60 tons but is much corroded. Calculations show that during its passage through the atmosphere a meteorite less than about 1 ton in weight will lose all its cosmic velocity, which may have been as high as over 150,000mph (70km/sec) relative to the Earth, and strike the ground with a velocity due only to gravitational attraction. Somewhat larger meteorites may retain their cosmic velocities; and those in excess of 100 tons will be hardly slowed by the atmosphere and so will impact at such high speeds as to be almost entirely vaporized in the resultant blast. For this reason giant meteorites are not found on the Earth, although some large craters are believed to be of impact origin.

The Arrival of a Meteorite. The fall of a meteorite of even quite modest dimensions is often accompanied by spectacular effects. In the absence of cloud cover, the meteorite itself is seen even during the day as a bright fireball, incandescent due to frictional heating, accompanied by a trail of ionized gases and dust which is brightly luminous by night and normally dark by day. Sometimes the meteorite is fragmented by the violence of its passage and a single fireball is observed to break into separate parts.

Sound effects which may be audible up to 50mi (80km) or more from the eventual impact point are variable and less easy to

describe. Most witnesses hear one or more loud reports. Other sounds, including whistlings, cracklings, and noises like thunder or the tearing of cloth or the roaring of fire, have also been reported. An observer close to the point of landing may hear the thud of impact. Shock waves may be detected by seismographs.

Meteorites which have lost all their cosmic velocity during their journey through the atmosphere are often found lying on the surface of the ground, although they may penetrate soft earth to form craters up to several feet deep. Stones from the 1869 Hessle fall in Sweden failed to break ice only an inch or two thick.

Contrary to popular expectation, freshly fallen stones are usually quite cool to the touch. If a meteorite breaks up in the air, the resultant fragments are scattered on the ground within an elliptical area whose long axis is aligned with the flight direction.

The External Appearance of Meteorites. Ablation entirely destroys a high proportion (20–100%) of a meteoroid entering the atmosphere: the amount depends on such factors as original size, shape, cosmic velocity and angle of incidence to the atmosphere.

Freshly-fallen meteorites are usually covered with a thin black fusion crust, produced by melting of the leading surface as the meteorite decelerates through the atmosphere, molten material streaming backward to coat most or all of the specimen. If the meteorite has remained in a stable orientation during this stage, ablation tends to produce a conical or dome shape, sometimes bearing rather regularly disposed furrows and pits, so that the leading surface can be readily identified.

Classification. Meteorites are classified broadly into three groups, irons, stony-irons, and stones. Members of the first group consist almost entirely of iron and nickel alloyed together as the minerals kamacite (4–7% nickel) and taenite (30–60% nickel). Many irons reveal a striking structure when sawn, polished and etched with acid. This Widmanstätten pattern consists of bands of kamacite bordered by taenite and arranged parallel to the octahedral faces of an original homogeneous crystal of nickel-iron.

The stony-iron meteorites contain, as the name suggests, nickel-iron together with silicate minerals, the precise nature of which allows subdivision into four classes: the pallasites (metal plus *olivine); the mesosiderites (metal plus *pyroxene and *plagioclase); and two further classes each known from only a single example.

93% of all observed falls are of the third group, the stony meteorites. This figure probably approximates to their actual extraterrestrial proportion (the fact that irons predominate among *finds* is ascribed to their greater resistance to terrestrial weathering and to their more obviously unusual character). The stones consist chiefly of the minerals olivine, pyroxene, nickel-iron, plagioclase and *troilite (iron sulfide).

A view over Mauritania looking southeast toward the El Djouf desert. Below, in old sedimentary and igneous rocks, rising out of the desert are the famous Richat structures. The larger is about 30mi (50km) in diameter; the smaller, a little toward the south, about 5mi (8km) in diameter. It is now considered that these craters are almost certainly of impact origin, showing that the Earth, like its neighbors, has been subject to meteoritic bombardment in the past.

Minor amounts of other minerals, some unknown in terrestrial rocks, are also often present. Most stones are characterized by the presence of small, approximately spherical aggregates known as chondrules, and these meteorites (84% of the total falls) are called chondrites.

Some chondrites, especially a subgroup rich in carbon and called carbonaceous chondrites, have chemical, mineralogical and textural features which suggest that they are primitive, well preserved objects, less highly evolved than other meteorite types and terrestrial rocks. In particular, the carbonaceous chondrites approximate closely in composition to the non-volatile material of the Sun, as determined by spectroscopy. There are a number of other reasons for believing that these meteorites may represent primordial Solar System material, and that other meteorite types, the irons, stony-irons, and those stones lacking chondrules – the achondrites – may be derived from this primordial material by a variety of secondary processes and events.

The Origin of Meteorites. A considerable amount of evidence indicates that these extraterrestrial fragments are travelling in elliptical orbits around the Sun, and are thus genuinely part of the Solar System. Moreover, they appear to have originated in

Extraterrestrial material reaches the Earth in several different ways. Giant meteoroids (1), of mass greater than about 100 tons, are reduced in size during their passage through the atmosphere owing to ablation. They retain most of their cosmic velocity, and are almost entirely destroyed on impact with considerable release of heat and other energy. Their impacts produce large craters (e.g., that in Arizona) and may also be responsible for the formation of tektites. Meteoroids of mass between 1 gram and 100 tons (2 and 3) lose most or all of their cosmic velocity, and may fragment (3). They come to rest on the Earth's surface – or, perhaps, form shallow craters. Their fragmentation in the atmosphere may contribute to (4), meteors or shooting stars. These are primarily formed by meteoroid grains, which are totally destroyed by ablation, though their passage is seen as a trail of light (a meteor). Their destruction contributes to (5), meteoroid dust. These minute particles survive their trip through the atmosphere to the surface largely undetected, and mix with terrestrial dust. Known as micro-meteorites, they have been identified in deep-sea sediments and from the polar icecaps.

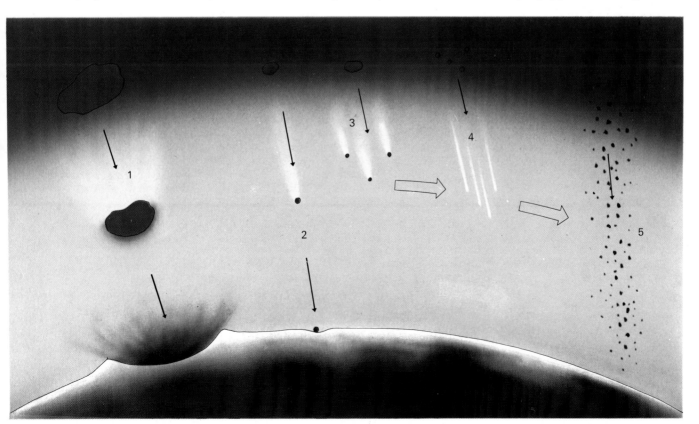

Meteorites. On the left is a polished and etched slice of the Amalia iron showing the Widmanstätten pattern. Behind it is a chondrite that fell in 1913; in the foreground is a cast of the Middlesbrough stone which fell in 1881.

established, but many meteorites undoubtedly show features indicative of transient events of great violence.

The Age of Meteorites. Radiometric dating techniques, based on the decay of radioactive isotopes (see *age of the Earth), are potentially capable of dating five separate events in the history of a meteorite. The five events are:·

(*i*) nucleosynthesis – i.e., the creation of the elements in the solar nebula which later accumulated to form the meteorites, asteroids and planets;

(*ii*) melting of the larger meteorite bodies when these had grown big enough to heat up spontaneously;

(*iii*) cooling of these parent bodies;

(*iv*) break-up of the parent bodies; and

(*v*) arrival on Earth.

The first event, nucleosynthesis, can in principle be dated by the measurement of an isotope of xenon produced by the decay of a short-lived and long-extinct isotope of iodine which is believed, for theoretical reasons, to have formed during nucleosynthesis. The melting and cooling ages of the parent bodies are determined, with rather more confidence, by comparing the amounts present of the long-lived radioisotopes of uranium, potassium and rubidium with the amounts of their decay products – lead, argon and strontium respectively. These first three events all occurred early in the life of the Solar System, within the period $4.5–4.0 \times 10^9$ years ago, and such studies of meteorites have played an important part in establishing the age of the Solar System at about 4.6×10^9 years.

Later events, the break-up of parent bodies and the arrival of a meteorite on Earth, may be tentatively dated using a somewhat different principle. When a parent body fragments in space, the smaller bodies thus formed become exposed to cosmic rays which produce, in amounts proportional to the exposure time, certain new radioactive and stable isotopes. When a meteorite falls to Earth, it is shielded from further cosmic-ray irradiation, so that stable nuclides cease to be formed and their concentration becomes fixed, while radioactive nuclides formed during exposure begin to decay at known rates. Measurement of suitable nuclides thus permits the estimation of both exposure ages and terrestrial ages.

There are some theoretical difficulties in this method and uncertainties as to the correct interpretation of results. One rather puzzling result is a disparity between the exposure ages of stones (mostly in the range $20–30 \times 10^6$ years) and irons (mostly in the range $100–1000 \times 10^6$ years). Terrestrial ages so far obtained on finds are all geologically very young, less than 1 million years, a finding to be expected for objects suscep-

the asteroid belt, the zone between the orbits of Mars and Jupiter which contains millions of small bodies that have failed to aggregate into a planet. Although most of the asteroids remain in more or less circular orbits beyond Mars, some travel in elliptical paths such that they cross the orbits of the inner planets. The origin of meteorites is thus linked with the nature and origin of the asteroids.

It is now generally held that the Solar System formed about 4.6×10^9 years ago from a rotating disc of dust and gas, and that the planets themselves were created by the progressive accumulation of small grains of solid matter. Initially, collisions were largely fortuitous but, as the bodies grew in size, the process was increasingly aided by the forces of gravitational attraction. Although smaller than the planets, the asteroid bodies formed in the same way, failing only to coalesce into masses more than a few hundred miles in diameter – Ceres, the largest, has a diameter of about 470mi (755km).

Recent spectrographic studies show that the spectra of the light reflected by the asteroids fall into distinct classes, each class closely resembling the spectrum, as determined in the laboratory, of a particular meteorite group. Some 80% of the asteroids (generally the smaller measurable bodies) give spectra indicating close affinity with the carbonaceous chondrites, and as we have seen there is good reason for suppos-

ing that these meteorites are representative of the original material of the ancestral solar cloud. The chondrules themselves may outline primordial dust particles. The primitive mineralogy, chemistry and texture of the carbonaceous chondrites and a few of the common chondrites, less heated and metamorphosed than the other meteorites, survived only in the small asteroid bodies which were never large enough to become heated internally. Inside larger bodies, heating due to release of gravitational energy as well as radioactive decay processes initiated melting and the segregation of metal from silicate phases. The stony-iron meteorites represent an intermediate stage in this process, and probably originated in bodies 60–125 mi (100–200km) in diameter. The iron meteorites and the achondrites probably represent the complementary core and outer shell regions of even larger, more fully differentiated bodies. The pallasites, for instance, appear to have formed in the core of bodies with a maximum diameter of about 370mi (600km). All these events are believed to have taken place within a relatively short time after the condensation of the Solar System. It is clear that, if the above sequence of events is broadly correct, then one or more of the larger parent bodies must have been fragmented in order to account for the arrival on Earth of small pieces of the more evolved meteorite types, including all the irons. The times of break-up of parent bodies have not been well tible to rapid weathering and erosion under terrestrial conditions.

Meteorite Craters. The heavily cratered surfaces of the major bodies in the Solar System owe their topography chiefly to the impacts of vast numbers of meteoritic objects, acquired mainly in the early history of the Solar System. It is inconceivable that Earth in its early life was not likewise subjected to large-scale cosmic bombardment. The evidence for this, in the case of an active, mobile planet such as Earth, is now difficult to find. With its mobile crust, constantly being created and destroyed by plate movements (see *plate tectonics), and ceaselessly being modified by orogeny, erosion and sedimentation, there remain few areas of ancient terrain to be searched for impact structures. A few score of such structures have been tentatively identified, of which only a small number are undoubtedly of impact origin.

Conclusion. It is clear that meteorites are to Earth scientists much more than interesting but irrelevant curiosities. Apart from providing important evidence concerning the nature, origin and age of the Solar System – and the fact that, prior to the advent of space exploration, they were the only extraterrestrial material available for first-hand study – meteorites supply strong clues concerning the nature of the Earth itself. A whole range of geological and geophysical evidence suggests that, apart from the superficial crust, the Earth consists of a nickel-iron core (partly molten) and a silicate-rich mantle made up, at least in its outer parts, of olivine and pyroxene. It is believed that the iron and stony classes of meteorites are analogous, respectively, to these two regions of the Earth's interior. The stony-iron meteorites may broadly correspond to terrestrial rocks in the region of the core/mantle boundary at 1800mi (2900km) depth.

However, the analogy should not be taken too far. The size of the Earth is much greater than the sizes attained by even the largest of the meteorite parent bodies, and meteorites thus lack the high-pressure minerals which must be present at depth within the Earth. Nevertheless, among all natural objects available for study in the laboratory, meteorites are the closest relatives to the inaccessible matter that forms the bulk of the Earth.   FBA

Tektites

A rare and problematic class of natural objects, tektites are much studied and little understood. They are small pieces of glass, varying in color from light green to black and having a chemical composition similar to that of acid *igneous rocks (about 75% SiO_2) but with a significant deficiency of alkalis. Many have distinct and characteristic shapes – spheres, buttons, dumbbells, etc. They have been found in only four areas of the Earth's surface, known as "strewn fields": southern Australia and

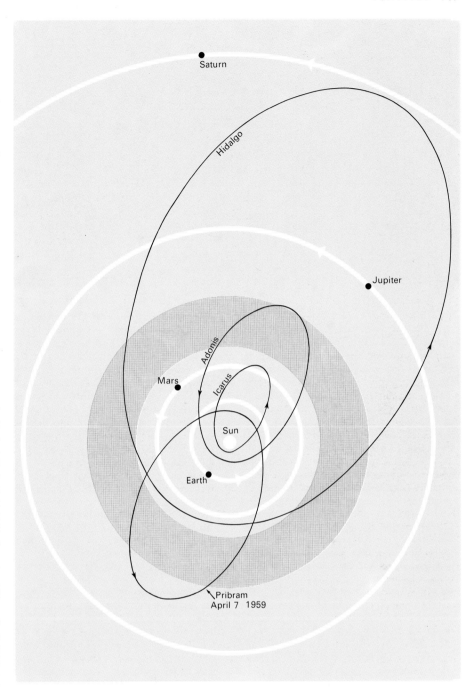

Most asteroids circle the Sun with orbits that lie within the asteroid belt, represented here as a stippled zone. Some, however, have much more elliptical orbits that intersect those of the inner planets: shown here are the orbits of Icarus and Adonis, the best known such asteroids. Hidalgo, the asteroid with the most eccentric orbit of all, approaches the orbit of Saturn at one extreme and that of Mars at the other. Also shown is the calculated orbit of the Pribram meteorite which fell to Earth on April 7 1959.

southeast Asia, the Ivory Coast, Czechoslovakia, and Texas and Georgia, USA. Each group has its own distinctive age, but all are geologically very young, the Australian, Asian and Ivory Coast tektites being of *Pleistocene age (about 650,000 years and 1,300,000 years respectively), and the European and North American tektites having *Miocene (15,000,000 years) and *Oligocene (34,000,000 years) ages respectively. Older tektites are unknown.

Any theory which seeks to explain the origin of these mysterious objects must take account of their restriction in both space and time, and the fact that they bear no discoverable relation to their surroundings.

Other highly significant features which must be explained are the presence within some tektites of minute grains of the meteoritic minerals kamacite, troilite and schreibersite, and the recent discovery that contained gas bubbles are at pressures of only about one thousandth of an atmosphere.

In the last 200 years there has been no shortage of theories for the origin of tektites, although many must be dismissed as fanciful: modern evidence discounts, for example, an artificial, man-made origin; and Australian tektites have not been shaped in the gizzards of emus, as was proposed in 1911! Indeed some of their

A selection of tektites showing clearly the aerodynamically molded shapes.

shapes have been shown by wind-tunnel experiments to have originated aerodynamically, by ablation and molding during transit through the Earth's atmosphere.

Modern theories for the origin of tektites can be divided into three groups. The first claims an entirely extraterrestrial provenance, that tektites are quite simply *meteorites, albeit with novel composition. Candidates for the parent body include planets, asteroids, comets and the Moon, although the latter now seems an extremely improbable parent since no lunar rocks of remotely similar composition have been found *in situ*. The second group of theories invokes an entirely terrestrial origin, involving special and speculative types of volcanic or cryptovolcanic eruptions and processes.

There are formidable weaknesses in both these groups of theories, and the weight of evidence increasingly appears to favor an origin involving terrestrial material ejected from the ground in violent meteorite or comet impact. In its modern form, this hypothesis demands that the impact is sufficiently catastrophic to vaporize large amounts of surface and subsurface rock, the gases being ejected into suborbital trajectories. On cooling, the more refractory components condense and accrete into droplets that incorporate bubbles of gas at pressures appropriate to the atmosphere about 20 to 25mi (30–40km) above the ground. Before returning to Earth in regions remote from, and perhaps even antipodal to, their source area the fragments are molded into aerodynamic shapes.

Spectacular and improbable though this hypothesis may appear, it is the best at present available, and it provides a model for future work on these enigmatic objects.

FBA

Geophysics

The classification of scientific research into neatly labelled compartments is a process traditionally alien to the geological sciences. Most geologists would consider that they were of necessity in close touch with many branches of chemistry, physics or zoology.

However, there is much scope within the Earth sciences for someone with a more specialized training in physics, and such a person is, quite logically, described as a geophysicist. In particular, various experimental techniques of a physical nature have been applied to studies of the Earth with spectacular success: the great revolution in the Earth sciences brought about by the concept of *plate tectonics would never have occurred without the evidence obtained from geophysical methods. The vast increase in the successful location of economic oil, gas and *ore deposits since the war has depended largely on the use of geophysical exploration techniques.

Seismology. Of all the methods available, seismic investigations are by far the most revealing in terms of structural contrast within the Earth's interior. An earthquake or explosion generates waves of elastic energy within the ground. The task of the seismologist is to record the portion of the wave motion that returns to the surface and study the recorded signals for information about the structures through which the waves have passed. The experimentalist is concerned with two basic types of waves, body waves and surface waves (see *earthquakes).

A body wave travels through the Earth as a simple pulse, whereas a surface wave

The distribution of tektites around the Earth: (1) Texan bediasites; (2) Georgian georgianites; (3) Ivory Coast tektites; (4) Czechoslovakian moldavites; (5) Indochinites; (6) Jawa and related tektites; (7) Philippinites; (8) Australites.

A seismic experiment in progress on the Moon. The leads trailing across the lunar surface are from individual sensors laid out at distance.

proceeds only along the surface of the Earth and its wave motion is spread out over a broad time interval. The reason for this dispersion of energy is that low-frequency portions of the surface wave travel through a thicker layer of the surface than do high-frequency portions, and hence in general there is a spread of velocities associated with the different frequencies of the surface waves in the initial "package".

This can be used to infer the average structure of the Earth between two recording stations. The inter-station velocity of the different frequency components of the surface wave can be measured directly from the seismograms made at the two stations. Since the different frequencies are sampling different depths within the Earth, these velocity/frequency data can be transformed into information about the variation of velocity with depth by a straightforward, though rather lengthy, computation. The method has been of great value in determining the Earth's gross structure.

A more recent development has been the detection of the natural vibrations of the Earth itself. These are excited to any measurable degree only by the largest earthquakes and are analogous to natural vibrations of a bell or of the air within an organ pipe. Models of the seismic velocity and density structure of the whole Earth are developed from these data in much the same way as surface waves are analyzed. However, very special instruments – normally called strain meters – are needed to detect these oscillations, which have periods of up to one hour. Strain meters consist essentially of two solid piers embedded in the ground some tens of metres apart. Apparatus which allows the very small relative displacements between them to be continuously measured, usually a laser generator and reflecting mirrors, is mounted on the two piers.

The interpretation of body-wave seismograms involves the correct identification as reflections or refractions from discontinuities within the Earth of different arrivals within the signals. For example, a seismic ray is refracted very sharply at the boundary between the core and the mantle. The result is that the core casts a large "seismic shadow" that is clearly observable if records from around the world are compared.

In the last few years, two abrupt increases in seismic velocity and density have been detected at depths of about 250 and 400mi (approximately 400km and 650km), and these are probably due to pressure-induced changes in the atomic packing of mantle material: a seismic body wave that has passed through these structures may consist of two or more interfering signals due to the reflections and refractions that occur at a boundary between materials that permit differing velocities of pressure waves.

Large spreads of seismometers have re-cently been set up, one of the largest being in Norway where 198 instruments are distributed over an area of about 15,500mi² (40,000km²). The advantage of such a distribution is that, when the signals from all the seismometers are summed together, scattered energy tends to cancel out so that the coherent phases are more obviously apparent. In addition, it is possible to determine the direction and angle of approach of the waves from the small differences in their arrival times at the individual seismometers.

In the interpretation of body-wave seismograms, a wave that travels along the interface between two layers is often recorded. The thickness and seismic velocities of the layers can be deduced from the slopes of time-vs-distance (from source) graphs constructed from the records.

In the search for oil-bearing strata, geophysicists make use of the seismic-reflection technique to the virtual exclusion of all other exploration methods. This involves the deployment of a dense line of seismometers (normally referred to as geophones in this context) as close as possible to the shot point, the object being to detect only the reflections from directly beneath the shot/receiver location. The location is progressively shifted until a pattern of vertical reflections over the whole survey area is obtained. Finally, the seismograms from each geophone are plotted side by side, so that laterally varying structures can be clearly seen.

In practice, the interpretation of this kind of data is much more involved than one might expect. However, great advances have recently been made in improving the clarity of the records. We have already considered the spatial filtering that can be carried out using a pattern of receivers: equally, the signals can be frequency-filtered using standard electronic techniques and, in addition, the energy source can be enhanced by using a pattern of shots.

Gravity. The reader will be very familiar with the law of gravitational attraction between masses, if only because one is drawn so firmly towards the Earth when falling off a ladder. The precise value of the gravitational force is very slightly variable over the surface of the Earth and the changes reflect lateral inhomogenities of mass within our planet's interior.

In the gravimeter we have an instrument that allows us to measure the gravitational force to very high precision and thereby learn something about the Earth's internal structure. There is no problem in detecting variations in gravity due to dense ore bodies or basaltic intrusions. The difficulty comes in the correct interpretation of the data: any number of different shapes or density contrasts can give rise to any one set of gravity readings. The main value of the method comes when it is carried out in conjunction with other geophysical techniques.

The gravimeter does not make friends easily. It insists on being treated with extreme care at all times and has an in-

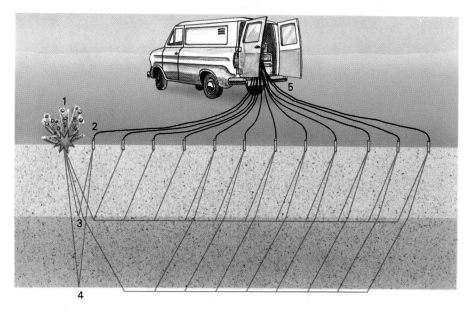

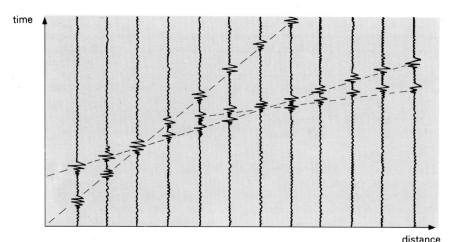

A seismic refraction experiment and an idealized trace of the results. By recording at different points the disturbance due to seismic waves generated by an explosion, a prospector can build up a picture of the underlying rock strata. This will indicate suitable sites for further exploration for oil or minerals. Shown in the diagram are (1) shot point; (2) first geophone; (3) and (4) direct reflections; and (5) equipment truck (not to scale).

cal conductivity of the ground over various depth ranges, and they have wider applications than to the location of mineral deposits: water content is a major factor in the conductivity of crustal rocks and consequently electrical methods are often used when an estimate of the depth of the water table is required.

From large-scale experiments that provide electrical conductivity values to depths in excess of 620mi (1000km) it has become possible to deduce (extremely approximate) temperature-depth curves for the Earth's interior. These estimates rest on the assumptions that the major constituents of the mantle are known, and that temperature is the dominant controlling factor on the electrical conductivity of mantle materials. For a variety of reasons, an improvement in our knowledge of the Earth's internal temperature would be of very great value, and there is currently in progress research aimed towards increasing our rather scanty knowledge of electrical conduction properties of Earth materials under high temperatures and pressures.

Electrical Prospecting Methods. The most straightforward approach to the measurement of Earth conductivity is the resistivity method. Two metal stakes are hammered into the ground and a direct or very low frequency alternating voltage is applied across them. The resulting distribution of current within the ground will depend on the variations in conductivity beneath the surface as well as on the separation of the two stakes, the separation being increased if a greater current penetration depth is required (there is a limit imposed by the power of the voltage source). The quantity that is measured is the drop in potential between two electrodes usually lying *between* the current electrodes. Generally speaking, a low drop in potential means that a region of high conductivity is being sampled. Correspondingly a large drop means low conductivity (high resistivity). Frequently, the interpretation of resistivity data is no more sophisticated than this: an anomalous region, once located, would be investigated further by other means. The association of particular distributions of conductivity with the shape of anomaly patterns in the readings taken at the surface is an extremely complex problem and an active area of current research.

Closely associated with the resistivity method is a technique known as induced polarization (IP). If, on completion of a resistivity reading, the current is turned off, the voltage measured across the potential electrodes may fall to zero virtually instantaneously or may do so gradually over as much as three minutes. The groundwater within the pores and cracks of the rock is an electrolyte – that is, it contains freely moving charged particles. These particles pile up at the interface of electrically conducting mineral grains when a current is flowing, and slowly diffuse back to an equilibrium state when the current is switched off. If ore minerals are spread out within the country

fallible habit of refusing to settle to a steady reading towards the end of a long day when an icy wind is numbing the fingers. It is simply a small mass suspended on a very sensitive spring, though some form of mechanical amplification is also included. It is always necessary to protect the equipment from changes of temperature, either by including thermostatically controlled heating circuits, or by building the springs and levers out of various carefully chosen metals whose different degrees of expansion on heating interact in such a way as to cancel each other out: in effect the device itself makes the corrections for changes of temperature.

The gravity variations over the surface of the Earth are due to a combination of local anomalies, some of which we have already mentioned, and broad regional anomalies spread over hundreds or thousands of square miles which are probably due to mass anomalies in the deep interior. Our

knowledge of these features has been vastly increased in the last few years by observing the orbits of artificial satellites. The satellites precess, or progressively change their orbiting path relative to the Earth's axis, due to these broad variations in the gravity field, and it is possible to determine the location and amplitude of these anomalies from the rates of precession of a large number of satellite orbits. Future work will doubtless reveal more and more details of the gravity field.

Electrical and Electromagnetic Techniques. Many of the economically important ores are good conductors of electricity, particularly compared to the country rock in which they are embedded. Such ores include *graphite; *pyrite, which is an important ore of sulfur and is sometimes associated with gold; *chalcopyrite, the copper ore; *galena, the principal ore of lead; and the iron ore *magnetite. There are various methods of determining the electri-

A contour map of the variations in the Earth's gravitational field obtained by observations from artificial satellites.

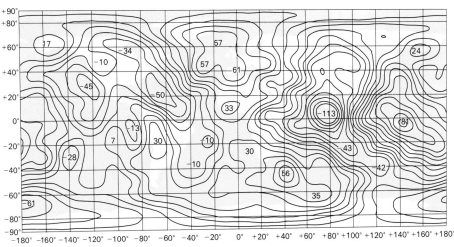

rock so that they have an effectively large total surface area, this effect will be enhanced and the measured voltage will take some time to die away.

In practice the interpretation of IP anomalies is much less clearcut than the above description suggests. Many other mechanisms have been proposed for the effect, and these may be applicable in particular circumstances.

Electromagnetic Prospecting and Deep-Sounding Methods. In general terms, electromagnetic (EM) prospecting equipment is like an oversized mine detector. An alternating current flowing in a large coil of wire gives rise to an alternating magnetic field in the surroundings. This field causes a current to flow in any conducting body in the vicinity, and a secondary magnetic field is then set up by the conducting body. All that is required is to detect the distortion due to the presence of the body of the primary magnetic field by the secondary. In the simplest type of EM detector, one measures the direction of the field by rotating a coil of wire attached to some earphones and listening for the minimum in the hissing sound produced by the induced current in the coil.

EM tests are frequently performed from the air as a preliminary search over a wide area with a view to locating regions that are worth studying in more detail on the ground. Surveys are usually flown at around 500ft (150m).

Magnetics and Paleomagnetism. No single field of research has contributed more to the general acceptance of the concept of *plate tectonics than the study of rock magnetism.

We can consider the building-block of all matter, the atom, as behaving like a tiny bar magnet. Normally the directions of the myriads of tiny bar magnets making up a lump of matter are random. However, in a few special cases, there is an interaction between nearby atoms within solids that are composed of a particular ordered distribution of certain elements, so that magnetic directions of the atoms are aligned either all in the same direction or, alternatively, all in opposing directions: in rocks, the most common material of this type is the iron ore mineral *magnetite. The result is that the sample will have a spontaneous magnetization due to the resultant of the individual magnetic alignments of the atoms.

For all but the smallest samples, an equilibrium (low-energy) state results in which regions within the solid about 0.01mm wide are uniformly magnetized while adjacent regions, or domains, have quite different directions of magnetization. In the presence of an external magnetic field the domain boundaries are forced to move

slightly to give a net magnetization in the same direction as the field.

For very small samples the equilibrium state is when there is only one domain: the magnetic directions of these single-domain grains are extremely stable because, although an external magnetic field can provide the energy to shuffle grain boundaries about a little, much greater energies are required to actually change the direction of magnetization *within* a domain. However, one rather efficient way to destroy any magnetic symmetry is to heat the material until the thermal agitation of the atoms overcomes the magnetic ordering.

We can now consider what happens to the magnetite within a rock that solidifies from an initially molten state. Below a

particular temperature, the thermal energy is no longer sufficient to randomize the atomic magnets against their tendency to align themselves in the direction of the Earth's magnetic field. Hence the direction of the Earth's field at the time of formation is "frozen" into the rock. During later geological periods the geomagnetic direction will in general be quite different – due principally to the movement of the rock relative to the magnetic poles. By the time the geophysicist collects his sample, only the most magnetically stable single-domain grains still retain their initial magnetic direction.

In the immediate vicinity of a rock containing magnetic minerals, the Earth's magnetic field is distorted. The magnetic pros-

Horizontal-loop electromagnetic equipment in use. Note the connecting lead to the other operator in the distance.

pecting method involves measuring the Earth's magnetic field at regular intervals across the area of interest using an instrument called a magnetometer. The geophysicist is then faced with the – now familiar! – problem of interpreting the anomaly pattern in the readings. His task is one degree harder than with gravity techniques, for he is faced with the uncertainty of the resultant magnetic direction of the body (the sum of all the individual magnetic grains) in addition to its shape, depth and gravity or magnetic contrast. However, much information about structure can often be gained by simply plotting a contour map of the magnetic readings. Any systematic features or trends will then show up. A classic example of this is provided by the magnetic lineations on either side of the mid-ocean ridges.

If the *in situ* orientation of a rock sample is noted, it can then be removed to the laboratory to measure its magnetic direction. This is normally accomplished by rapidly rotating the sample on a platform, which has the effect of inducing a small alternating current in a set of pick-up coils. The direction of the sample's magnetism can then be determined by comparing the signals induced in the different coils. As we have seen, the resultant direction will be the combination of the directions of individual grains. However, by a process known as "magnetic cleaning", which normally involves successive heating and cooling of the sample in the absence of a magnetic field to demagnetize all but the most stable single-domain grains, the magnetic direction of the sample at the time of its formation can be extracted.

The data thus obtained have been used with great success to chart the motions of continents relative to the magnetic pole through geological time. One problem of this technique is that a continent could move only along a line of latitude, in which case the relative direction of the Earth's magnetic field would not vary: the result is that only changes of paleolatitude can be observed. However, the *relative* motions of different continents can often provide information on their past positions.

Conclusions. It has been pointed out more than once in this chapter that geophysical methods do not often give specific answers to the problems that they are supposed to solve, although the situation is normally improved by use of a combination of meth-

Above, polar wandering curves for the various continents through geological time, based on paleomagnetic data. The numbers refer to: 1, Precambrian; 2, Cambrian; 3 Ordovician; 4, Silurian; 5, Devonian; 6, Carboniferous; 7, Permian; 8, Triassic; 9, Jurassic; 10, Cretaceous; 11, Tertiary; 12, Quaternary. Since these curves, which describe the apparent positions of the north magnetic pole as determined from different continents, are not only not colinear but also show remarkable differences of form, the only apparent explanation of polar wandering would seem to be that the continents have moved relative to each other. *Below,* in more detail, the data and the resultant curve using paleomagnetic results from the North American continent alone.

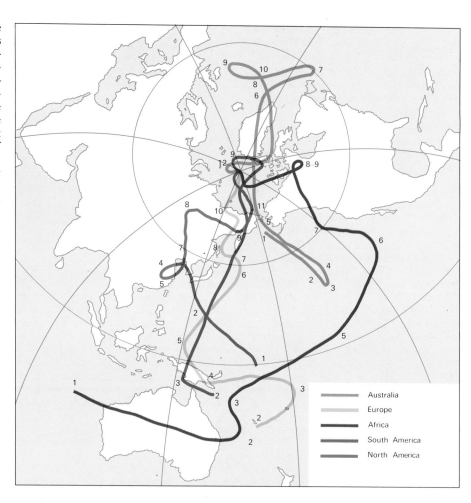

	Australia
	Europe
	Africa
	South America
	North America

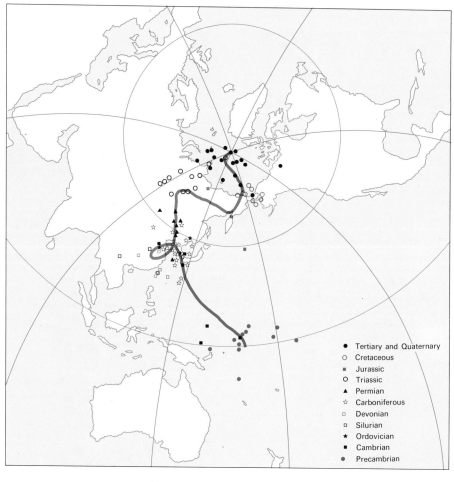

- ● Tertiary and Quaternary
- ○ Cretaceous
- ■ Jurassic
- ○ Triassic
- ▲ Permian
- ☆ Carboniferous
- □ Devonian
- ▢ Silurian
- ★ Ordovician
- ■ Cambrian
- ● Precambrian

ods. Our discussion has been concerned chiefly with techniques that are loosely combined under the heading "geophysics". However, these techniques, and their results, should never be considered in isolation from the other branches of geology, since they are often most effective when combined with geological constraints. MHW

Geochemistry

Nature is a very poor chemist – but an excellent experimental annealing oven. Man has learned to purify and concentrate small parts of the outermost skin of our planet so that chemists may work with and study the detailed behavior of pure substances. However, the rocks and fluids of Nature's experiments have not been subjected to the thousands of years of human effort which have produced pure substances for the chemical laboratory. Natural rocks and minerals, the oceans and atmosphere are in almost all cases complex mixtures of different chemical substances which are continually reacting in order to achieve a final condition of chemical equilibrium.

Geochemistry is the field of study dealing with the many diverse aspects of these reactions. It may be defined briefly as the study of the natural chemistry and evolution of the Earth and, more generally, of other cosmic bodies.

Formation of the Elements. The chemical compositions of the Sun and other stars, and of interstellar gas clouds, can be determined by observing their spectra. Such measurements show that, although the compositions of individual stars differ to some extent, all stars show similar general abundance patterns. From these data, together with analyses of meteorite compositions, relative "cosmic" abundances of elements in the Universe can be estimated.

Hydrogen (92.7%) and Helium (7.2%) together constitute 99.9% of all the matter to be found in the universe. The heavier elements, in particular oxygen, silicon, magnesium and iron, which make up the bulk of the Earth, together amount to a small fraction of 1% of the available matter.

The shape of the abundance pattern, where abundance is plotted against increasing atomic number (see *elements), carries several clues as to the manner in which these heavier elements were formed: the relative abundances decrease rapidly with increasing atomic number; the pattern has a characteristic "zig-zag" shape resulting from the greater stability of elements with even atomic numbers; the light elements lithium, beryllium and boron are present in anomalously low amounts; iron has an excessive abundance; and the abundances of elements with atomic number greater than 45 are approximately similar.

It is believed that the only mechanisms capable of supplying the vast amounts of energy radiated by a star are thermonuclear reactions. The most important of these is thought to involve the conversion of hy-

drogen into helium. In this "hydrogen-burning" the combined masses of the products are slightly less than the mass of the reactants, the lost mass being converted into energy. At higher temperatures, approaching 180×10^{6}°F ($100,000,000$°C) or more, the helium produced in this way can react further to produce carbon. At still higher temperatures more fusion reactions may occur, to produce oxygen, neon, sodium, magnesium, aluminum, silicon, phosphorus and sulfur.

However, as the nuclear charges become higher, the repulsive forces between the nuclei also increase, so that impossibly high temperatures would be required to produce elements of higher atomic numbers by continued fusion alone. To produce such elements, different mechanisms (beyond the scope of this book) have been proposed.

Thus, starting with hydrogen, all the other elements can be built up in the interior of stars by a variety of nuclear reactions. The anomalously low abundances of lithium, beryllium and boron are thought to result from the rapid destruction of these nuclei in subsequent nuclear reactions. On the other hand, iron and silicon are unusually stable, as a result of their nuclear structures, and so are present in greater abundance than expected.

It is believed that Earth and the other planets formed by condensation of these various elements released after their formation in preexisting stellar reactors. The nature of the condensation process is still an active topic of research: however, it has been found that certain types of *meteorites have chemical compositions similar to the

cosmic abundances. These meteorites may represent relatively primitive material left over from the formation of the Solar System. The composition of the Earth, however, has changed since then as a result both of the loss of volatile elements and of chemical differentiation to produce the present distribution of elements on the planet.

Composition of the Earth. Direct observations can be made only of the compositions of the atmosphere and oceans, and of rocks near the Earth's surface. However, as a result of studies of nodules carried up in *kimberlite pipes from regions of high pressure, and analyses of seismic data (see *geophysics), the internal structure of the Earth is quite well understood.

The first task of the geochemist is to analyze the rocks and minerals which make up the Earth's crust. Once their compositions are known, experiments can be carried out over a wide range of temperatures and pressures to determine how the rocks may have been formed. Some of the techniques for doing so are discussed below.

Atomic Absorption and Emission Spectrometry. The rock to be analyzed is first ground to a fine powder and dissolved in hydrofluoric acid. After neutralizing or evaporating off any unreacted acid, the resulting rock solution is then sprayed into a hot flame. In the flame the high temperature causes some atoms to be excited into higher energy states. When electrons in the excited atoms drop back to their ground states, radiation of a characteristic color is emitted by each element. This is the basis of flame *emission* spectroscopy, which can itself be

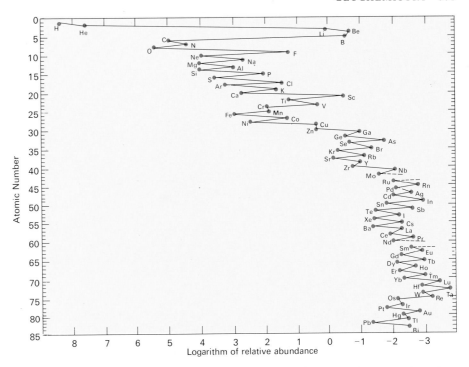

Relative cosmic abundances of the elements, referred to a value of 10⁴ for silicon (Si: 4 on the logarithmic scale). Elements with even atomic numbers are plotted in blue, those with odd atomic numbers in red. Hydrogen (92.7%) and helium (7.2%) together constitute 99.9% of all the matter in the universe. The heavier elements, and in particular oxygen (O), silicon (Si), magnesium (Mg) and iron (Fe), which make up the bulk of the Earth, together amount to a fraction of 1% of the available matter.

X-ray diffraction photograph of finely powdered quartz. The film is curled into a cylinder, the sample mounted at its center, and a beam of X-rays passed in through a hole in the film. The beam is diffracted into a series of cones, represented on the film by pairs of curved lines whose positions and intensities provide a unique "fingerprint" of the mineral. (The marks on the right are later additions.)

used as a direct method of analysis. It is also used in the determination of the compositions of the atmospheres of stars.

Many atoms, however, are not excited in this way. If a lamp emitting the wavelengths of light characteristic of the element to be determined (e.g., red light for calcium, green for barium) is shone through the flame, the radiation can be absorbed by the atoms of that element present. The logarithm of the ratio between the intensities of the light before and after passing through the flame is found to be proportional to the concentration of the particular element in the rock solution, and hence in the rock itself. This is the basis of *atomic absorption spectroscopy*. This method of analysis is particularly useful for determining small or trace quantities of minor elements.

X-ray Fluorescence Spectroscopy. Another commonly used analytical technique involves the bombardment of a rock sample with X-rays. The rock may be finely powdered and pressed into a pellet, or fused into a glass bead using a low-melting-point flux. The pellet or glass bead is then exposed to radiation from an X-ray tube.

The atoms of the rock sample are again excited into high energy states. On decaying they emit fluorescent X-rays whose wavelengths, which are characteristic of the particular atoms present, can be measured.

The method of X-ray fluorescence spectroscopy has been further developed to allow a complete chemical analysis to be performed on a single mineral grain. Instead of exciting the specimen with a beam of X-rays, a focused beam of electrons is used. The electron beam, which can be focused into a spot less than a thousandth of a millimetre in diameter, again excites atoms into high energy states from which they fall back, emitting fluorescent X-rays. By collecting the X-rays from this tiny spot the chemical composition of the area hit by the electron-beam can be determined. This is the basis of the *electron microprobe microanalyzer.*

Chemical Compositions of Different Rock Types.

Although *sedimentary rocks and *metamorphic rocks are frequently exposed at the Earth's surface, it is estimated that 95% of the Earth's crust is composed of *igneous rocks.

The ocean basins which constitute around 70% of the Earth's surface are floored with *basalt*. Sometimes the igneous processes supplying basalt to spreading mid-oceanic ridges break through the surface to produce volcanic eruptions, as in the case of the island of Surtsey which was "born" in November 1963 (see *ocean floor; *vulcanicity). Large amounts of basalt are also found on the continents, together with other volcanic rocks and their intrusive slowly-cooled analogs.

Although analytical methods give data on the molar or atomic amounts of the different elements present, it has become standard practice for analysts to recast their determinations into the weight percentages of different *oxides* present. These analyses show that common igneous rock-types may vary from 48% to 72% silica (SiO_2) by weight, and an even larger relative change is shown for magnesium oxide (MgO) – from 8.1 to 0.5 wt%.

How can such variations in chemical composition be produced?

Once the chemical composition of a rock is known, laboratory experiments can be performed to determine how the minerals in the rock react under changing pressure and temperature conditions, and in particular how that rock composition melts. Most igneous rocks contain the minerals clinopyroxene (see *pyroxenes) and *plagioclase feldspar. In natural rocks neither is ever pure. Plagioclase feldspars are framework silicates ranging in composition from $NaAlSi_3O_8$ (Albite) to $CaAl_2Si_2O_8$ (Anorthite). Of clinopyroxenes the most important end-member composition is that of *diopside, $CaMgSi_2O_6$.

The system diopside-anorthite can therefore be considered as a (much-simplified) model basaltic rock composition. How does such a system behave at high temperatures?

Consider a rock consisting of 80% diopside crystals and 20% crystals of anorthite. Its temperature can be raised up to 2300°F (1260°C) without appreciable amounts of reaction between the crystals: however, at this temperature a melt starts to form. This melt has a composition richer in anorthite than the average composition of the rock, since more anorthite melts than diopside. This process continues at 2300°F until all the anorthite has been melted. Once this has happened, the temperature can continue to increase and the remaining diopside can dissolve in the melt, which becomes successively richer in diopside with increasing temperature.

This simplified summary shows that, when a rock melts, the composition of the melt formed may be quite different from that of the original rock. When melting begins inside the Earth, the small quantities of liquid formed in this way may coalesce to form a body of molten magma. Since the magma is less dense than the surrounding rocks, the liquid may rise towards the Earth's surface, leaving behind a residue of minerals with higher melting points.

This process, partial melting, whereby melts having different compositions from the starting material may form and then migrate upwards has operated over the 4.6 thousand million years of the Earth's history, and is considered the primary mechanism of chemical differentiation of the Earth.

The Earth's Core and Mantle.

Most geochemists now consider that the Earth formed by a gradual condensation and accretion of particles from the nebula which gave rise to the Solar System (see *planet Earth). In the earliest stages of the Earth's evolution, short-lived radioactive isotopes caused a rapid increase in temperature and so melting as described above. The core separated out as a dense metallic liquid rich in iron, nickel and possibly silicon and/or sulfur, and gravitional forces caused it to migrate to the center of the planet. At the same time, volatile elements were expelled as gases to form an early atmosphere.

The crust formed – and is probably still forming – from the less dense silicate melts, rich in magnesium, aluminum, silicon, sodium, potassium and calcium, which migrated upwards on partial melting.

The mantle represents the residual high-melting-point material left behind after partial melting. It is likely that the mantle consists dominantly of magnesian *olivine, $[Mg,Fe]_2SiO_4$, together with smaller amounts of *enstatite ($MgSiO_3$), diopside ($CaMgSi_2O_6$), pyrope *garnet ($Mg_3Al_2Si_3O_{12}$) and perhaps some phlogopite *mica ($KMg_3Si_3AlO_{10}(OH)_2$).

Evolution of the Atmosphere.

It is likely that the proto-Earth had very little or no atmosphere at all. However, the heat liberated by gravitational collapse and by the decay of short-lived radioactive isotopes would soon result in melting of the Earth's interior to produce silicate melts and liquid iron. This heating would also liberate gases which would rise to the surface and escape. It is very likely that the entire atmosphere originated as volatile constituents expelled

as volcanic gases from the interior of the planet.

Three states in the evolution of the atmosphere are recognized. In the initial stage, the volcanic gases emitted would be in equilibrium with metallic iron in the mantle and would therefore have a much more reduced (less oxidized) character than those observed today. These volcanic gases would provide an initial atmosphere consisting largely of hydrogen, water vapor and carbon monoxide (H_2, H_2O and CO) with minor amounts of nitrogen, carbon dioxide and hydrogen sulfide (N_2, CO_2 and H_2S). The primeval atmosphere is therefore likely to have been quite different from that of today. As the gases cooled, H_2O condensed as water and the CO and CO_2 may have reacted with H_2 to form methane (CH_4), leaving an atmosphere of mainly H_2 and CH_4.

This stage came to an end following the separation of the metallic iron from the mantle to form the core. This allowed the oxidation state of the mantle to become much higher so that the volcanic gases in equilibrium with the mantle became more oxidized and were probably similar to those found today: H_2O, CO_2, CO, H_2, SO_2 (sulfur dioxide), N_2, Cl_2 (chlorine) and other minor constituents. In this second stage of evolution, the atmosphere probably contained mainly N_2, CO_2 and H_2O. The light gases, like H_2 and He (helium), continued to escape into space. Small amounts of free oxygen could have been produced in the upper atmosphere, but the oxygen would be rapidly consumed in the oxidation of the volcanic gases.

The third stage of evolution is marked by the appearance of free oxygen when oxygen production exceeded consumption. This is likely to be associated with the onset of green-plant photosynthesis – paleontological evidence suggests the existence of algae at least 2 thousand million years ago, and probably much earlier still. By 1.2 thousand million years ago, sufficient oxygen was present in the atmosphere to allow the formation of extensive sedimentary "red-beds" containing ferric iron.

The present composition of the Earth's atmosphere is 78% N_2, 21% O_2, 0.9% Ar (argon) and 0.03% CO_2, plus other gases such as Ne (neon), He, CH_4 and Kr (krypton) in smaller amounts (the amount of H_2O is variable, of course, depending on the degree of saturation). It is likely that the oceans play a crucial role in controlling the composition of the atmosphere by absorbing CO_2, which is later deposited as carbonates and organic carbon in *sedimentary rocks.

It is worth noting that the Venera and Mariner spacecraft sent to Venus found an atmosphere consisting of 97% CO_2 at temperatures around 860°F (460°C). It had been suggested that these conditions are the result of initially small build-ups of CO_2 in the Venusian atmosphere triggering a disastrously increasing greenhouse effect, caused by the retention of heat by CO_2 molecules. It appears possible that if the carbon dioxide content of the Earth's atmosphere were to exceed a critical level (perhaps as a result of the increased burning of fossil fuels), the Earth's surface temperature would rise, thereby releasing more CO_2 from the oceans and producing a similar effect.

A temperature of 860°F, as found on Venus, is clearly sufficient to vaporize all our rivers and oceans. Such a temperature would even release most of the CO_2 locked up in sedimentary carbonates. However, long before then, Earth would be, like Venus, a dead planet. It is therefore of obvious importance to increase our understanding of the controls on atmosphere composition and temperature on Earth.

Isotope Geochemistry. The number of protons (positively charged particles) in an atom's nucleus determines its atomic number, and hence its chemical properties. However, each *element may have different numbers of neutrons (non-charged particles) in the nucleus. Thus each element can have a number of different *isotopes* of different mass numbers (sum of protons and neutrons). Some of these isotopes may be radioactive, and can be used for radioactive age determinations (see *age of the Earth). Others are stable. Each element may therefore exist in nature as a mixture of different stable isotopes (as well as any radioactive isotopes that might remain).

Although the chemical properties of different isotopes of the same element are virtually identical, the differences in mass can give rise to small differences in both equilibrium and kinetic properties: when a cloud loses rainwater, the rain is enriched in heavy isotopes and the remaining vapor is richer in light isotopes. Isotopic measurements have made it possible to study the total circulation of water on the Earth.

Different isotopes of the same element can be separated using a *mass-spectrometer*. Modern mass spectrometers can measure variations in isotopic abundances to within about 1 part in 10,000. These measurements make it possible to measure isotopic variations for elements with atomic number up to about 20. Since the effects of relative differences in atomic mass are so small, they become much less important with increasing mass number, and variations in isotopic abundance cannot be detected at all for elements of atomic numbers above about 20. There is one group of important exceptions to this rule, isotopes of radioactive origin. Thus rather large variations in the isotopic composition of strontium, argon and lead are found in nature, due to the production of *strontium from radioactive *rubidium; argon from radioactive *potassium; and *lead from *uranium and *thorium.

The fractionation of light isotopes is most efficient in systems involving a gas phase when there is effectively a continuous fractional distillation. Thus, as mentioned above, the isotopic composition of water vapor in equilibrium with seawater indicates a depletion in heavy isotopes.

Current Topics of Geochemical Research. Considerable effort is being expended on efforts to place further geochemical constraints on possible mantle models and to elucidate the genesis of different igneous rocks. An understanding of the geochemistry of the igneous rocks erupted at spreading and destructive plate boundaries (see *plate tectonics) is expected to be of critical importance in investigating the mechanisms of plate movement.

To test models for the genesis of igneous rocks, detailed measurements are required not only of the phase chemistry of natural systems but also of the behavior of trace components. Experimental determinations of the distribution coefficients of trace components between minerals and melts are being carried out over wide ranges of temperature, pressure and melt composition. Recently improved techniques have extended the range of experimentation to 1.5 million atmospheres of pressure. This may make it possible to investigate the behavior of mantle materials at pressures near to the pressures experienced at the core-mantle boundary.

Experimental investigations of this type are carried out in conjunction with detailed theoretical treatments of the thermodynamic properties of the mineral and melt solutions. Thus studies in geochemistry can yield fundamental information to the fields of solid-state chemistry and thermodynamics – in addition to answering old questions and formulating new problems about the origin and chemical evolution of the Earth. DGF

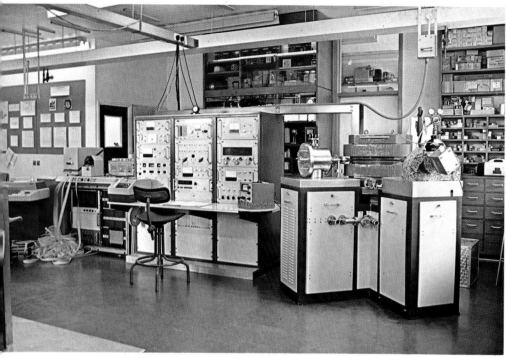

Climatic Zones

Any planet revolving round a sun inevitably has climatic zones. This arises from the simple fact that some parts of the planet receive a greater net amount of light and heat than others, and so there must be some sort of heat-flow from one part to another.

The variations which occur between the patterns of climatic zones of the different planets in our own Solar System depend not only on their possession or non-possession of a fluid mantle, but upon the period of rotation of the planet on its own axis, and the obliquity of this axis (i.e., the angle between its axis and the plane of its revolution around the Sun). The Earth's climatic zones have been subject to change through geological time, not only because its period of rotation and the obliquity of its axis have been subject to some variation, but because the fluid mantle has changed. Moreover, the changing distribution of land and sea, especially in relation to the position of the poles, greatly affects the heat-flow in the oceans and in the atmosphere. There have been changes in some other factors also, such as in the radiation output from the Sun, distance of the Earth from the Sun and from the Moon, and so on.

However, once the Earth had developed a solid core and a fluid mantle, it must have had climatic zones with a recognizable similarity to the present ones, corresponding to a circulation in the atmosphere resembling in general that of today. Given that the Earth has, during geological time, always been rotating daily on its axis with a period much shorter than its rate of revolution round the Sun (now just over 365 days), there will always have been a zone near to the equator where more radiation was absorbed than reflected, and polar areas where more was radiated outwards than

received. The area of net absorption lies today between the Tropics of Cancer and Capricorn, each at an angular distance of 23.5° from the equator, corresponding to the 23.5° obliquity of the Earth's axis at the present time. The zone of maximum net absorption varies with the seasons of the year – i.e., the period of revolution of the Earth around the Sun. Correspondingly, the area of net loss of radiation varies through the year, the extreme variation being beyond the polar circles, whose latitudes are 66.5° (90° less 23.5°). The poles themselves experience continuous daylight for one half of the year, and continuous night for the other half. In between the Tropics and the polar circles are 43° of latitude in which the Sun is never vertically overhead, and in which there is never total darkness or total daylight for 24 consecutive hours at any time of the year.

Whether the Earth were rotating upon its axis or not, there would be a meridional (north-south) flow in the atmosphere to effect the necessary heat compensation between the tropics and the polar regions. There would be between the tropics, as today, rising air (upward convection), which necessarily spreads out at higher levels to flow northwards and southwards, to descend after travelling between a third and half-way to the poles, where there is in general a lack of upward convection. Some of this air then flows equatorwards close to the surface, to compensate for the rising air in the tropics. It follows that low pressure is usual near the equator, and high pressure in mid-latitudes. The vertical circulation here described is known as a Hadley Cell.

The basic situation near the poles, most marked in winter, is that the heavy, cold air – i.e., at high pressure – is always tending to spread equatorwards. It will be realized that the situation is inevitably somewhat complex where this air of polar origin en-

counters the descending air of mid-latitudes, and indeed this is where the Earth's most variable weather is experienced.

One now has to take into account the effect of the Earth's rotation, expressed as the Coriolis force, whose value is nil at the equator. The net effect of this force, combined with frictional drag, is to deflect the meridional flow more and more as one moves polewards. In the northern hemisphere deflection is to the right, so that, for example, the surface equatorwards flow (the Trade Winds) in lower latitudes becomes a northeast wind. In the southern hemisphere the corresponding winds are deflected to the left, becoming the southeast Trade Winds. The slowly outward-spreading air of the polar regions is similarly deflected. Some of the descending air just north of the Hadley Cell moves polewards, and the often strong surface winds are deflected to become (in the northern hemisphere) southwesterly or even westerly: the westerly wind belts are of considerable but varying width. In the southern hemisphere, the strong west winds of these latitudes have long caused them to be described as the Roaring Forties.

The vertical circulation is particularly complex in these latitudes. It is rendered all the more complex by the present distribution of oceans and continents, which in fact modifies the circulation everywhere. The oceans are more heat-conserving than the continents, and the effect of this is that the continents have much greater seasonal ranges of temperature, to the extent that winter in eastern Siberia is colder than at the poles, and this region experiences the highest atmospheric pressures known on Earth. Subsiding cold air tends to spread out then from these "cold poles". The converse is summer heating, leading to rising warm air and a compensatory flow of surface air in toward these areas: the Indian monsoon is the classic example of this.

It will be seen that there are areas which experience, at least seasonally, converging surface winds, of which the warmer is forced to rise over the cooler. When the differentiation between the two air masses is sharp there are distinct fronts, highly characteristic of the westerly wind belt. Rather less distinct fronts, occurring where there is strong convection, are found near the equator – the Intertropical Convergence Zone – between the Trade Winds of the two hemispheres.

The major climatic zones as they exist on the Earth today may be summarized as follows (see also p. 787):

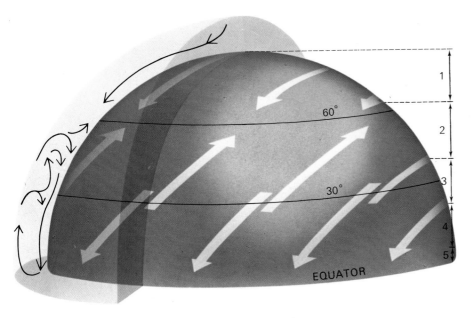

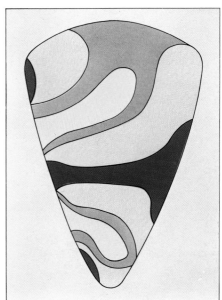

A cross-section of the northern hemisphere showing the climatic zones and a simplified representation of the atmospheric circulation patterns. Reading from the north pole toward the equator the zones are: (1) the polar zone; (2) the westerly wind belt; (3) the Mediterranean zone; (4) the Trade Wind belt; and (5) the equatorial region. Winds blow southward from the pole, and to both the northeast and southwest from roughly 30 latitude. On the left this circulation pattern is shown in its vertical aspect.

The pattern of precipitation that might develop on a hypothetical continent lying from 60° south to 80° north. Due to the rotation of the Earth, the pattern is not symmetrical about a north-south axis. Wet areas are shown in dark green, humid in pale green, sub-humid in brown and arid in pale brown.

(*i*) Equatorial regions, which are hot and wet throughout the year, as a result of continuously strong insolation (amount of solar heat received) and hence upward convection of moist air.

(*ii*) Tropical regions. Beyond about 5° latitude, north and south, the seasonal apparent shift of the Sun north and south begins to be reflected in the emergence of a dry season, which increases in length toward the Tropics of Cancer and Capricorn. The effect of the configuration of land and sea is that the length of the dry season increases more rapidly on the western sides of continents than on the eastern.

(*iii*) Sub-tropical deserts. The last mentioned effect is very noticeable in the Trade-Wind belt, for these deserts in no case extend to the eastern coasts of continents. The greatest extent of desert and semi-desert is, not unexpectedly, in the broadest land mass in the world, from the Saharan coast eastward *via* Arabia to inner Asia. It does of course border the Arabian Sea, but, although this brings it to the eastern coast of Africa, this is not in broad

perspective the main eastern coast of the land mass known as the Old World.

(*iv*) The so-called Mediterranean and China climates embrace those areas where the effect of the north-south apparent movement of the Sun is a seasonal variation of the climatic zone between about 30° and 40° latitude (north and south) between the Trade-Wind belt in summer and the westerly wind belt in winter. In winter the onshore westerlies bring rain to the western ("Mediterranean") coasts, while the easterly Trade Winds bring summer rain to the eastern ("China") coasts. Because of the barrier imposed by the north-south mountain chains in the American continents, the "Mediterranean" zones there are very narrow, and only in the European Mediterranean area has this zone a large east-west extent. The seasonal range of temperature is much greater in the "China" than in the "Mediterranean" type of climate.

(*v*) The westerly wind belt, which tends to have rain throughout the year. The seasonal range of temperature is relatively slight on the western margin of continents, as in the

British Isles, but gradually increases eastwards as the total annual rainfall generally diminishes. But this is the zone of most complex meteorological activity and is characterized by travelling depressions and fronts, which, together with summer convectional activity, bring adequate rain in the growing season to large inland areas.

(*vi*) Polewards of the westerly wind belt is an area of less stormy conditions, but which becomes increasingly cold as one approaches the pole. It has a greater latitudinal extent on the eastward side of the northern landmasses – there is almost no land in the southern hemisphere until one reaches the ice-covered polar areas. In Siberia and northern America, there is sufficient warmth in summer for considerable vegetative growth, but not enough to thaw the soil at depth, and so the zone is characterized by permafrost (see *tundra landscapes).

There are of course various anomalous areas, such as the monsoon climate zones, but these may be regarded as major perturbations of the general zonation, and not as something entirely separate.　　　FG

Processes that Shape the Earth

Continental Drift

For those interested in the history of science, in the interplay of fact and hypothesis, of competing schools of thought and the pervasive influence of intellectual climates of opinion, there are few subjects more fascinating than the long-continued controversy over continental drift. Only within the last decade have the vast majority of geologists and geophysicists come to accept that the continents have moved with respect to each other, splitting up in some regions and colliding elsewhere. It is now customary to discuss such lateral mobility in terms of the theory of plate tectonics, involving both continents and oceans, so that the older name, "continental drift", is falling into disuse. (See also pp. 740–5.)

Although a number of scholars had been impressed by the congruence of the (eastern) South American and West African coastlines, it was not until 1858, with the publication of *La Création et ses mystères dévoilés* by Antonio Snider-Pellegrini, that the first clear suggestion of a break-up and drifting apart of the Atlantic continents emerged. Snider's revolutionary views had no impact, however, upon the contemporary scientific community, mainly because of the fantastic nature of his old-fashioned catastrophist beliefs, for which the only support brought forward was the "jigsaw fit" of the two South Atlantic continents.

Although a few other, rather more respectable, figures speculated upon the possibility of lateral mobility of the continents, at the beginning of this century there was near-unanimity among geologists in favor of the alternative stabilist view.

This hypothesis stated that the continents had remained fixed in their relative positions since the time of their formation early in the history of our planet, and that therefore the ocean basins were permanent physiographic features.

The Earth was supposed to be still in the process of progressive solidification and contraction from a molten mass. Lighter rock materials had moved towards the surface to give rise to granitic-type rocks, and were underlain by denser rocks resembling, if not exactly matching, *basalt, *gabbro or *peridotite. Mountain ranges were produced by contraction in a manner somewhat analogous to the crinkles developed on a shrinking, drying apple. On a larger scale, an overall arching pressure caused certain sectors of the Earth's surface to collapse and subside, giving rise to the oceans, while the continents remained emergent.

Evidence of former land connections, or land-bridges, across what was now deep ocean was provided abundantly by the total or near identity of many fossil animals and plants found on different continents. Unless such transoceanic land-bridges had existed in the past these striking similarities were inexplicable in terms of Darwinian evolution, for genetic isolation should have given rise to morphological differences in the faunas of the different continents.

The first person to make a serious challenge to this long-standing orthodoxy was, strictly speaking, an outsider, because Alfred *Wegener was qualified professionally not in geology but in astronomy and meteorology. However, a man of wide interests and broad vision, he was able to perceive weaknesses in the conventional theory, and put forward an impressive array of evidence from several different research fields in support of his revolutionary theory, continental drift. This received its first public airing in a lecture in Frankfurt in 1912 and was followed later that year by two scientific papers. An enlarged version appeared in book form in 1915 but it was not until the translation into English of the third edition of his book, *The Origin of Continents and Oceans*, in 1924, that the theory began to attract widespread attention.

Wegener postulated a huge, primeval supercontinent, christened by him Pangaea (from the Greek, meaning "all land"), which had begun to split up late in the *Mesozoic era. Its various components had moved apart at different times: South America and Africa had started separating in the *Cretaceous, as had North America and Europe; the Indian Ocean had begun to open up in the *Jurassic but the principal drift movements had taken place later, during the Cretaceous and *Tertiary; Australia–New Guinea had split off from Antarctica in the *Eocene and moved northward, driving into the Indonesian archipelago in the late Tertiary. During the westward drift of the Americas, the western Cordilleran mountain ranges had been produced by compression at the leading edges; while a large area of land to the north of India had crumpled up in the path of the subcontinent during its northward movement, so forming the Himalayas. The Alpine ranges were likewise the consequence of north-south compression between Africa and Europe.

Supporting evidence for continental drift was brought forward from a variety of fields of study. The celebrated "jigsaw fit" of the Atlantic continents was, Wegener considered, no more than suggestive, because it could have been merely coincidental. Much more significant were the many indications from the geographic distribution of distinctive types of *fossil that there had been land connections between the southern continents in pre-Tertiary times.

To give just two examples: *Mesosaurus* is a small Permian reptile known only from South Africa and southern Brazil; and *Glossopteris* is a fossil leaf abundant in many deposits of the same age in South Africa, South America, Madagascar, India and Australia. The *Glossopteris* flora had indeed been known for some time and was the principal argument for the former existence of a southern supercontinent called Gondwanaland (the name is derived from that of a region in India).

Wegener's reconstruction of the map of the world for (1) the upper Carboniferous (Pennsylvanian), (2) the Eocene and (3) the lower Quaternary.

Opposite: a satellite picture showing how separation of the African and Eurasian plates has led to the formation of the Red Sea and the Gulf of Aden.

Wegener argued that the traditional explanation of sunken land-bridges to account for such similarities of organisms between continents now separated by deep ocean was untenable on geophysical grounds. The principle of isostasy implies that lighter, continental crust cannot sink into denser, oceanic crust (the two types of crust were distinguished early this century on the basis of regional gravity measurements and differences in *igneous rocks). The only reasonable alternative explanation was that the various continents in question had drifted apart at some time in the geological past. Indeed the younger faunas, of the Tertiary and *Quaternary, tend to be quite different in each continent.

Another of Wegener's approaches was comparison of geological structures such as *mountain chains, or distinct groups of rocks, in the different continents. He pointed out a number of striking trans-Atlantic resemblances. For instance, the Cape fold mountains of South Africa appear to have a continuation in Buenos Aires Province in Argentina; and the late Paleozoic/early Mesozoic series of largely non-marine strata known in South Africa as the Karroo System are remarkably similar in many respects to what is known in Brazil as the Santa Catharina System. In Wegener's own (translated) words: "It is just as if we were to refit the torn pieces of a newspaper by matching their edges and then checking whether the lines of print run smoothly across. If they do, there is nothing left but to conclude that the pieces were in fact joined in this way."

A third line of argument was based on the reconstruction of ancient climates by investigating the distribution of certain types of sedimentary rocks. A number of distinctive boulder beds signifying deposition from an ice sheet (tillites) occur in late Paleozoic rock sequences in the southern, "Gondwana", continents. In South America, South Africa and India they are of late *Carboniferous age but in Australia there are important *Permian tillites as well. The distribution of these makes no kind of sense with the continents in their present relative positions but, if they are brought together as part of Pangaea, a position for the South Pole in the Carboniferous can be inferred just east of South Africa and within Antarctica.

Wegener suggested that the presence of Permian tillites in Australia and the disappearance of such deposits elsewhere at this time signified an eastward shift of the pole. Confirmatory evidence came from the Northern Hemisphere. Wegener found abundant evidence of a humid equatorial zone, in the form of thick beds of late *Carboniferous coal, extending from the eastern USA through Europe into China. These coals contain fossil plants of tropical type as indicated by, for instance, the lack of seasonal rings in the wood. In the overlying Permian deposits of Europe and the USA there are huge salt deposits, signifying a warm, arid climate. To Wegener this was good evidence of the same polar shift inferred for the southern hemisphere, this time causing a change from a humid equatorial zone to an arid trade-wind zone.

One further line of evidence on which Wegener relied should be mentioned. Geodetic observations made early this century seemed to indicate that Greenland was moving westward from Europe at a measurable rate. Such a movement might constitute a direct proof of continental drift. Unfortunately, however, it has not been confirmed by recent measurements employing more sophisticated and accurate techniques.

The geophysical basis of Wegener's theory was closely related to the principle of isostasy. Both assume that the substratum underlying the continents acts as a highly viscous fluid. Wegener argued that if a landmass could move vertically through this fluid, as was widely accepted, it should also be able to move horizontally, as indeed was indicated by evidence of the *folding of strata in mountain belts. Again, the Earth is an oblate sphere, bulging slightly at the equator: this equatorial bulge is of just the size to be expected for a sphere of perfect fluid spinning on its axis at the same rate as the Earth does. Under short-term stresses, such as those that result in *earthquakes, the Earth behaves as an elastic solid, but in the long term it acts as a fluid. Wegener made an analogy with pitch, a material which shatters under a hammer blow but which over a much longer period flows slowly under its own weight. Movement of the continents was thought to be under the control partly of tidal forces, accounting for the westward drift of the Americas, and partly of a so-called *Pohlflucht* (or "flight from the poles") force, causing movement of India and compression of the Alpine and Himalayan mountain belts.

Initially the reaction of geologists and geophysicists to Wegener's theory was mixed, but by the mid 1920s opinion had hardened against him and he had few supporters. A wide variety of criticisms was put forward. The supposed "jigsaw fit" of the Atlantic continents was inaccurate and did not allow for vertical movements of the crust. The similarity of distinctive rock types and geological structures between different continents had been exaggerated; furthermore, mere similarity did not prove former contiguity. The paleontologists upheld land-bridges of reduced size to account for similarities in ancient faunas and floras—despite the geophysical objections. The Carboniferous and Permian tillites of the Gondwana continents were deemed probably not glacial and the northern-hemisphere coals not necessarily tropical.

Part of Wegener's theory involved a contradiction: if the American continents could move laterally by displacing the ocean floor, how could the Cordilleran mountains have been produced by compression, which implies a significant resistance from the supposedly weaker oceanic rock? More-over, why did the supercontinent Pangaea remain intact for most of the Earth's history and then abruptly break up within a few tens of millions of years?

Perhaps the most serious objection, certainly to geophysicists, was the proposed mechanism of drift. It was not difficult for experts to show that the forces which Wegener proposed were far too weak; polar wandering was likewise regarded as geophysically impossible. Some incensed critics even challenged Wegener's credentials as a scientist: He was a mere advocate, selecting for presentation only those facts that would favor the theory. To quote, he "took liberties with our globe" and "played a game in which there are no restrictive rules and no sharply drawn code of conduct".

Wegener died on the Greenland ice cap in 1930 and it was left to a few enthusiastic disciples to battle on in the attempt to persuade the community of Earth scientists that continental drift was more than mere fantasy. One of these was the South African geologist Alexander *du Toit, who pointed out all kinds of hitherto unemphasized and yet remarkable geological similarities between the Gondwana continents, and also eliminated some of the weaknesses of Wegener's theory, adding modifications of his own. Another was the British geologist Arthur *Holmes, who in 1929 proposed convection currents in the mantle as a driving force for drift, an idea which closely anticipated modern views.

Nevertheless the great majority of geologists remained unconvinced, and opinion in some quarters, especially in the USA, was so hostile that it was advisable for "drifters" to keep their views to themselves if they wished to be considered respectable scientists. It was not until the new discipline of paleomagnetism (see *geophysics) began to produce some astonishing results in the 1950s, followed by equally striking oceanographic discoveries in the 1960s, that the consensus swung dramatically in favor of laterally mobile continents and young ocean basins. With the almost universal acceptance of the theory of *plate tectonics the revolution begun by Wegener over half a century earlier was complete.

The question inevitably arises, "Why was opinion so generally hostile to continental drift for so long?" A number of possible answers can be suggested. Many found Wegener's proposed driving forces totally unconvincing and felt obliged on this ground alone to reject the theory: there are many examples, however, of scientists accepting the existence of a phenomenon without understanding the fundamental cause—the *Pleistocene Ice Age is a good geological example. It has been argued that Wegener's theory was "premature" in that it could not readily be fitted into the framework of existing knowledge. Some might say that for the stability of science any observation or idea that contradicts the established view of the world must be presumed invalid and set aside in the hope that it will eventually turn out to be false or irrelevant. Since geologists like to see things for themselves, more Europeans and Americans might perhaps have been persuaded of the reality of drift if they could have personally investigated the critically important Paleozoic rock successions of South Africa and Brazil. As a final justification, our knowledge of the 70% of the Earth's surface covered by ocean was negligible until the development of new techniques in the last few decades.

But when full allowances are made, it is difficult to avoid the conclusion that much of the hostile reaction to Wegener's ideas was based on prejudice (influenced no doubt by the consideration that he was a geological amateur) rather than on any objective assessment of the facts. The prevailing climate of opinion was such that he was not given a fair hearing. There is perhaps a moral here, that scientists should always strive to avoid dogmatism in their opinions and be receptive to interesting new ideas, however disturbing they may be to the established body of knowledge.   AH

Plate Tectonics

It is rare in the history of science that a single idea or group of closely related ideas can, within a decade of their conception, cause virtually every aspect of their subject to be viewed afresh, and can set into one consistent and intelligible framework the accumulated observations of more than a century. Yet this is no overstatement of the impact of the ideas of plate tectonics upon the Earth sciences as a whole. Geologists, geophysicists and geochemists had for years been studying limited aspects of Earth history, whether it were the distribution of certain kinds of volcano, or the variation in thickness from place to place of the Earth's crust, or the periodic extinctions of groups of ancient organisms. It was as if Earth scientists had been engaged in the completion of an enormous jigsaw puzzle; each making progress with his own group of pieces, but with little consensus on how the groups should be assembled to make the complete picture. And then a crucial piece was found and it at once became obvious how the groups must fit together and what the overall picture must be. Naturally, it has emerged that some earlier pieces which perhaps never fitted too well have had to be lifted out and placed elsewhere; equally there remain parts of the puzzle which have yet to be completed; but at least the broad outlines are now clear.

Early Evidence. In order to discuss and explain plate tectonics it is necessary first to review the background to the discovery. There had long been speculation (see *continental drift) that the continents might have moved with respect to each other during the geological past. Evidence had been of two major kinds—"fit evidence" and "wrong-latitude evidence". The fit evidence was simply that many con-

tinental areas today separated by oceans had shapes which suggested that they had at one time fitted together; furthermore, if continents were reassembled according to shape, there were in many cases similarities between the rocks and fossils of the regions thus brought together. This evidence was suggestive—but not conclusive, because both shape and geological similarities could be coincidental.

The "wrong-latitude" evidence was, however, rather different. Various rocks and fossils which were thought to require rather special climatic conditions for their development were found at latitudes at which such conditions seemed impossible; for example, the occurrence of coal near the south pole (*coal forms in warm subtropical conditions similar to those found in the Florida everglades). Conversely, evidence is found in India of the former presence of huge continental ice sheets such as are today restricted to very high latitudes. Clearly it was very difficult to reconcile observations of this kind with the present pattern of climatic belts, and one solution was to allow that the continents had moved so as to occupy different latitudes at different times.

Although probably the balance of geological evidence favored such large-scale movements, much geophysical theory tended against them. The Earth was known from observations of the transmission of seismic waves to be made up of essentially solid, crystalline silicate material with a partially molten metallic core. It was impossible to conceive of any energy source sufficiently great to power these large-scale motions in solid rock.

In any case, the proponents of continental drift left many questions unanswered concerning the details of the process: the crust of the continents was known to be very thick, ranging from 15 to 43mi (25–70km) with an average of about 22mi (35km). Crust under the oceans was much thinner, only 4mi (6km) or so, and, judging from seismic observations, made largely of different material from that in the continents. Was the crust of the continents to be visualized as ploughing through, or overriding, the crust of the ocean basins?

Some geophysical evidence, however, supported the geological observations insofar as it seemed that some rocks had magnetic characteristics (in fact, a "frozen in" magnetic declination and inclination) acquired at the time of their formation and which could not have been acquired at their present latitude. The movements suggested by the magnetic observations were virtually identical to those required to satisfy the "wrong-latitude" evidence of the rocks and fossils.

Thus, about the middle of the 20th century, there was a stalemate with irreconcilable yet apparently unassailable arguments on either side. In passing, however, it is worth noting one other result of the paleomagnetic studies of the 1950s which at the time seemed of only academic interest.

It became established that the polarity of the Earth's magnetic field could periodically reverse: this simply means that, after such a reversal, a compass needle that today points north would point south. A magnetic field such as we have today is conventionally called "normal" and the opposite "reversed". It seems that the Earth's field has changed polarity frequently in the past. A change in polarity takes about 5000 years to accomplish, and the field then remains constant for periods that mostly last for between ten thousand and one and a half million years. It became possible to draw up a "reversal time-scale".

Mid-Ocean Ridges and Sea-Floor Spreading. About the same time that this work was being done, important observations were being made in the ocean basins. The role of submarine warfare in the WWII had led to the development of very effective acoustic sounding devices that made it easy to map the topography of the sea floor—which submarines might use for concealment. By the mid '50s enough information was available to demonstrate that the ocean floors were topographically at least as interesting as the continents and, in some ways, possibly more informative. Because the influences of weathering and erosion, which continuously modify the shape of mountains and valleys on land, do not operate in deep water, the processes that led to the formation of a submarine topography can often clearly be read in its form. In particular, huge ranges of submarine mountains which rise between 1.9 and 3mi (3–5km) above the *ocean floor (the oceans average about 3mi (5km) deep) became known; these ranges were more or less symmetrical and were about 930mi (1500km) wide. Along their crests had often had a curious "median valley"—a rift-like valley with relatively steep sides, 1.2 to 1.9mi (2–3km) deep and 37 mi (60km) wide. There was a striking similarity to the rift-valley system of East Africa where it had long been thought that the Earth's crust was being stretched apart. In the case of the Atlantic Ocean in particular the overall trend of the mountain range (the mid-Atlantic ridge) was striking. It was central within the Atlantic, and mirrored faithfully the changes in curvature of the margins of the continents on either side. In changing direction to follow the continental shapes the ridge did not simply swing round but was offset repeatedly along great numbers of parallel fractures (now known as transform faults).

It became clear that the mid-Atlantic ridge was part of a more or less continuous world-wide system of ocean ridges more than 25,000mi (40,000km) long; not all divided oceans symmetrically, and not all had rifts along their crests.

Frequently, at the same time as shipboard instruments were being run to survey the ocean floor, another instrument, a seaborne magnetometer, was being towed some distance behind the ship in order to measure the intensity of the Earth's mag-

Magnetic stripes across a mid-ocean ridge. The pattern of stripes is symmetrical on either side of the ridge crest. Moreover, the same pattern and symmetry are shown even when two sections of ridge are separated by a transform fault. The distribution of these magnetic stripes is one of the major evidences in favor of plate-tectonic theory.

netic field. It had been expected that in oceanic regions the field would be rather flat and uninteresting; in the event it was found to be extremely variable. It appeared that there were very striking elongate magnetic highs and magnetic lows which ran parallel to the crests of ocean ridges, and that this pattern of parallel highs and lows commonly extended all the way from the ridge to the flanking continents.

It was these observations, and an intriguing suggestion put forward by an American, H. H. *Hess, a couple of years earlier, that sparked the imagination of two Cambridge University geophysicists, Fred Vine and Drummond Matthews. They noticed two features of the oceanic magnetic field which had previously escaped attention. They saw that not only were the magnetic stripes of the ocean floor parallel to ridge crests but that they were *symmetrical* across any particular ridge, that any peculiarities of the pattern on one side of the ridge could be matched on the other. The second feature which they noticed was that, starting at the ridge and working out to one side, the widths of successive magnetic stripes on the ocean floor exactly matched in proportion the known durations of periods of normal and reversed polarity of the Earth's magnetic field going back in time from the present.

To interpret these observations they put forward a bold and completely original hypothesis: they suggested that the floors of the oceans were behaving as the magnetic tape in an enormous tape recorder which was recording the changes in polarity of the Earth's magnetic field. It worked like this: the Atlantic, for example, was imagined to have been initially closed with Africa fitting up against South America – and so on. The continents moved apart and partially molten material from the Earth's interior welled up to occupy the gap in between. Rocks have no magnetic properties while they are

hot, but as they cool below about 850°F (450°C) they can become weak permanent magnets, "freezing" into their mineral structure some "memory" of the ambient magnetic field in which they cooled (see *geophysics). Thus the first material to well up between the separating continents would acquire thermoremnant magnetism which reflected the polarity of the Earth's field at that time. As the separation continued, material would continue to well up and cool along the axis of separation; as soon as a reversal of the magnetic field occurred, however, further cooling would produce rocks which were weak permanent magnets oppositely oriented, and this would continue until the field reverted to its previous polarity. In the case of the Atlantic the axis of separation is believed to be the line of the median valley along the crest of the mid-Atlantic ridge; new material (i.e., lavas) can be observed by submarine photography to be welling up along it today – this will cool with magnetic properties related to the Earth's present magnetic field. Moving out to either flank we find progressively older ocean floor, with the transition from each magnetic stripe to its neighbor recording a change in the polarity of the field at some time in the past, and each stripe recording the polarity of the field at an earlier stage in the opening of the ocean, when that stripe was being formed at the ridge crest. By processes such as these it was possible not only to explain why the crust under oceans was different from that under continents – it owed its formation to quite a different process – but also the way that the magnetic stripes formed and the reason they were symmetrical across each ocean ridge.

When these ideas were first presented in the early '60s they were received with considerable scepticism. The Vine and Matthews interpretation of the magnetic stripes did, however, fit exactly with a

comprehensive sea-floor spreading model for continental drift put forward by Hess a few years earlier. Within two or three years it became clear that virtually all ocean ridges for which there were reliable observations showed the same magnetic characteristics, and that the new interpretation had to be taken very seriously. One important consequence of the model was that, if its magnetic signature allowed an age to be assigned to each piece of ocean floor, it was possible to calculate a velocity for sea-floor spreading. Consistent, and consistently varying, velocities have now been established for ridges on a world-wide basis: oceans are widening at rates ranging from a little over 0.8 to about 5.5 inches per year. (2–14 cm/y).

Subduction. Earth scientists now faced something of a predicament. The evidence for sea-floor spreading seemed very strong but the rate of spreading was very high, amounting to a present-day rate of generation of new surface area for the Earth of about 0.5% per million years (the Earth's age is about 4600 million years). Only two possibilities were open: either the Earth was increasing in volume to accommodate this new surface area or in some way surface area was being destroyed as fast as it was being created. Although the expanding Earth hypothesis has had several distinguished advocates, the weight of opinion has been opposed to it for a variety of reasons: if the Earth had been of much smaller diameter in the past, its density and the acceleration due to gravity experienced at the surface would both have been much greater than today; according to one proposal, all surface objects would have weighed four times as much 200 million years ago, with a host of more or less inevitable consequences for the Earth's surface processes (e.g., the weight of certain large land animals would have exceeded the strength of their bones – not *all* of them could have spent their lives up to their necks in water!). Changes in density would also have affected the Earth's rotational speed and hence the length of the day. Studies of growth patterns in fossils of marine organisms which maintain daily and monthly rhythms (e.g., in response to daylight and tides) show that the changes which have occurred in the length of the day are too small to permit any major changes in the Earth's density.

For these reasons attention was paid to the alternative possibility – the destruction of surface area as proposed by Hess. He had pointed to the importance of the so-called deep-ocean trenches which were found in many oceans, but which were particularly well developed around the western and northern sides of the Pacific Ocean. These had been known about in a general way for many years but had become much better understood during the post-WWII era of sea-floor exploration. The trenches are elongate furrows in the ocean floor and in them the water depth ranges between 5.6 and 6.8 mi (9–11 km), roughly twice the average depth of the oceans: they are normally 150–190mi (250–300km) wide. In the western Pacific they form a semi-continuous chain along the western side and commonly have the form of a series of intersecting arcs. On the concave side (generally the side towards the continent) there is everywhere a parallel ridge, which from place to place breaks the surface to give small islands that are volcanic in origin, although some now carry a surface capping of recent coral growth. Virtually all the present-day volcanic activity of the western Pacific lies along such ridges, immediately west of the deep trenches. The strings of volcanic islands are known as island arcs.

Hess drew attention to other anomalous features of the island-arc areas. A series of pioneering experiments carried out by the Dutch geophysicist F. A. Vening Meinesz in the '30s had shown that there were very strong anomalies in the Earth's gravitational field in the neighborhood of island arcs. These suggested that, under the trenches, low-density crustal rocks had been deflected downwards into the denser material of the mantle. Island-arc regions had also long been known to be seismically active; in particular, earthquakes occur on an inclined zone which intersects the surface above the line of the deep ocean trenches, and dips away under the island arcs at somewhat variable angles averaging about 45°. This inclined zone of seismicity extends down into the mantle for about 430mi (700km).

Hess proposed that at these trenches the ocean floor which had been generated some time earlier at a ridge turned downwards and was subducted into the mantle: the inclined seismic zone was thought to track the downward path of the descending material. This proposal could satisfy the gravitational observations and, in a less obvious way, explain the volcanic activity, thought to be triggered by the descending mass.

The next step had to wait until the last years of the '60s. A decade earlier the US government had set up a world-wide network of high-precision seismic observations (checking adherence to any nuclear test-ban agreement requires that the normal pattern of world-wide seismic activity be known). After ten years of observation it became clear that virtually all earthquakes were restricted to a small percentage of the Earth's surface, and that they were distributed along continuous and very well-defined narrow zones. These zones surrounded huge areas which were virtually unaffected by earthquakes. Once more, this had been known in a general way for a long time, but the observations were rather poorly distributed over the Earth's surface and so the patterns had not been very obvious. It became apparent that seismicity was virtually restricted to mid-ocean ridges, island-arc areas and narrow, linear zones which linked arcs to ridges, arcs to arcs or ridges to ridges.

Theory and Proofs. These observations, coming on top of the discovery of sea-floor spreading, led a number of groups of wor-

A satellite photograph of the Andes. This range, which contains some of the highest mountains in the world, is a result of the interaction between the westward-moving (oceanic) Nazca plate and the eastward-moving South American plate. As the Nazca plate is subducted, mountain-building, earthquakes and volcanic activity occur.

kers separately and simultaneously to the essential ideas of *plate tectonics. The idea was that the surface of the Earth comprised a relatively small number of internally rigid plates and that these were in continuous motion with respect to each other. At mid-ocean ridges they continuously moved apart, new material welling up from the mantle and being welded onto their trailing edges; along the lines of trenches plates converged, one plunging down into the mantle under its neighbor; and along a third sort of boundary (conservative boundaries) plates neither gained nor lost area but simply slipped past each other. This latter kind of boundary frequently had very little topographic expression on the ocean floor except perhaps as an elongate scarp. Virtually all seismicity thus resulted from interactions between plate margins.

The importance of the distinction between continental crust and oceanic crust now becomes clear: plates may be capped by either kind of crust (and in practice most plates are in part oceanic and in part continental) but each plate moves as a coherent entity; continents move apart as if on a conveyor belt, by the generation of new crust at a spreading ridge, and move together by the destruction of oceanic crust at a trench (or *subduction zone*) between them. Oceanic crust has therefore a rather ephemeral existence: the oldest known is about 200 million years old. In contrast, continental crust seems not to be able to be returned to the Earth's interior, at any rate not in any quantity, for it is not only much thicker than oceanic crust but also less

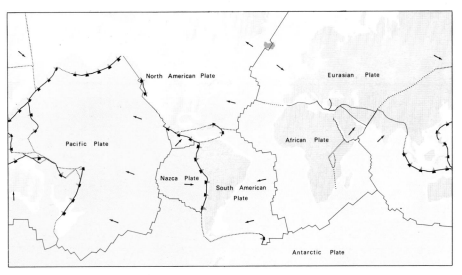

The major plates of the Earth's crust and the directions in which they are moving. Dotted lines show probable plate margins, arrowheads destructive plate margins with underthrusting in the direction of the arrowheads.

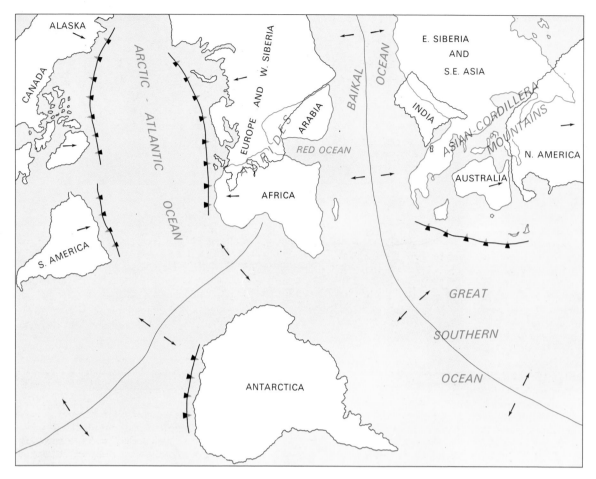

A map of the Earth as it will appear in 150 million years' time.

dense, and it seems to have developed over a long period: the oldest known, in Greenland, is about 3800 million years old.

For any hypothesis to be worthy of serious attention it must be testable, and a great deal of effort has gone into testing the predictions of plate tectonics. One approach was by means of fault-plane solutions. Faults are fractures at the surface of the Earth along which movement occurs between adjacent blocks: sometimes this movement is steady and continuous but occasionally a projection on one block will engage with the opposite wall and the fault will be temporarily locked; locked, that is, until the local stress concentration is sufficient to cause rupture with explosive energy release, giving rise to an *earthquake. At the instant of rupture, the surface of the Earth may be viewed as four quadrants, two of the quadrants being thrown into instantaneous compression and the other two into extension. Examination of seismic records from stations round the world can reveal the orientation of these quadrants for any particular earthquake.

A photograph from space of the Himalayas. Unlike the Andes, where oceanic plate is being subducted beneath continental plate, the more complex folding and faulting of the Himalayas are a result of the collision of two continental plates. The main folding of the Himalayas took place comparatively recently, in the Miocene.

Insofar as the orientation is quite different for movement on a fault along which blocks are sliding past each other from the situation when blocks are moving apart, and different again from when they are converging, it is possible to assign a type of motion to each earthquake for which there are sufficient data, and to compare that motion with what is expected from plate tectonics. The agreement is striking.

A second and more ambitious test was planned: the *ocean floor is subjected to a steady and continuous, but very slow, rain of fine particulate matter settling through the water and accumulating on the bottom. This fine sediment is partly organic in origin – the skeletons of minute marine organisms such as *foraminifera and *radiolaria – and in part made up of fine clay, either washed out into the ocean basins from the continental shelves or made up of fine volcanic dust. Clearly, other things being equal, the older the ocean floor the thicker should be its veneer of sediment. Furthermore, the age of the lowest layer in the sedimentary pile should be close to that of the formation of the volcanic crust upon which it rests. A program of deep-sea drilling was therefore carried out to core the sediments of the ocean floor and to compare the age of the lowermost sediment (as determined by fossils) with the age of the volcanic rocks of the oceanic crust predicted by plate tectonics and the interpretation of the magnetic stripes.

Sufficient results have been obtained from both the Atlantic and Pacific Oceans to demonstrate that both the thickness of the sedimentary accumulation and the age of the lowest sediment in the pile increase systematically away from ocean ridges.

It is now very difficult to see any way in which the general concept of plate tectonics can be shown to be in error, although undoubtedly ideas will undergo modification in many matters of detail.

The Physics of Plate Tectonics. The silicate materials of which the Earth is largely made have some of the properties of ice. Ice in a glacier may be considered either as a very viscous fluid or as a brittle solid depending on the time-scale of interest: struck with a hammer the ice will shatter; left to flow under its own weight down a valley it changes shape continuously as a fluid. Both ice and rocks "flow" in the solid state most readily when they are close to their melting point, and at temperatures much below their melting point behave in a highly brittle fashion and scarcely flow at all. These observations not only help explain the existence of plates but also resolve the classical continental-drift paradox in which it appeared that on the one hand continents must have moved, yet on the other no forces existed powerful enough to propel them if rocks were as strong as they seemed to be.

The silicate material of the Earth's mantle is close to its melting point a hundred miles or so below the surface: it behaves as a crystalline solid for the trans-

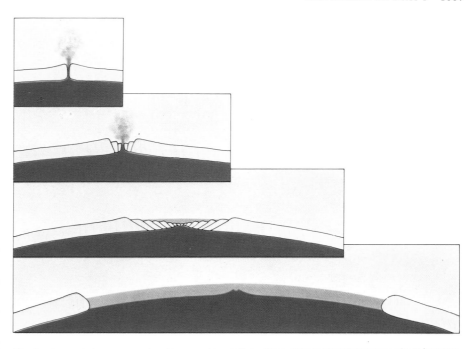

The development of an ocean and a mid-ocean ridge. Initial arching of the continental crust results in fractures and consequent vulcanicity as molten magma from the mantle escapes to the surface. This volcanic activity and slight separation cause downfaulting. As the arch collapses water is able to fill the central area in the form of a shallow sea: by this time major separation is underway and new oceanic crust is in the process of formation. The end result is complete separation of the continental masses, between which stretches an ocean. Centrally placed is a mid-ocean ridge, the site of further sea-floor spreading.

mission of elastic waves, but if subjected to small stress differences will flow readily at the rates required for plate tectonics. As continents move apart, hot ductile mantle material wells up between them to form the new ocean floor. The ocean floor is, however, maintained by the circulation of sea water at a temperature close to $40°$F (about $4°$C), more than $1800F°$ ($1000C°$) below the temperature required for the start of melting of the mantle. The new ocean floor and the immediately underlying upper mantle are both therefore rapidly chilled, and for that reason become strong, giving rise to oceanic plate. The effects of cooling penetrate the mantle quickly at first and then

more slowly, and thus plates thicken with time, achieving an average thickness of about 50mi (80km). Because oceanic plates are cooler than the underlying mantle they are also more dense and thus tend to sink into it: this is what happens at oceanic trenches.

Plate tectonics is the surface expression of thermal convection within the Earth. Heat is generated in the mantle by the radioactive decay of uranium, thorium and potassium faster than it can be lost by conduction: plate tectonics allows a continuous upwelling of hot material to the surface where it can cool and, once cooled, be "quickly" returned to the mantle.

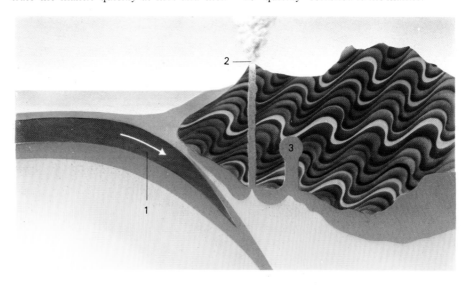

The development of a mountain range at a destructive plate margin, where an oceanic plate (1) is being subducted beneath a continental plate. This results in volcanic activity (2) and igneous intrusion (3) as well as contortion of the continental crust to produce a mountain chain.

Part of the Giant's Causeway near Portrush in County Antrim, Northern Ireland. This columnar structure of basalt consists of tightly packed prisms. Jointing occurred first near the surface of the lava, where there were contractions towards a large number of discrete centers: the result was a polygonal, generally hexagonal, pattern of joints. These developed in depth to produce the columns as cooling penetrated the lava.

justly been described as a "revolution in the Earth sciences". As we have seen, what is essentially a rather simple concept explains satisfactorily many of the problems that have concerned geologists, geophysicists and paleontologists for decades. While it is not in the nature of any scientific discipline to remain static, and so any theory must necessarily be expected to undergo modifications with time, we can say that with the idea of plate tectonics we are close to a full understanding of the physical basis of most, if not all, of the processes that shape the surface of the planet that we live on. ERO

Weathering

Weathering is the breaking down and alteration of rocks at the Earth's surface by the direct effects of local atmospheric conditions – otherwise known as weather. Physical and chemical processes attack the rocks to the extent that they and the products of their weathering may bear little resemblance to the original materials of which they were made up, and may even be completely destroyed. Thus durable granites are reduced to clays, and friable sands and hard limestones simply disappear in solution to leave only minute residues. The biological activities of plants and animals also provide physical and chemical means for rock breakdown.

In the break-up of rocks it is difficult to separate physical disintegration from chemical alteration, and it is true to say that there is little physical weathering that is not also partly chemical. Unlike the situation on the *Moon, where only physical processes operate, atmosphere and water occur everywhere on the Earth and they react chemically with the rock-forming minerals. The new materials which result are relatively more stable and in equilibrium with conditions at the Earth's surface.

Physical Weathering. Rocks are broken down mechanically with little or no chemical change by a variety of causes, some of which can originate within the rock itself while others are of external origin. The deeper a rock is buried beneath overlying material, such as rock or ice, the greater is its strength; but when this material is removed, a rock expands upwards and eventually ruptures, forming a series of cracks or joints. The rock splits along these joints, sometimes parallel to the land surface to form *exfoliation* domes, which are common in granites and sandstones: a good example of their occurrence is in the Yosemite Valley, USA. Joints can also be formed by contraction during cooling of rocks, as in

The development of *mountain chains (*orogenic belts*), within which the rocks have been highly deformed and in many cases recrystallized in the solid state under abnormal temperature conditions, occurs at convergent plate margins (i.e., with one of the plates undergoing subduction) where at least one of the plate margins is continental. At the eastern Pacific margin, the Andes seem to have formed in response to the continued subduction of the Pacific plate in the Peruvian trench; volcanic material has risen from the subduction zone and thickened and elevated the crust. In contrast,

the Alpine–Himalayan mountain belt has developed by the collision of continental masses following the subduction of all intervening ocean floor. Both continental masses are of too low a density to be carried down into the mantle and have come to rest with one having partially overriden the other. The zone of contact is one of enormous geological complexity and the highly deformed rocks within sometimes contain material once deposited on the now vanished intervening ocean floor.

Conclusion. The almost universal acceptance of the theory of plate tectonics has

Large deposits of scree at the foot of Cholatse, Nepal. Scree is composed of rock fragments physically weathered from the mountainside and transported for at most a short distance by gravity. The finest particles have usually been removed by water.

the basaltic lavas of the Giant's Causeway, County Antrim, Northern Ireland. This jointing is important, as it is the means by which all kinds of weathering agents can attack a larger area of the rock.

Rocks can also be exfoliated by granular disintegration, best seen in dry climates with little vegetation, particularly where marked changes in the amount of heat received from the Sun cause thermal expansion and contraction: coarse-grained rocks are affected by this process more rapidly than fine-grained ones. The growth of salt crystals, especially in porous rocks, also causes granular disintegration and such growth can be very disruptive. Most salt weathering takes place in arid areas, where its effect on building materials has been much studied.

Because water expands by about 9% on freezing, frost shattering is probably the single most important physical agent in weathering, particularly (for obvious reasons) in cold climates. If water freezes after entering a joint or crack then its expansion can disrupt the enclosing rock and break it into pieces: angular screes accumulate in this way. In unconsolidated rocks, frost heaving is caused by the movement of water through capillaries from unfrozen ground to ice nuclei.

Chemical Weathering. The main processes of chemical weathering are solution and leaching by water derived largely from rain, and oxidation and carbonation which depend upon the oxygen and carbon dioxide content of the atmosphere. In a general way, chemical weathering is an acid attack on the rocks of the Earth's crust and in particular an attack on the most abundant minerals – *quartz (sand) and aluminosilicates (*clays).

Rainwater, together with soil and groundwater, is a mixed electrolyte containing varying amounts of negatively charged anions (e.g., chloride, bicarbonate and sulfide ions), and positively charged cations (e.g., sodium, potassium, and calcium ions). Ion exchange (a simple reaction between ions in the solution and those held by the mineral grains) is the most important process in chemical weathering. The clay minerals are chiefly responsible for the ion-exchange capacity of rocks, the different clay minerals which are formed by weathering depending upon the parent rock and the degree of leaching. Clay minerals can also change from one to another under suitable conditions; *kaolinite may occur in well drained areas of granitic rocks, *montmorillonite in ill-drained alkaline situations, and *illite in cool temperate climates. The acidity of the weathering environment is highly important, especially to those solution processes that remove minerals like *gypsum, *calcite and

*dolomite. *Feldspars, common minerals in granites, are decomposed by hydrolysis to clays.

Because the Earth's environment is an oxidizing one, many rock minerals combine with oxygen. The best known oxidation process is that of *iron from the ferrous to the ferric state, which, particularly in the presence of water, produces rusting.

There is no absolute scale of degree of weathering, but minerals may be ranked into a series according to general ease of

weathering – quartz, *zircon and *tourmaline being very stable minerals, and *biotite and the feldspars being less stable. Most rocks consist of minerals that are not easily soluble, but over geological time weathering rates can be significant. In general, the rate of chemical weathering is greatest in the moist humid tropics (where it is considered to be 20–40 times that in temperate latitudes) and is least in arid areas (see *arid landscapes). The time taken to weather 3.25ft (1m) of granite in the forest

Rust, an example of the results of chemical weathering. Iron, on exposure to the atmosphere, combines with the oxygen and water present to give hydrated ferric oxide ($Fe_2O_3.nH_2O$). Unlike many tarnishes, rust does not protect the iron beneath from further corrosion.

Chemical weathering at work on a gravestone. Studies of gravestones can be of great value in this context since in most cases the date of erection is accurately known.

zone of the Ivory Coast is considered to be about 22,000 years; in northern England approximately 2ft (60cm) of *Carboniferous limestone has disappeared in about 12,000 years, a rate equivalent to 3.3ft/20,000y – an estimate based on the chemical weathering of naturally occurring limestone and of public monuments.

Chemical weathering can produce a rotted rock-form known as a saprolite, which is the product of chemical changes which have taken place *in situ*. The depth or level to which weathering has taken place, sometimes known as the basal surface of weathering, can be over 1000ft (300m). As a result of chemical changes within this rotted rock, distinct layers or horizons occur, and these make up a weathering profile. Under conditions of heavy leaching, silica is dissolved and insoluble minerals such as alumina and ferric oxide accumulate in the upper part of the profile, forming a weathering crust; this process is sometimes called laterization: the laterites of India have been formed in this way (see *bauxites and laterites). Bauxites (aluminum ore) have also been formed under conditions of leaching, usually under alkaline conditions.

Few landforms are produced by the sole agency of weathering. But rocks that have been shattered or rotted by the effects of extreme weathering are easily removed by gravity or worn away by agents of *erosion such as rivers or glaciers. The removal of deeply weathered profiles in granitic areas, for example, is believed to provide the origin of tors, and of dome-like hills (bornhardts) in savannah areas. Many kinds of tunnels and pits are caused by solution of soluble rocks such as limestones, producing distinctive landforms called karren.

The importance of chemical weathering cannot be overstressed. The changes produced in the rocks form the basis, with biological processes, for soil formation and also affect soil fertility and productivity. Furthermore, chemical weathering is the mechanism for the concentration of many valuable substances, including bauxites, opals and iron ores.   MMS

Erosion

The word "erosion" is derived from the Latin, *erodere*, to gnaw or eat away, and refers to the many processes which wear away the Earth's surface. Rock fragments are first loosened by *weathering (the physical and chemical break-up of rocks by the action of weather) and are then eventually removed by gravity, water, ice or wind. It is difficult to say where weathering ends and transport and erosion begin, but erosion usually implies wearing away by moving agents. In general the agents themselves have only a small effect – it is the material that they carry that is responsible for most of the erosion. The combined effects of weathering, transport and erosion are known as denudation (Latin *denudare*, to strip bare) or degradation.

Water. The downslope migration of rock waste and the displacements of bed rock are commonly referred to as *mass movements*. Such movements include falls of dry material, slides, soil creep and various types of flow, depending upon the amount of water or ice present. Sliding requires a slip surface between the moving mass and the underlying stable ground. Where frost occurs frequently, ice needles push up rock fragments (because water expands on freezing) which, when the ice thaws, slide downhill. All these processes reduce the gradient and lower the ground surface; and of course they act with different intensity depending upon the orientation of the slope.

The washing action of rain is an important agent of particle removal, especially on steep slopes and in areas of intensive rainfall and little vegetation: up to one hundred tons of soil per acre may be shifted by one storm. Rain may become concentrated into

The end-product of fluvial erosion: rounded pebbles in a river pothole in Cape Province, South Africa. The water itself is not the primary agent of erosion, but it contains particles of weathered material and it is these that are responsible for the rounded appearance of the pebbles and the edges of the pothole.

rill wash, which in easily erodible deposits forms intricate gullies and ravines, such as those found in badlands. In mountainous areas where unconsolidated deposits contain large boulders, rain may wash out finer particles, leaving the larger ones behind as protective caps to the less resistant material. This process forms earth pillars which may be several yards high.

Material moved downhill by these means may be channelled into rivers, which are responsible for many types of erosion. One of these is *corrasion*, which refers to the material dissolved in the waters of the river (the dissolved load), representing about 30% of the total removed by river erosion. Rivers also move fragments along their beds which abrade and drill into the bedrock: this process is known as *vertical corrasion* and produces the rounded forms known as potholes. Rock fragments, both suspended and bedload, are jostled by rivers and are broken down by the process of *attrition*. The river's banks are undermined by a scouring process known as *lateral corrasion*. It is estimated that the material brought into the sea by rivers is equivalent to a lowering of the world's land masses by about 3.25ft (1m) in 30,000 years.

A river's volume varies throughout the year, and by far the greater amount of its erosion occurs during its flood stage. The erosion is largely accomplished by turbulent water flow. In steeply graded streams, vertical cutting takes place at rates as great as 20 inches (0.5m) of rock in 3000 years. In mountainous areas or in regions of little weathering, steepsided gorges like the Grand Canyon of Arizona are formed. Most rivers have a winding or meandering habit, eroding the banks on the outsides of the bends and depositing material on the insides. Lateral cutting (i.e., cutting into the banks) is in general much more important than vertical downcutting; it abrades the rock floor to produce rock-cut platforms.

Erosion can also occur when water is not concentrated into river channels. This usually takes place in arid and semi-arid areas where, after storms, flow is in the form of sheet-floods, comparatively shallow floods running over a broad area. Material is transported by such flow over gentle slopes, often at the foot of steep mountains, a delicate balance being maintained between the material delivered to the slope and the rate of its removal. Erosional-transport slopes, pediments, are formed and so the process is called pedimentation.

Ice. Glaciers and ice-sheets are bodies of ice which move slowly over the ground under the action of gravity. Rock fragments loosened by snow and frost become incorporated into the moving ice: if enough of this debris is included in the lower part of

Earth pillars in the Goreme Valley, Turkey. The cappings of rock were originally boulders lying on the surface of the ground: as rain eroded this surface these boulders protected the earth beneath them while the surrounding earth was removed. These particular earth pillars possess an additional point of interest: they have been hollowed out and are used as houses.

the ice, scraping and scratching of the embedded material over the bedrock surface causes *glacial abrasion*, which gives rise to smoothened rock surfaces as well as scratches known as striae (or striations) parallel to the ice movement. The grinding up of rock fragments also forms rock flour, fine sediment associated with rivers draining from glaciers.

At the base of a glacier there are pressure variations which, together with the effects of frost action under the ice, cause joints in the rock to be prized open: blocks become detached and are incorporated into the glacier. This process is called *glacial plucking* or joint-block removal, and is especially important in the coldest glaciers where the ice is frozen to the bedrock, and in rocks where the joints are spaced 3.25–23ft (1–7m) apart. Plucking gives a shattered and broken appearance to the landscape. *Roches moutonnées*, swarms of rocks which have a smooth, gradual slope on one side and a steeper, rougher slope on the other, are caused by abrasion (on the smooth side) and plucking (on the rough).

Glacial erosion modifies river-formed valleys into U-shapes. Relatively small bodies of ice erode corries or cirques, which are amphitheater-like hollows characteristic of glaciated highlands. Glacial erosion is both variable and selective: it is most effective where large volumes of ice are confined in narrow, steeply descending valleys; and in these situations glacial erosion rates can greatly exceed those of rivers. However, in close proximity to areas of intense glacial erosion there may be *plateaux where the effects of ice have been negligible and where the relief is much as it was before the glacier's arrival.

Wind. The wind is an important transporting agent, and this is reflected in the great dust storms which take place in desert areas. The sand grains suspended in the air are the smaller ones, movement of larger particles being along the ground by *saltation* – by a series of jumps. The height reached by such larger particles is rarely more than 6.5ft (2m) above the surface, and so the erosive force of the wind is generally limited to this low level when it meets higher obstacles. The wind picks out structural weaknesses in the rocks, so that their bases are fluted and undercut to form caves, mushroom rocks and irregularly carved ridges known as yardangs.

Sand grains carried by the wind also cause abrasion and polishing of desert surfaces by the natural sandblast – vehicles used in the desert often lose all their paint. Sand grains are blown for vast distances and suffer considerable attrition, becoming almost perfect spheres with frosted surfaces like ground glass, known as millet-seed grains. The wind removes the finer com-

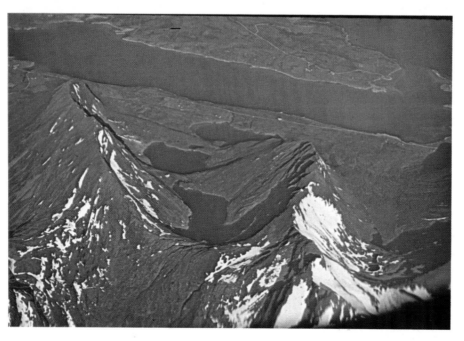
End-products of glacial erosion: a cirque and a characteristic U-shaped glacial valley set high in the mountains of Norway.

ponents of the broken rock, leaving behind a gravelly or bare rock surface, called a desert pavement. Shallow basin-like depressions are formed by this process, known as *deflation*, particularly where soft unconsolidated and friable rocks are exposed: in the Kalahari desert these shallow depressions are known as pans.

In desert areas, much of the wind's energy is used to redistribute sand accumulations. Wind erosion outside these regions becomes important whenever vegetation cover is thin, as in the areas surrounding the polar ice caps: in the Pleistocene period, thick deposits of wind-blown dust and silt (loess) accumulated beyond the glacial limits.

The Sea. Erosion by water, glaciers and wind can act over the whole of the Earth's surface, resulting in an overall reduction of the land (subaerial erosion). But the action of the sea is confined to relatively narrow limits. Wave erosion can occur a metre or so above the level of the highest spring tides; the depth to which wave erosion (as distinct from wave motion) occurs below the lowest tide level is uncertain, though about 23ft (7m) is the usual figure quoted. Clearly, the longer the coastline, the greater the area exposed to the waves.

Though tides and currents may perform erosive and transporting activities, waves are by far the most important marine agents of erosion. This is due both to the hydraulic action of the water itself and to the action of stones and boulders moved by the waves.

Wave size depends largely on the length of *fetch*, the distance at the disposal of the wind for the generation of the waves, which itself depends largely upon local topography. Two main types of waves are recognized: constructive waves, relatively widely spaced, which tend to build up a beach; and destructive waves, which are closer together and tend to erode and comb down a beach. In a destructive wave, the forward wash is weak but the backwash is powerful and removes material seawards.

When waves break against cliffs during storms, they can exert pressures of over 5000lb/in² (35MN/m²), and very high pressures may also result from air compressed between the wave and the cliff. Such wave action concentrates on and opens up cracks and joints in the rocks. Stones and boulders moved by the waves cause attrition; and are hurled at cliffs which become undermined by caves and overhangs. Cliff and cave-roof collapse is aided by surface weathering, and blowholes, arches and eventually stacks (like the famous Old Man of Hoy in the Orkney Islands, off the north coast of Scotland) are produced. In unconsolidated rocks, such erosion may be severe.

Sand and pebbles worked by the waves also abrade the rocks on the foreshore, especially in regions where the difference

Sipapu, the largest of the three natural bridges in the Natural Bridges National Monument, Utah. The bridge, which spans 265ft (81m), was initially formed by one of the two streams that meander through the park, being later enlarged by wind erosion.

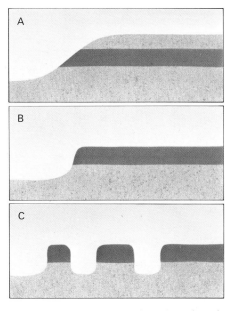

The development of plateau formations through erosion, where a roughly horizontal mass of resistant rock lies in more easily eroded rocks. Initially a table-top is produced, to be fragmented by further erosion so that buttes and mesas are formed.

A dramatic example of marine erosion at work is provided by these cliffs at Bonifacio, Corsica, where the coastline is retreating owing to wave action and subsequent rock falls. Note also the depositional markings displayed in certain of the strata.

between high and low tide is large, and in this way wave-cut platforms are formed. Corrosion (chemical weathering) by sea water and by marine organisms assists in the development of marine platforms.

The Results of Erosion. Erosion is the complement of *deposition, in which material is laid down to form new land. Given enough time, erosion agents cut across bedrock to form erosion surfaces. The ultimate eroded condition of the land is envisaged as a low-relief plain, the peneplain, across which meander sluggish streams.

The stages in the development of the peneplain have been termed the cycle of erosion. Recent work has been critical of the erosion-cycle concept, but there is no doubt about the existence of eroded surfaces; and, with the help of modern techniques, we can now distinguish between the products of the different agents of erosion and so trace the history of such surfaces.   MMS

Deposition

There are many economic and environmental problems where knowledge of sediment transport and deposition can play a part; for example, the design of harbors to minimize silting or of undersea pipeline routes to minimize the damage done by scouring. Such knowledge is also vitally important in investigating ancient *sedimentary rocks, where ability to predict the extent and trend of rock bodies can be of value in assessing and exploiting natural resources such as coal, natural gas or groundwater.

The products of the weathering and erosion of older rocks are distributed on the Earth's surface by a variety of processes. In some environments sediment is simply in transit but in many others deposition is significant, leading to accumulations of sediment which, in favorable circumstances, may become part of the sedimentary-rock record. Knowledge of the processes of sediment transport and deposition, as observed in present-day natural environments and in laboratory experiments, enables us to interpret *sedimentary rocks as the products of such processes.

Agents and Processes. Sediment is moved at the Earth's surface by four main agents, water, wind, ice, and gravity, operating in a variety of processes: these

A blowhole in Corfu. Blowholes are formed when, initially, waves erode deeply into the coastal cliffs until eventually a section of the undermined rocks collapses into the cave beneath it. At high tides waves rush into the blowhole at pressures sufficient for water to be forced out at the landward end, as is happening in this picture. In time the "bridge" of material roofing the seaward part of the cave will also collapse, so that a new inlet is formed.

processes are not exclusive to individual agents, and some agents move sediment in more than one way. It is important to realize that gravity not only plays a part in driving the flow of water and ice but also, in some instances, acts directly on sedimentary particles, causing them to move and be deposited elsewhere. Such direct gravity-produced movement may be aided by the lubricating effect of water or of finer particles between the larger grains.

We will discuss deposition with reference to the four major transport processes, solution, suspension, bedload and mass flow: if we understand these then we are a long way toward understanding deposition, which is merely the cessation of transport.

Solution. Chemical *weathering of unstable minerals causes some of their ions to go into solution. The dissolved ions are transported by rivers into the sea or, more rarely, to an inland lake. In both cases, if addition of ions continues for a long time, there comes a point when the water body is saturated with certain salts, which then precipitate to maintain an equilibrium of input and extraction. The sea achieved an equilibrium in the distant geological past, and this has since been maintained by certain minerals being precipitated from solution in favorable conditions. While sodium chloride (common salt or *halite, $Na^+ Cl^-$) is the most abundant ionic pair in

the sea, it is not the one nearest to saturation: calcium carbonate, the main constituent of limestones and chalk, being far less soluble, is the compound most easily precipitated from seawater, forming the minerals *calcite and *aragonite.

The uppermost layers of the ocean are saturated with calcium carbonate, particularly in tropical latitudes, and so it comes as no surprise to find this material being deposited in great abundance on warm, shallow sea floors such as the Bahama Banks, the Persian Gulf and the Florida Keys. There is also some precipitation of calcium carbonate in colder waters, though here the process is assisted by organic agents. Even in warm seas, such organic agents play a predominant role in precipitation, although straightforward physical processes may also contribute. Many organisms, both animals and plants, secrete calcium carbonate as shells, skeletons or supporting structures, and most naturally occurring calcium carbonate is of this origin. Some aragonite is probably precipitated by inorganic means as ooliths – small rounded particles, a millimetre or so in diameter, which grow by the addition of concentric layers while being rolled about on an agitated sea floor.

Many of the products of organic precipitation are readily recognized as such; for example, the shells of *bivalves, *corals

or *echinoids; but other particles may need to be examined by microscope or electron microscope before their organic origins can be shown. The coccoliths which make up the famous *Cretaceous chalks are a very good example of this.

The only other minerals which precipitate from seawater of normal salinity are certain iron minerals, mainly iron silicates, which accumulate locally off the mouths of some major tropical rivers. Most other minerals that are precipitated from the sea require the salinity to be much greater than normal. In fact a whole suite of minerals is produced by the progressive concentration of seawater. These are collectively referred to as *evaporites. Seawater must have, for example, ten times its normal concentration for sodium chloride to precipitate: clearly, unusual climatic and topographic conditions are needed for this to be achieved naturally. The combination of a hot, arid climate, where the evaporation rate is high, and a basin with a very restricted connection to the open sea allows concentrations to build up as more and more seawater is sucked into the basin to replace

A river delta on the shores of the Arafura Sea. Deltas are a result of the deposition by rivers at their mouths of weathered and eroded material transported by the water. If conditions are favorable (i.e., the water fairly still) the delta will gradually advance seaward.

Weathered and eroded material being transported in suspension colors the water of this river in Sulawesi. Deposition of such sediment at river estuaries may result in formation of a delta. The animals being washed are water buffalo.

that lost by evaporation. The *salinas* of the west coast of Mexico provide examples of these conditions.

Elsewhere, as in the coastal flats (sabkhas) of the Trucial Coast of the Persian Gulf, evaporite minerals precipitate from water within recently deposited carbonate sediments. Evaporation from the exposed sediment surface draws seawater landward through the sediment (rather as coffee seeps into a dry sugarlump), concentrating the water as it moves until *gypsum and *anhydrite (forms of calcium sulfate) precipitate as layers or nodules below the sediment surface.

Suspension. Anyone who has witnessed a dust storm or observed the turbid nature of a river in flood will testify to the ability of both wind and water to carry material in suspension. The sedimentary particles are supported by the turbulence associated with the rapidly moving fluid. Virtually all natural flows of wind and water are fully turbulent – that is, there is a random movement of parcels of fluid superimposed upon the overall fluid movement. The breakdown into discrete clouds of a gently rising column of smoke in still air is a common illustration of the onset of turbulence.

Particles carried in suspension are supported by the upward components of turbulence and, clearly, smaller particles are more likely to be carried than large ones. Normally only the smallest grains are carried in suspension, most typically those in the clay and silt grades (less than 0.0025in (0.0625mm) in diameter), though sand or even larger material may be carried in very strong flows. For particles of silt grade or finer, suspension is the only mode of transport: on *erosion, they go directly into suspension, with no intermediate phase of movement in contact with the bed.

In order for material to be deposited from suspension, the level of prevailing turbulence must be reduced, so that the flow is no longer able to support such coarse, or so much, sediment. Because of the tendency of larger particles to be deposited more rapidly, the deceleration of a flow carrying a range of grain-sizes in suspension may lead to the deposition of a graded bed; that is, one in which there is a gradual upward diminution in grain-size. In cases where only the finest sediment is transported, fine silt or mud will be deposited with no obvious upward grain-size change, though often with a thin parallel lamination such as that seen in many ancient *shales. All *mudstones are the product of gentle deposition from suspension and originate in environments of low current or wave strength; for example, lakes, lagoons, the sea or ocean floor below the wave base, or the more sheltered parts of tidal flats. Once deposited, fine sediment often develops cohesive strength and may be able to resist erosion by subsequent strong currents.

An unusual but geologically very important type of suspension deposit is that produced by a turbidity current. This is a dense current which flows down a slope beneath a body of clear water, the current's greater density being due to its carrying sediment in suspension: the material is there by virtue of the turbulence which is, in turn, due to the flow's existence in the first place. In other words, the current is a dynamic system with a feedback loop involving sediment, slope and turbulence.

Such currents are a common occurrence in freshwater lakes and reservoirs, where sediment-charged rivers spread material out over the lake floor by under-riding the lake water (see *deltas). Temperature differences may also aid the density current. More important geologically are the turbidity currents which introduce and distribute sediment of quite coarse grain-size (sands and fine gravels) in deep-ocean settings, where normally only the finest grains are deposited from suspension. These oceanic turbidity currents are generated on the continental slope, often in the heads of submarine canyons, and flow, normally by way of a canyon, to build up a submarine fan at the foot of the slope where they begin to decelerate. Such activity is particularly common off the mouths of major rivers, where high sediment input can cause the accumulation of large volumes of sediment in unstable settings: periodic removal down the slope relieves this instability. The most spectacular present-day example is the Bengal submarine fan which is fed by the Ganges and Brahmaputra Rivers: this fan extends out into the Bay of Bengal for some 2200mi (3500km), testifying to the distances over which turbidity currents can transport sediment.

The layer of sediment laid down by a turbidity current is called a turbidite, and is normally a parallel-sided sheet of sand, which, in the geological record, will be interbedded with finer background sediment, normally mudstone. The sand or sandstone may show evidence of small-scale erosion on its base and internally may show graded bedding, reflecting the gradual waning of the current. There is often some evidence, in the form of lamination and ripples, of the reworking of deposited material by the later stages of the flow or even by more permanent bottom currents. Thick sequences of turbidites are common in the stratigraphic record; for example, the Silurian *graywacke sandstones of the British Southern Uplands.

Bedload. Many of the complex and interesting structures left on a sandy beach or tidal flat by the ebbing tide, or produced on the bed of a sandy river or even in gutters after a storm, are due to transport and deposition of material which has been carried as bedload. Near to the bed, sand and coarser-grained material normally moves by the rolling, bouncing and jumping of the individual particles. In water, grains up to the size of large boulders can be shifted, though in wind only particles less than 0.08in (2mm) across are generally moved. For sand, the processes of movement and the structures produced are similar in both wind and water, and so can be considered together.

Almost as soon as sand begins to move as bedload under a current flowing in a single direction, the bed becomes molded into small-scale ripples which have their crestlines at right angles to the direction of flow. The ripples have an asymmetry in the direction of the flow (i.e., across the crests), with a gently sloping upstream surface and a more steeply inclined downstream surface, the lee face. Ripples move downstream by erosion of material from the upstream surface and deposition on the lee face; and this is reflected in the internal structure of the ripples, which shows inclined laminae representing the successive positions of the lee face. This lamination, known as cross-lamination, is a common feature of ancient sands and sandstones, and its presence makes it possible for us to interpret the deposit in terms of a current of strength appropriate to the formation of ripples, and whose direction of flow can be deduced from the direction of the inclined surfaces.

With stronger flows, a new form of surface structure develops. This has a shape very similar to that of the ripples, but it is considerably larger and is known as a dune. (The word "dune" is often thought to refer only to those forms built by wind, but it is now used equally for water-lain structures.) Dunes range in size from structures with a relief of about 12in (30cm) up to forms several tens of yards high in windblown deserts or on shallow sea floors like that of

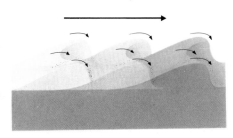

Dune migration. Material is carried up the windward (or upstream) face and drops over the crest onto the lee face. This results in the progressive migration of the dune in the direction of the wind (or water) flow.

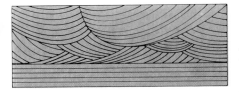

Cross-bedding overlying evenly bedded strata.

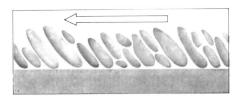

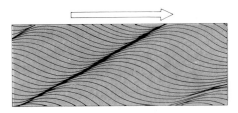

Above, imbricate stacking of pebbles, the planes of the pebbles being inclined in the direction of current flow. *Below*, cross-lamination, resulting from the migration of ripples in the direction of flow by erosion of material from the upstream side and its deposition on the downstream side.

the North Sea. The mechanisms associated with dune migration are very similar to those operating in the case of ripples, and inclined lamination on a larger scale (this time known as cross-bedding) is the characteristic internal structure. This can occur in units up to several tens of yards thick though units of less than 3.25ft (1m) are more common. The largest units are most commonly the products of wind-blown dunes. (See *arid landscapes.)

When the flow strength is greater than that appropriate for the formation of dunes, the bed becomes flattened and a phase of transport is developed where grains close to the bed travel as a rapidly moving sheet (plane-bed transport). Deposition of particles transported in this way produces a parallel lamination in the sand with the laminae, each a few grain diameters thick, showing very slight grain-size differences. The reasons for this sorting are not clear. Parallel laminated sandstone, when split along the lamination, shows a marked linear structure on lamination surfaces, the so-called parting or primary current lineation. This is a common feature of pavement flagstones and is thought to be due to spiral vortices in the flow. It can be used as an indicator of current direction when found in ancient sandstones.

In the case of the most rapid flows, the bed may again be molded into a wave-like form, but the rapid, sheet-like movement of the sand continues and so the waves are much more rounded and symmetrical, and have only a low relief: they often grow and disappear quite rapidly, and can move in an upstream or downstream direction. Such features, called antidunes or standing waves, are often seen in streams running across beaches at low tide or in gutters during heavy rain. They are then obvious because not only is the sediment surface distorted but also the water surface takes on a similar form in phase with the sediment waves below it. The internal structures of these forms are poorly understood and probably involve gently inclined internal lamination. They are unlikely to be preserved in deposits and very few examples have been described from the stratigraphic record.

When the sediment in transport has a substantial proportion of pebbles and coarser particles, the transport and depositional mechanisms and structures are somewhat different from those occurring with sand. In pebbly rivers, the gravel is commonly molded into bars which often split the flow to give the stream a braided pattern. The growth of these bars is complex, but involves both vertical accretion of material to the upper flat surface and extension of the downstream end by avalanching of material swept over the top. This avalanching produces cross-bedding, as in dunes, while the vertical accretion produces a crude horizontal stratification in which the more flattened pebbles show an imbricate stacking, like tiles on a roof, with the inclined planes dipping in an upstream direction.

Imbricate stacking of pebbles deposited in a powerful current. These pebbles have been jostled, transported and roughly sorted; and deposited tilting upward in the direction of flow.

Slumps in dune bedding near Route 89, Utah: the bedding is particularly clear in the lower strata. Note the closely horizontal boundaries between the layers of dune-bedded strata, the layers themselves being termed "cosets".

Ripple drift in beach sand. This occurs because deposition is of greater extent on the lee side of ripples, which therefore migrate downstream.

So far we have only discussed the nature of bedload transport by unidirectional flows, but such movement is also important in wave-dominated environments such as shorelines – the oscillatory nature of the water movement in waves is the dominant cause of differences in the structures produced. Ripples are commonly produced by the action of waves on sand, as a walk on any beach will reveal, but the ripples differ in several respects from those produced by currents. They are much more likely to have a symmetrical profile, with rounded or sharp crests. The crest-lines, which are oriented parallel to the wave fronts (i.e., perpendicular to the direction of wave flow), often show great lateral continuity: where two or more wave systems coexist, complex interference patterns may result. Internally, lamination may be wavy with the laminae inclined in opposed directions.

Some beaches are devoid of ripples: here breaking waves on the ebb tide create flow conditions analogous to the plane-bed mode of transport for unidirectional currents. Gravel beaches show good sorting of the pebbles and, if the shapes are suitable, these may be packed with a good imbricated fabric.

Mass Movement. Viscous material on a slope will flow by shearing within the material. Ice is one such material and, flowing in glaciers, it carries and eventually deposits large quantities of sediment (see *glaciation). Similarly, on submarine slopes or on terrestrial hill slopes during heavy rain, masses of sediment may flow as a highly viscous liquid if sufficient muddy material is present to act as a lubricant. In both ice- and mud-flow situations, because of the viscosity, it is possible for large particles, up to the size of very large boulders, to be transported and deposited.

Glaciers transport vast quantities of sediment of a wide variety of grain-sizes, from the finest rock flour to large boulders. All are transported together within the ice with little sorting of grain-sizes and with little abrasion between the grains. Most deposition takes place at the end of the glacier as a dumped mass of unsorted sediment, a moraine of boulder clay, though this can be reworked by meltwater as bedload or in suspension. Where glaciers end in the sea, material is dropped from the melting sole of the ice sheet or from icebergs floating far from the parent glacier. The deposits of such processes are recognized by the presence of "dropstones", incongruently large grains in an otherwise finer background.

High-viscosity flows produced on slopes by an abundance of muddy sediment occur in both submarine and subaerial environments. The best known mudflows occur on alluvial fans in deserts, where deep weathering gives abundant fine sediment which is periodically flushed out in periods of heavy rain. Such mudflows can travel many kilometres and deposit elongate lobes of poorly sorted conglomerate.

Submarine mudflows are less well understood, but are probably generated by slumping on continental slopes, and may evolve downslope until they come under the influence of turbidity currents. The deposits of supposed mudflows are sometimes found interbedded with turbidites in sequences of deepwater sediment in the stratigraphic record.

Conclusion. The transport and deposition of the weathering products of the Earth's surface involve complex and varied phenomena. Environments of deposition are characterized by the processes operating within them, and control of the development of these environments depends on a clear understanding of the processes. Equally, a knowledge of the products of various sedimentary processes is an essential pre-requisite to any environmental interpretation of ancient sedimentary rocks, and this can often be an important consideration in planning the exploitation of sedimentary natural resources.   JDC

Glaciation

Today, ten per cent of the Earth's land area is covered by ice with a total volume of 6 million cubic miles ($26 \times 10^6 km^3$) and 18,000 years ago nearly thirty per cent was covered by ice with a total volume of around 18 million cubic miles ($76 \times 10^6 km^3$). Some seventy-five percent of this planet's fresh water is currently in the form of ice.

A fine example of a terminal moraine only a few years old near Athabasca, Canada. Terminal moraines are made up of rock particles eroded from the mountainside by the glacier during its descent and deposited as the ice melts (note the "dirtiness" of the ice at the toe of the glacier) or washed out by subglacial streams. Further in the background a cirque can be seen.

Glacial ice forms in cold areas of the Earth's surface where annual snowfall is greater than the amount of snow which melts during the year. Newly fallen snow has a density of about $3lb/ft^3$ ($0.05g/cm^3$), but as it is progressively buried, individual grains are pressed together and the spaces between them may be filled by frozen meltwater; when the density has risen to $51.46lb/ft^3$ ($0.83g/cm^3$) we have ice. Ice masses build up in this way in cold regions, either near the poles or at high altitudes in more temperate latitudes (there are several glaciers on the equator).

Although glacial ice appears to be a rigid material, it is able to flow to a certain extent and so has a tendency to sag under its own weight. Thus the ice masses which build up in cold regions do not continue to grow upwards, but flow away laterally toward warmer regions. The effect of this slow flow can be seen on the surfaces of many glaciers, where bands of debris may show complicated patterns of folding. Large ice sheets are in fact dome-shaped, having typically a parabolic surface-profile which results from the physical properties of the ice. Where glacier ice moves down very steep slopes, the ice is unable to flow

sufficiently quickly to take up the new shape needed to conform to the changing shape of the glacier bed, and so the ice fractures, producing crevasses.

There are three principal types of glacier: ice sheets, valley glaciers and cirque glaciers.

In polar regions great dome-shaped *ice sheets* such as those of Antarctica and Greenland completely submerge the land. The beds of these ice sheets descend below sea level and include high mountain ranges which do not pierce the ice surface. The discovery of the technique of radio echo-sounding has made it possible to determine the shape of the bedrock surface on which these ice sheets lie.

Valley glaciers occur in mountain areas where ice flows away from the main centers of accumulation. Because of the high rates of accumulation in such areas, valley glaciers need to flow very rapidly in order to discharge the accumulating ice. They are thus often highly crevassed and erode deep valleys.

Very small glaciers often form on mountainsides where the net accumulation is relatively small. These erode small hollows on the mountainside to form *cirque glaciers*.

Glaciation in the Past. We often assume that the modern Earth environment is in some way fixed. In fact there is evidence for all to see that Britain and North America were cold enough to maintain very large glaciers until as recently as 10,000 years ago. In the mountain areas of Britain we find armchair hollows known as *cirques*

(cwms in Wales, corries in Scotland) scooped out by cirque glaciers. We find deep U-shaped trenches typical of those cut by valley glaciers, and over much of Britain we find the typical deposit of glaciers, *till*. This is a mixed deposit ranging from clay to large boulders (often striated by glacial action), and represents material eroded by the glacier from the rocks over which it has passed, transported by the moving ice, and finally dumped when the ice melts. It forms the subsoil of much of Britain. We also find evidence of old *terminal moraines*, which are ridges pushed up by the advancing margin of the ice sheet, and which allow us to reconstruct the position of that margin. (See ★deposition; ★glacial landscapes.)

If we consider the last 100,000 years in northwest Europe and North America, extensive glaciation has been much more common than the temperate conditions under which we live at the moment. Evidence from North America in particular shows how, time after time, the great ice sheets thrust to the south, then retreated, reaching at their maximum extent some 18,000 years ago the outskirts of what are now New York and Chicago. These great southward advances were associated with southward movement of the climatic zones, with tundra conditions in, for example,

A spectacular example from Strandflat on the Norwegian coast of a U-shaped valley eroded by the glacier that still partly occupies it. On the surface of the glacier can be seen lateral moraine. The fjord in the background is another U-shaped valley that has been invaded by the sea.

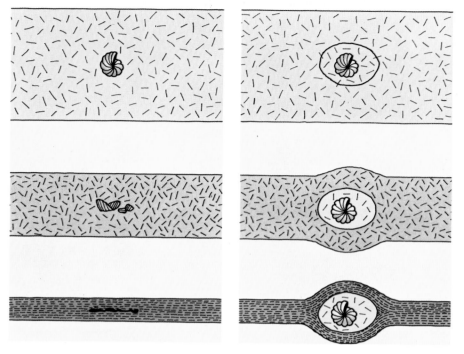

Differential compaction of clay sediments as sedimentary rocks are produced. In the left-hand column, lack of cementation results in the crushing of included organisms during diagenesis of the sediments. In the right-hand column, there is early carbonate concretion around an included organism, protecting it so that even after diagenesis it may be perfectly preserved.

southern Britain and northern and central France, and the prevalence of floating pack ice in the Atlantic down to the latitude of Madrid.

As we have seen, ice sheets have a typical shape, and if we know the areal extent of an old ice sheet from the distribution of till and moraines, it is possible to reconstruct its surface form. Such a reconstruction shows the last ice sheet over Scandinavia to have had a maximum thickness of 1.5mi (2.4km) over its source area. Because of this great weight of ice, the Earth's crust was depressed beneath the ice sheet: when this melted, the crust began to spring upward again, a process which is still continuing. (The process by which the Earth's crust is depressed by superincumbent loads is known as isostasy.)

It has been possible, by radioactive dating of organic material associated with the moraines which mark the successive ice-front positions during retreat, to reconstruct how the great North American ice sheet slowly melted away. We see that by 6000 years ago the ice sheet had collapsed completely in the North American mainland, leaving only remnants in the Canadian Arctic archipelago. The remnants of the European ice sheet are the small glaciers found in the Scandinavian mountains.

Ice Ages. Fluctuations of the Earth's climate and physical environment between glacial episodes (such as that between about 70,000 and 10,000 years ago) and interglacial episodes (such as that between 10,000 years ago and the present day) have been characteristic of the last two million years or so. This is known as the *Quaternary period, during which there have been about seven major glacial epi-

sodes. Before this period, the Earth's climate seems to have been generally warmer, and the great Antarctic ice sheet, which is so important in influencing the Earth's climatic and oceanic circulation, does not seem to have existed prior to about five million years ago.

There are, however, earlier periods of the Earth's history during which we find widespread glacial tills, striated boulders and evidence of glacial *erosion, leading us to think that the Earth has from time to time been subject to ice ages similar to those of the Quaternary. The reason for periodic ice ages, and the glacial and interglacial episodes which occur within them, is still an enigma, but there are two principal hypotheses currently in favor to account for their origins.

Firstly, ice ages could develop when continental plates (see *plate tectonics) move into polar positions so that large ice sheets may build up on them. This hypothesis could explain the initiation of Quaternary ice ages after the Antarctic continent had moved into a polar position in late *Cenozoic times, and might also explain the *Paleozoic ice ages when Gondwanaland lay in a polar position.

However, glaciers seem to have penetrated the tropics during the late Precambrian ice ages, and it may be that for such events we need a second hypothesis, a postulated slow "flickering" of the Sun, whereby its luminosity is (minutely) reduced for a period of time. Astronomical observations of other stars tend, to some degree, to confirm that this is a possibility.

The succession of glacial and interglacial periods within ice ages is most probably related to variations of the Earth's orbit

which affect the intensity of solar radiation reaching the planet. However, there are many other possible mechanisms of climatic change, both on this and on smaller scales, which are internal to the Earth and thus more difficult to identify. For instance, it is possible that the Antarctic ice sheet is unstable, and might flow rapidly into the southern oceans, thereby cooling them and raising world-wide sea levels. With more of the Earth's surface covered by water, the planet's reflectivity (albedo) would increase, so that more of the Sun's light and heat would be reflected back into space, causing global cooling and possibly producing glaciation in temperate latitudes.

Many scientists are now searching for clues about the origin of climatic changes, largely in order to be able to predict future changes in the Earth's climate, on which so much of our economic structure depends. The problem is an important one for, if the immediate geological past is any guide to the future, the present interglacial will one day deteriorate into a glacial period.   GSB

Diagenesis

When sediments are buried, all kinds of physical and chemical processes take place which may lead to quite radical modifications of the original material. Diagenesis is the term used to cover all those transformations occurring at relatively low temperatures and pressures in environments not too far beneath the Earth's surface: at greater pressures and temperatures there is the rather different process of metamorphism (see *metamorphic rocks).

Perhaps the most obvious effect of diagenesis is the transformation of loose, unconsolidated material into hard, compact *sedimentary rock. This aspect (for it is only one) of diagenesis is termed lithification. Good examples are the conversion of sand into sandstone, mud into shale and peat into coal.

Compaction and Cementation. We can recognize two essentially independent components of diagenesis. The first is physical and reflects the increasing overburden pressure as the sediment is buried. Individual sediment particles pack closer and closer together and, in so doing, forcibly exclude some of the sediment pore-water: this is known as compaction. The second component is chemical rather than physical. New minerals precipitate in pore spaces, displacing yet more pore-water, and bond sediment grains together: this is cementation. The cementing material arises from chemical reactions between unstable sediment particles and pore-waters. It may, as in the case of *limestones, amount to wholesale recrystallization.

Compaction and cementation generally progress side by side throughout diagenesis. Occasionally one is directly related to the other, as in the case of "pressure solution" when physical compaction stress causes recrystallization.

Unlike metamorphism, which generally alters beyond recognition the superficial forms of the rocks involved, diagenesis, at lower pressures and temperatures, can preserve superficial forms intact. The ripples on the beach in the upper photograph have been formed by the action of the sea; and it is clear that the quartzite rock in the lower photograph was originally deposited in a similar environment.

In other cases the total diagenetic modification of a sediment may be dominated by either compaction or cementation. The two extremes may even occur side by side when very early cementation occurs locally within a sediment: this results in ellipsoidal concretions, or nodules of hard carbonate-cemented sediment, around which are "wrapped" layers of shaley sediment demonstrating differential compaction. This effect is sometimes beautifully illustrated by perfect preservation of delicate fossils within a concretion, whereas the same organisms are crushed or flattened in the surrounding shale.

The extent of differential compaction is large, especially in mudrocks. At *deposition, muds contain 80% or so of water by volume. Early cementation preserves this open fabric and the true three-dimensional nature of any included organisms. Compaction then reduces the overall volume of the mudstone to one-fifth of the original, but does not affect the early-cemented material.

The Starting Point – Sediments at Deposition.
Fresh sediments contain a variety of mineral constituents from two principal sources.

*Erosion of the land surface contributes soil matter, coarser mineral particles (especially *quartz) as well as much finer clay particles (*illite, *kaolinite, *chlorite, and *montmorillonite). Also present are amorphous mixtures of iron and aluminum hydroxides together with organic matter. Sedimentary processes tend to sort these components into different classes according to size (or, strictly, hydrodynamic equivalent).

The second main source is the depositional water itself. Calcium carbonate (as *calcite or *aragonite) is precipitated, either directly or as the skeletal remains of marine organisms, from the warmer water regions of the world's oceans. These sediments are the forerunners of limestones.

There is a third component of sediments at deposition – water trapped within the sediment pores. This can be fresh or a strong salt solution, as in marine sediments. The very large volume of water trapped in mud sediments means that dissolved salts may constitute a significant fraction of the initial sediment.

Mineral Stability.
Chemically precipitated minerals are stable when surrounded by the waters from which they have been deposited. The fine-grained constituents of soils, however, form under the influence of very dilute aqueous solutions (rainwater) and an oxygen-rich atmosphere. Instability of these components is to be anticipated. The coarser constituents of soils are the more resistant to the *weathering process. They are less likely to be reactive during diagenesis unless, for some reason, they have had little chance to react in the weathering environment. Glacial or volcanogenic sediments contain coarse particles which can be very unstable.

Diagenetic Environments and Reactions.
Recent research programs based on the analysis of sediments and squeezed pore-waters from offshore drilling programs point to the existence of definite diagenetic zones at different depths in buried sediment sequences. Sediments containing organic matter become oxidized just below the sediment/water interface as molecular oxygen is destroyed. From here down to a hundred feet or so, sulfate-reducing bacteria are active in marine sediments: sulfate from the overlying depositional waters and organic matter are consumed and hydrogen sulfide and carbon dioxide produced. The former reacts quickly with unstable iron minerals to produce *pyrite (iron sulfide). Reactions between clay minerals, unstable carbonates and bacterial carbon dioxide lead to the precipitation of calcite (or dolomite) cement. Concretionary bodies are often cemented by pyrite and calcite or *dolomite. These "early" precipitated minerals are sometimes termed authigenic.

Sulfate, like oxygen before it, eventually becomes exhausted as one goes deeper in a sedimentary pile. Conditions then favor bacterial fermentation reactions. Organic matter is converted to methane (*natural gas) and more carbon dioxide. Iron carbonate (*siderite) is a common precipitate in this zone. It should be noted that fermentation will occur at much shallower depths in non-marine sediments – as confirmed by the common generation of "marsh gas" in freshwater swamps.

At burial depths of the order of thousands of yards, temperatures are reached which preclude life, and hence, of course, further fermentation. Unstable minerals continue to react with pore-waters, however, and organic matter evolves towards *coal or liquid *petroleum, depending upon its original nature. Some silicates dissolve, others alter: gradual conversion of

montmorillonite to illite is a common phenomenon. Carbonates continue to precipitate or recrystallize to more stable compositions and crystal structures.

Eventually, of course, temperatures and pressures become so high that there is wholesale silicate-mineral recrystallization with total exclusion of pore-waters. The sediment has then become a *metamorphic rock.

The End Product.
Sedimentary rocks represent the interaction between some or all of the above processes for variable time intervals, with the vast variety of different sediments produced in different depositional environments. Some general patterns do exist.

Slowly deposited marine clay sediments almost invariably contain pyrite, sometimes in sizable quantities. Ancient limestones are almost always entirely recrystallized to low magnesian calcite. The relative reactivity of carbonate minerals in aqueous systems is amply demonstrated. Sandstones exhibit a bewildering range of diagenetic mineralogy and sequences of alteration. Perhaps this demonstrates most effectively of all the dependence of diagenetic reaction upon the presence and involvement of an aqueous phase. Whereas clay sediments eventually exclude most of their pore-waters and become closed systems, most sandstones remain significantly permeable throughout their geological history. They are therefore migration pathways for aqueous solutions, from any source, and naturally the passage of these solutions leaves its mark. CC

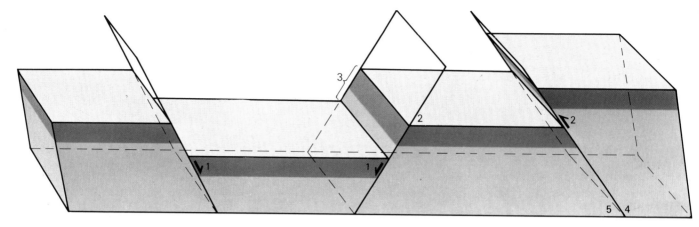

Fault terminology: (1) normal fault; (2) reverse fault; (3) displacement; (4) hanging wall; (5) foot wall.

Faulting

Faults occur on all scales, from the microscopic through to structures that can be traced for a thousand or more kilometres.

The recognition of faults and the terminology used to describe them date from the early days of mining. The faults that concerned the miners were the inclined shear-fractures (dip-slip faults) which disrupted workable seams of coal or metal ores. When these inclined faults were encountered in mine-workings, the rock mass adjacent to the fault plane (the plane along which there had been relative movement) and sloping upward away from the miner was termed the foot wall, the other rock mass adjacent to the fault plane being termed the hanging wall. When the seam in the hanging wall has been displaced downward relative to the same seam in the foot wall, the fault is known as a *normal fault*, because in British mines it was the type normally encountered. When the relative movement has been in the other direction the structure is termed a *reverse fault*.

The orientation of any geological plane is defined by the trend of a horizontal line drawn on that plane, known as the *strike* direction, and the angle of greatest inclination of the plane, the dip angle (or *dip*). Normal and reverse faults both result from slip in the dip direction.

Another common type of shear – which caused little trouble to miners and so was unrecognized for many years – is variously known as a strike-slip, wrench, tear or transcurrent fault. The fault plane is vertical and the sense of movement along it is classified as left- or right-handed, relative to an observer facing the fault. The classification is not as arbitrary as it might appear, since the same sense of movement will be recorded no matter on which side of the fault the observer stands.

Faults which exhibit *oblique slip* – that is, where there has been movement in both the dip and the strike direction – do not fit into the simple system of nomenclature set out here. However, as strike- and dip-slip faults are remarkably common, the terms defined

Small-scale faults. In this rockface can be seen normal faults, reverse faults and strike-slip faults, as well as jointing. Faults may be on far smaller scale even than these – they may be microscopic – or may extend for hundreds of kilometres, as in rift valleys.

The development of an imbricate structure. As the mass of rock flows down the gentle slope its front end encounters a resistance to further motion, while the rearward parts of the block continue to move. This results in compression at the forward edge and the development of a series of faults, often curved.

above are in widespread and frequent use among geologists.

When two faults intersect they may form conjugate fractures. Small-scale normal faults may, in combination, form a graben, and larger fractures and groups of similar fractures having the same general arrangement result in major crustal features known as grabens or *rift valleys: examples are the Rhinegraben and the African Rift System.

During the formation of normal faults and grabens, the main compression which brings about failure in the rock acts vertically (for this reason, normal faults are sometimes termed gravity faults): for both wrench and reverse faults, the main compression acts in the horizontal direction, the type of structure developed being determined by the direction in which the least compression has acted.

Because of limitations set by thickness of the crust and the principle of isostasy, large-scale normal and reverse faults with displacements of more than half a mile are rare. In contrast, major wrench faults (e.g., the Great Glen Fault of Scotland) exhibit displacements of 60mi (100km) or more. Similar large-scale structures, such as the San Andreas Fault complex, California, and the Anatolian Fault, Turkey, are currently active and have caused catastrophic damage to cities in recent times. Such large structures are thought to be related to plate boundaries (see *plate tectonics).

The other type of fault which exhibits displacements of up to 60mi (100km) is the major overthrust. These comprise thin sheets which have moved over horizontal or gently inclined thrust planes (the whole complex may subsequently be folded). Because these structures are associated with

the major fold belts they were originally considered to be the direct result of the compression which gave rise to the fold belt itself – hence the emotive term overthrust. However, it can be demonstrated that many, if not the majority, of such structures were emplaced by a relatively thin (0.6–1.9mi (1–3km)) sheet of rock sliding down a gentle slope with a gradient of one or two degrees. Sliding on such low-angle slopes is possible when the sheet is resting on certain clays (e.g., the Scaley Clays of Italy) and *evaporite rocks such as salt or gypsum. It is now believed that these structures moved downhill because they were supported on weak rocks in which the water pressure balanced the weight of the rock in the sheet such that the frictional resistance to sliding of the sheet was reduced to virtually zero.

When the front end of the gliding block encounters an obstacle of some kind, it slows and stops. However, the rear of the block continues to move, and the compression thus developed at the front end of the block causes the formation of folds (see *folding) or faults. The fault structures which develop at the front end of the block are true thrusts or reverse faults. Often they are curved features which, when they occur close together, are collectively termed imbricate structures.

Joints and Veins. Faults are certainly spectacular structures, but by far the greater majority of fractures one observes in rocks are not faults but joints. These exhibit little or no shear displacement and are mainly the result of minor extensions. Joints usually form clear patterns which influence or control topography.

In the undeformed sediments of the

Elaborate patterns of quartz veins decorate these boulders from Cornwall, Great Britain. The veins occupy preexisting faults.

Grand Canyon the causes of the individual sets of joints cannot readily be inferred: indeed, only when joint sets are related to folds can one deduce how the various fractures are related to the direction of compression.

Sediments and *metamorphic rocks at depth in the crust contain water under high pressure. When water at sufficiently high pressure enters fractures in the rock and the water pressure is sustained for long enough, minerals which have been held in solution crystallize on the fracture walls, held apart by the water pressure, so that veins are formed. The vein material is commonly *quartz or *calcite, though sometimes it includes *gold, *silver, *lead, *zinc or other ore minerals (see *ore deposits). Veins of economic importance are less frequently encountered than the non-economic quartz veins widely developed in deformed *sedimentary rocks. However, to compensate for this, economic veins are sometimes of great extent, as for example the Mother Lode of California (the cause of the '49 Gold Rush), which is many metres wide and extends through a significant part of California.

Conclusion. As we have seen, current movement on faults results in destructive *earthquakes; veins are sometimes productive and of economic benefit; while joints are the bane or the blessing of most engineering or mining projects. From this bald statement alone it is clear that faults, joints and veins are of the utmost importance to us all.   NJP

Earthquakes

Perhaps 60,000 people died in Lisbon on All Saint's Day, 1755, in what was one of the most violent earthquakes on record. At least two major tremors struck the city, causing enormous structural damage and sending the waters of the River Tagus rushing through the streets. The death toll was especially high because the churches were packed, and because of the fire that ravaged the city after the tremors had passed.

Earthquakes are probably the most dramatic of Man's natural enemies; and for that very reason they are worth our study. By developing an understanding of both the causes and effects of earthquakes we can hope to reduce the horrifying toll of lives in the future, not only by selecting suitable building materials and sites but also by playing an active part in modifying the earthquake itself. Before taking any steps in this direction, we have to be able to predict where earthquakes are likely to occur.

Seismic Waves. When some volume within the Earth fractures or implodes, shockwaves are generated. These seismic waves travel away from the source region (or hypocenter) at speeds that depend on the structures through which they pass.

Although earthquakes occur down to a depth of approximately 400mi (700km), an extension of the initial rupture to the surface would occur only for hypocenters within the upper few tens of miles of the Earth. For example, the main shock of the Alaskan earthquake of March 27 1964, one of the largest earthquakes ever recorded, had a hypocenter at a depth of 12–19mi (20–30km).

The shockwaves can be detected by an instrument known as a seismometer, and recorded in the form of a seismogram. The seismogram gives a measure of actual peak-to-peak motions, usually of the order of 0.1in (2mm). The problem of measuring motions while being unavoidably attached to the moving object is overcome by suspending a large weight on a spring. As the ground moves, the mass and the recording

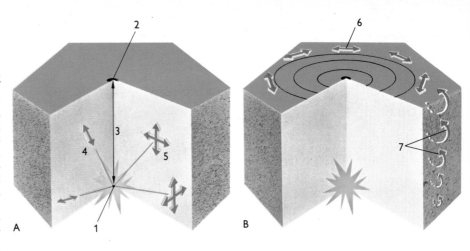

Types of seismic wave generated by an earthquake in relation to the hypocenter (1) and the point on the Earth's surface directly above the hypocenter, the epicenter (2). The distance between these two points is the focal depth (3). Body waves, shown in diagram A, consist of P waves (4) and S waves (5). In B are shown surface waves, comprising Love waves (6) and Rayleigh waves (7).

pen remain approximately stationary because of their inertia, while the rest of the equipment moves. Such a device is a seismometer in its simplest form. In most modern instruments the metal weight swings through an electric coil, thus inducing a current that is used to drive an electrical recording system.

In practice, the natural oscillation of the system has to be critically damped so that it responds faithfully to the varying motions of the ground throughout the signal and not just to the first impulse that arrives. Even so, any seismogram will, to a greater or lesser extent, be a reflection of the characteristics of the seismometer used to make it. If high sensitivity is required, the seismometer is tuned to respond vigorously to the natural frequency of a particular phase rather than displaying a high-fidelity broad-band response: in this way amplifications of as much as 200,000 are commonly achieved.

Two types of seismic wave are generated by the rupture, body and surface waves.

Body waves follow ray paths within the Earth that conform to the rules of simple optics: they are reflected and refracted at boundaries of different density; and are

diffracted, or spread out, round the corners of objects that are of a size similar to their wavelength. The motion of the particles in the ground as the wave passes is either in the direction of propagation of the wave front (for the P or compressional waves), or is at right angles to the direction of propagation (for the S or shear waves). In most rocks, P waves travel at about one and a half times the speed of S waves. In the air or a liquid, P waves are identical to sound waves (S waves do not exist in these media since a shearing motion cannot be sustained).

The common feature of surface waves is that all motion is confined to near the surface of the Earth, the amplitude of the motion dying off rather rapidly with depth. They also are of two types, depending on the particle motion: Love waves have a shearing particle motion at right angles to the direction of propagation and in the plane of the surface, and Rayleigh waves have a slightly more complicated, backward elliptical motion with no shearing component. An important feature of their surface dependence is that the long-period (low-frequency) portions penetrate deeper

Major earthquake foci in relation to plate margins.

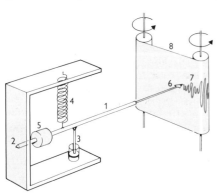

A simplified seismometer. A horizontal bar (1) is pivoted at one end (2) and suspended from a spring (4). A damping mechanism is incorporated (3). As the ground moves, the mass (5) ensures that the bar remains approximately stationary: thus movements are recorded by the pen (6) which draws a seismogram (7) on a chart moving between rotating drums (8).

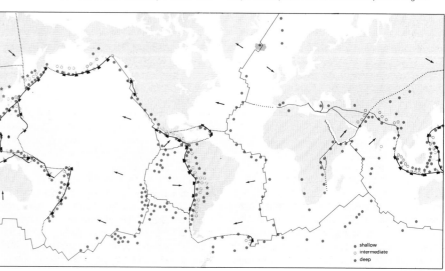

shallow
intermediate
deep

into the Earth than do the short-period (high-frequency) portions. Since seismic velocity generally increases with depth, the long-period surface waves will be traveling through a thicker layer with a higher average velocity than the short-period waves. Within a range of less than a hundred miles from major events, surface waves with periods of 10–20 seconds and amplitudes of an inch or two may be responsible for such effects as earthslides or the slow swaying of tall buildings.

Earthquake Zones. If the locations of major quakes are plotted on a map of the world, differentiating between shallow, intermediate and deep events, two things become immediately apparent. The first is that the distribution is strictly limited to a number of belts; the second that the deep earthquakes are virtually all associated with ocean trenches and island arc structures bordering the Pacific Ocean. Why, we may ask, should this be so?

The answer lies in the theory of *plate tectonics. This theory had its genesis in the theory of *continental drift as well as in studies of earthquake and volcanic action, and the effects of its general acceptance have in recent years radically altered our ideas about the planet we live on. Briefly, the theory implies that the Earth's crust consists of a number of semi-rigid plates that are in motion relative to each other. At margins where plates are meeting, one edge is forced under the other (subducted); and this is compensated for by the emergence of new material in mid-ocean in the process known as sea-floor spreading.

The belts of deep earthquakes are an indication of where oceanic plates and the lighter continental blocks are meeting: as the oceanic plate is subducted, arcs of volcanic islands, mountains and deep ocean trenches are formed. Coupled with this there is, as one might expect, deep seismic activity. In a similar way, the belts of

The remains of Montevago Cathedral after the earthquake that struck Sicily in 1968. Mild tremors began on January 14, and on the night of the 15th an event of magnitude 5.6 occurred, levelling three towns including Montevago. Hundreds lost their lives and more than 83,000 their homes.

shallow earthquakes indicate areas of active sea-floor spreading. The rather more scattered earthquakes throughout Europe, the Middle East and the Himalayas are a result of the collision of continental blocks.

There is a similar correlation between plate movements and earthquake magnitude. In general, the larger events – those with Richter magnitudes greater than 5 or 6 – do not occur in regions of plate creation but are associated only with the more violent process of plate underthrusting. A clear example of this is the zone of activity along the west coast of North America, which defines a region of lateral slip between the Pacific plate and the American plate. The San Andreas Fault system of

California is a clear expression of this; and the San Francisco earthquake of 1906, in which 500 died and a half billion dollars' worth of damage was done, a direct result.

Magnitude and Intensity. The ascribing of a magnitude to an earthquake is accomplished with reference to data obtained at a number of distant stations. The generally used scale is based on one derived by C. F. Richter to compare the magnitudes of earthquakes in the Californian region. The magnitude M is defined by

$$M = \log_{10}\frac{A}{T} + B,$$

where A and T are respectively the amplitude and the period of either the P pulse or the portion of the surface-wave packet with greatest amplitude; and B is a correction factor that takes account of the distance between the event and the recording station. The use of a logarithmic scale is for convenience, since different events release greatly differing amounts of energy: in the Alaskan earthquake ($M = 8.4$), for example, there was about 10^{13} times more energy (or 100 times more energy than in a 100-kiloton nuclear explosion) released than in the smallest recordable earthquake.

The original Richter magnitude scale is applicable only to local earthquakes in California, the distance correction factors being based on the local structure. However, the general formula above, as applied to any region of the world, is used to calculate what is frequently referred to as a Richter magnitude. On average, only nineteen events a year have magnitudes greater than 7, and of these only one would have a magnitude greater than 8; so that, in terms of total energy released, one need consider only nineteen or so earthquakes annually.

In the immediate vicinity of the earthquake source it is sometimes found useful to determine isoseismal lines – that is, lines of equal shaking – throughout the region. Use is made of the Mercalli intensity scale which reads not unlike the Beaufort scale for wind forces. There are twelve rather arbitrarily defined levels of intensity, and so we find that Intensity III is "felt by persons at rest on upper floors and favorably placed"; Intensity VII is "Difficult to stand. Noticed by drivers of motor cars. Fall of plaster. Waves on ponds . . ."; and the final level, Intensity XII or "Catastrophic", is described: "Damage nearly total. Large rock masses displaced. Lines of sight and level distorted. Objects thrown into the air."

The intensities experienced in different places are clearly related to their distances from the source; and a pattern of isoseismal lines, which may provide information about distribution of the *faulting, can be deduced. For example, a long horizontal fracture would normally result in a sausage-shaped pattern of isoseismals; and an extremely localized rupture would produce isoseismal lines roughly following concentric circles.

The ground displacement due to the seismic waves near to the source of a destructive earthquake is of the order of a few centimetres or less. Recordings made some 2.5mi (4km) away from the surface faulting of the San Fernando earthquake (February 9 1971, $M = 6.4$) showed displacements of about 10in (25cm). However, the structural damage to be expected depends upon the acceleration of the ground and the duration of the shaking as well as on the amplitudes of the waves. Gentle heaving of the ground is clearly less destructive than the violent motion of a wave of similar amplitude but very much higher frequency. Moreover, buildings will often withstand high accelerations for short periods but succumb to any prolonged vibration. In addition it should be noted that the horizontal motions of the seismic waves are generally more destructive than the vertical motions.

Fault-Plane Solutions. Detailed information about the present distribution of earthquakes has been a major factor in the study of plate-tectonic processes. In addition, a technique known as the determination of fault-plane solutions has played a large part in confirming the theory.

When a volume of rock fractures along a fault plane, the amount of seismic energy recorded by an observer will depend on the direction, relative to the fault plane, of his observation. Moreover, the sense of the first motion will be either compressional or, in the opposite direction, dilational.

So here we have a way of inferring the orientation of the faulting surface. Observations from stations in different parts of the world can be correlated, and from these it is fairly simple to work backwards to find the direction of the fault plane. There is only one problem: exactly the same results would be obtained for a fault at right angles to this were the sense of the *faulting to be reversed.

This is less of a problem than it might seem, since what we are in general really interested in is the direction of maximum compression, and at right angles to this, the direction of maximum tension.

The fault-plane technique was early on applied to the phenomenon, then only beginning to be accepted, of sea-floor spreading. Spreading occurs along the mid-ocean ridges. At intervals along these there are discontinuities, where sections appear to have been displaced "sideways". It had been suggested that a feature called a transform fault lay between the end of one portion of ridge and the beginning of the next.

If these offsets were due to simple displacement along a *fault the sense of motion would be parallel to the fault in both directions; but if new oceanic crust were being formed at the crests of the ridges and then spreading away, the sense of motion in the region of the fault would be outward in both directions from each of the sections of ridge. Fault-plane solutions were determined for earthquakes located along certain of these faults, and the results con-

formed perfectly with the hypothesis that new material was being created. Sea-floor spreading is one of the foundations of plate-tectonic theory, and so these studies were a substantial contribution toward our understanding of the nature of the Earth.

Earthquake Prediction and Control. Knowledge of where earthquakes are likely to occur is only part of the battle: we also want to know when; and, if possible, whether or not there is anything that can be done to modify the effects of the fracture.

In 1966 an increase in the number of small local earthquakes was observed in the vicinity of Denver, Colorado and it appeared that this increase was related to the disposal of fluid waste down a deep borehole. At roughly the same time it was shown that underground nuclear explosions at the Nevada test site were responsible for a similar increase there: the explosions were thought to act as a trigger, disturbing an existing distribution of stress that was already close to some critical value.

It wasn't long before somebody suggested that it would be a good idea to bore holes along the San Andreas Fault and pump water down them, on the principle that a number of small earthquakes now is preferable to the catastrophically large one that is bound to happen at some point in the future. The firing of a number of small explosions along the fault seemed an equally good idea, for exactly the same reasons. However, the uncertainties were – and still are – much too great, and the consequences of error too serious, for an exercise of this type to be carried out.

For earthquake prediction to be possible, we need some measurable and unambiguous phenomenon that precedes the fracture. Fortunately there is one. Large earthquakes are often heralded by smaller events, known as foreshocks. These seem to be the first signs of a major stress redistribution, which they in fact trigger. (It is equally logical to expect the period before a major quake to be seismically quiet while energy is steadily accumulated, and this "ominous silence" has also been observed in some cases. It too can serve as an effective warning.)

Foreshocks seem to be due to a phenomenon known as dilatancy hardening. Anyone who has walked across wet sand at the seaside will recall how a dry patch appears round each footprint. The sand grains, which had been closely packed together by the sea, have been disturbed by the pressure of the foot. Space between the grains has increased, and for this reason the intergranular water pressure has dropped, resulting in the apparent dryness.

The same sort of process occurs in rocks, and it is called dilatancy. Other studies have shown that decreasing the pore pressure increases the resistance of rock to fracturing, and this increase in strength is, logically enough, termed dilatancy hardening.

It is believed that, as stress build-up approaches a critical value, cracks begin to open and thus the pore pressure drops. This

Earthquake damage in California, the result of movement along the San Andreas Fault. The most recent large-scale movement, reflected in the devastating San Francisco earthquake, was in 1906 when the land to the west of the fault moved some 6.5m (21ft) to the northwest.

results in dilatancy hardening and so the earthquake proper is delayed until water has had time to percolate into the region of low pressure from the surrounding rock. This theory has been tested both by observation of changes in the seismic waves received and by electrical testing of the wetness of local rocks. The results of the tests bear out the theory admirably.

Despite successes of this kind, earthquake prediction is still a long way from becoming a practical reality. Recent researches have shown that precursory phenomena are often very dependent on the orientation of the cracks and the shape of the dilatant region, and for these and other reasons they might go unnoticed. The converse is also true: a region can show all the symptoms of preparation for a quake – and then no quake occurs! As if to add to the present infeasibility of accurate prediction, some workers suggest, and for very good reasons, that the dilatancy-hardening model may be invalid. Nevertheless, we can say with confidence that within a comparatively short space of time geologists will be able to accurately predict and ameliorate the effects of earthquakes.

Associated Phenomena. A variety of phenomena are associated with earthquakes. Effects such as avalanches, earth slumps or the movement of water are relatively easy to explain; but reported occurrences of visible ground waves, sounds or lights in the sky are extremely hard to evaluate. Part of the trouble is that, hardly surprisingly, psychological and physiological effects may well influence observers. However, it is generally agreed that this is at best only a partial explanation for such reports.

Abnormally high-amplitude waves in enclosed stretches of water such as lakes, rivers or narrow channels are known as seiches. When the seismic waves happen to excite the natural frequency of the water in the enclosure, a standing wave results, and this can happen well over 100 miles (160km) away from the epicenter (position on the Earth's surface directly above the hypocenter) of the earthquake due to the long-period surface waves.

Tsunamis or tidal waves, associated with earthquakes, probably come about through a sudden block movement or earthslide on the sea bed displacing a large body of water.

Along shorelines where there are rapidly narrowing U- or V-shaped inlets the amplitudes of the resulting waves can sometimes build up to heights of 65–100ft (20–30m). The east coast of Japan has such a topography, and is surrounded by an earthquake belt which is seismically the most active in the world; and hence this area suffers particularly badly from such waves. Tsunamis can travel a very great distance: for example, the 1960 Chilean earthquake resulted in waves in Sydney Harbor over 3ft (1m) in height.

Consideration of the three effects of visible ground waves, earthquake sounds and earthquake lights is hampered by their being very transitory and poorly documented phenomena. The speed of propagation of seismic waves, measured in kilometres per second, is too fast for the eye. However, it is possible that standing waves could be set up within some structure such as a valley floor, and that this interference pattern then migrates at a visible speed. Similarly, the passage of seismic energy through a corn field would be visible because each blade of corn would sway at its natural frequency.

The conversion of seismic energy in the ground to sound energy in the air is well understood: it would normally give rise to a deep rumbling sound near to the lower limit of our aural range. However, there are still problems in explaining all the reported earthquake sounds; and it must be borne in mind that it is difficult, if not impossible, to separate the sounds produced directly by the earthquake from sounds produced merely by moving structures.

Earthquake lights are even more puzzling. Many reports may arise from hallucination, others through electric arcing when, for instance, a power cable falls down. But there are a sufficient number of sightings for scientists to take seriously the possibility that electrical potentials are set up within the rocks as a result of the stress changes. Some Earth materials are known to possess this type of physical property. The problem is to understand how potentials sufficiently large to cause arcing at the surface can be produced.

Some observers claim to have seen aurorae (polar lights) at the time of earthquakes, and certain of the lighting phenomena may be attributable to this effect. Recently some rather inconclusive evidence has been presented that does suggest a possible causal connection between aurorae and earthquakes. Briefly, the evidence rests on observed correlations between properties of the Earth's upper atmosphere, magnetic field and rotation. By a mechanism that is not yet fully understood, the Earth's magnetic field appears to influence the mean altitude contours of tropospheric pressure in high latitudes. The main source of small changes in the length of the day (rate of the Earth's rotation) is believed to be zonal wind circulation patterns, which in turn are influenced by upper atmospheric weather. There is some evidence of a correlation between changes in the rates of rotation and earthquake activity, which is understandable on consideration of the large amounts of elastic energy stored in the Earth as a result of its rotation. A small change in this rate of rotation could trigger an otherwise delicately balanced set of stresses.

Finally, fluctuations in the Earth's magnetic field due to current flows in the ionosphere, at least partly a consequence of sunspot activity, are manifested in the form of aurorae. And it has been claimed that there is a detectable similarity between the periodicity of sunspot activity and earthquake activity. Although this may turn out to be so much geofantasy, the correlations are tantilizing enough to stimulate considerable current research interest.

Moonquakes. Earth is not alone in experiencing quakes. Seismometers placed on the surface of the *Moon during the Apollo missions have detected hundreds of seismic signals believed to be due to "moonquakes". They are all of fairly low magnitude – indeed, earthquakes of the same size would probably go unnoticed, even by people close to the focus.

There is no evidence of any currently active tectonic processes on the Moon similar to those operating on Earth. However, a strong correlation exists between the times of closest Earth/Moon approach and moonquake activity, and it would therefore seem likely that tidal forces act as a trigger to the release of strain within the Moon: the origin of the strain itself is not known.

This correlation suggests an interesting question: does the presence of the Moon influence the pattern of quakes on the Earth? So far there is no evidence of such an effect, but it will probably be some time before a definite answer can be given. MHW

Folding

Though it is easy to recognize a fold in a rock, it is far less easy to define exactly what is meant by the term "fold". A fold is a curved or flexed arrangement of a set of originally parallel surfaces. These surfaces usually define beds (or layers of rock of specific composition) which were originally

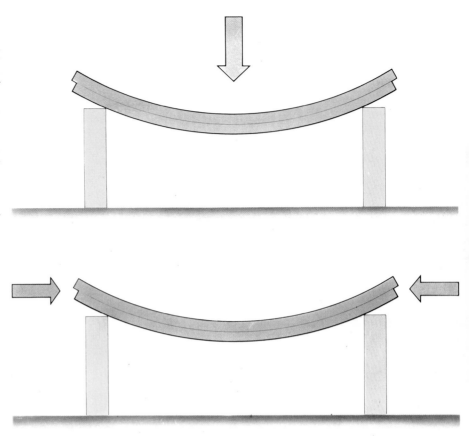

not only parallel but in the form of flat sheets, frequently horizontal. Folds range in size from the microscopic to structures which extend for many tens of kilometres.

From the mechanical viewpoint, folds may result from bending or buckling. Bending is the term used when flexure is induced by pressures applied at high angles to a pile of sheets, whereas buckling occurs when flexure is caused by compression acting inward along the original direction of layering.

Flexures which are the result of bending are known as *drape folds*. Large scale examples of such structures are particularly well developed in the Basin and Range Province of the western USA, where sediments have flexed in response to the vertical component of movements along faults developed in the basement rock beneath. Gentle flexures of considerable lateral extent may develop as the result of differential compaction, as for example where a relatively rigid block of *limestone grades laterally into *mudstone which originally possessed a high porosity (i.e., a high proportion of void spaces). As compaction takes place, the void spaces in

Flexure resulting from bending (*above*) and buckling (*below*).

the mudstone close and the depth of the mudstone layer decreases. Overlying sediments are then flexed as one would expect. In favorable circumstances, drape folds form important traps for hydrocarbons such as *petroleum.

The folds which have received most study are those which have developed in *mountain chains such as the Alps and Rocky Mountains, and the many fossil mountain chains which occurred as the result of earlier orogenies. The dimensions of folds which occur in such chains are extremely varied, their wavelength (i.e., the distance between adjacent peaks or troughs) being largely controlled by the thickness and strength of the individual rock units in

Fold terminology: (1) upright symmetrical; (2) asymmetrical; (3) overturned; and (4) recumbent. A series of folds such as this often culminates with a fold (5) cut by a thrust plane (6) to form a nappe. Also shown is an axial trace, or axial plane (7), the wavelength of one of the folds (8) and the fold axes (9).

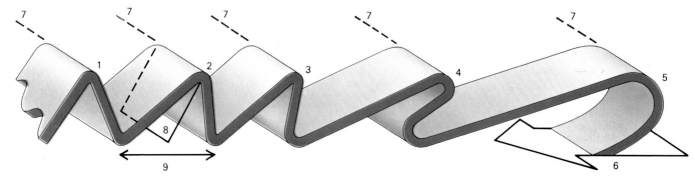

Folds may be on the very large or the very small scale – the former case being exemplified by this photograph of the McDonnelly Range of fold mountains in Australia. Note how the folds die away in the direction of their fold axes (that is, towards the front of the picture).

Medium- and high-grade *metamorphic rocks often exhibit complex geometrical forms that are the result of *multiple folding*. Indeed, the unravelling of these complex structures which show the imprint of two, three or even four separate and consecutive phases of folding has absorbed the interest of many geologists for the last two decades. The interference patterns which develop by the folding of folds are many and varied.

One often observes folds with smaller folds "upon their backs". These minor structures were at one time termed drag-folds, but are demonstrably not related to drag and are better termed *parasitic folds*. There are many other forms of minor structures: *pinch and swell* and *boudinage* (so named because it resembles a series of *boudins*, or sausages, resting on a slab) are the result of the extension of beds. These structures occur when relatively strong rocks are distorted, disrupted and spread by the flow of adjacent, weaker rocks. In the environment of high temperature and pressure in which such flow will readily occur, one frequently finds that recrystallization of the weaker rocks results in the development of slaty cleavage, typically aligned parallel to, or gently fanned about, the axial plane of the fold (that is, the plane between the crest and the core of the fold running through the crest of each of the folded beds).

The lateral compression which gave rise to the majority of fold structures in mountain chains developed either as a primary feature of the mechanisms giving rise to *plate tectonics, or as a secondary feature induced as a result of gravity tectonics, the effects of the force of gravity. With regard to the latter, deep-seated disturbances in the lower crust or mantle can result in variations in surface relief. Under suitable conditions, large slabs of rock can glide down gently inclined slopes under the action of gravity – hence the term gravity tectonics (see *faulting). While the sediments slide down the slope they remain undeformed. However, at the front end of the block, where resistance to gliding is first encountered, folds and/or faults develop as a result of induced lateral compression.

Model experiments indicate that, contrary to certain theoretical predictions, such folds form serially, one after the other. These model folds, produced by simple horizontal compression, show a similarity to natural folds which develop in the Jura. Identical model folds can be produced by the gliding mechanism of gravity tectonics. It is exactly this similarity in fold form produced by the two basic types of tectonics which has resulted in the long-lasting controversy regarding the relative importance of primary and secondary lateral compression in producing the fold structures in mountain chains.   NJP

which the structures developed. For example, massive limestones of the type seen in the Jura Mountains develop structures with a wavelength of 0.62 to 1.25mi (1–2 kilometres). *Sandstones and *shales with average bed thickness of less than a yard form the smaller, but still impressive, *box folds*, which have a more or less rectangular cross-section, while thin laminations of sediment give rise to the development of small-scale *kink folds*. This trend is continued into the microscopic level where one can find individual minerals, such as *mica, which contain folds.

Folds are frequently observed and drawn in profile, or section, and it is often tacitly assumed – or even stated – that the fold form can be projected in the direction at right angles to the profile (i.e., along the direction of the fold axis) for long distances. Such folds are termed cylindroidal. In real examples, where folds can be traced in three dimensions, it is found that the structures die out along their fold axis and, where suitably exposed, form *whalebacks*. One of the apparent difficulties in interpreting fold development in terms of cross-sections of a landscape is that the beds in portions of the section may be deformed into folds, yet elsewhere in the section be unfolded or only gently flexured. This relationship is readily understood when one realises that folds not only die out along the direction of the fold axis, but also upward and downward.

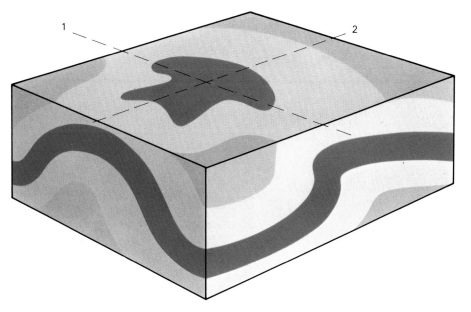

The mushroom interference fold, which develops on a flat outcrop when an initial fold with fold axis (1) is subsequently folded by a second event with axis (2) at right angles to that of the first fold.

A recumbent fold in Carboniferous rocks from Dyfed, UK. In this photograph it can be clearly seen how the degree of flexure dies out both above and below: in the central strata the contortion has been so severe that faulting has resulted. Much of the upper strata has been eroded away.

Dikes are tabular igneous intrusions oriented in such a way as to cut across the bedding planes: they are generally vertical or near-vertical. These dikes, situated near Ullapool, northwestern Scotland, are of quartz pegmatites in gneisses. Similar intrusions, but parallel to the bedding planes, are termed sills.

Igneous Intrusion

Magma which does not erupt as lava or ash from a volcano gradually solidifies below the surface to form an igneous intrusion, or pluton. The rocks so produced are usually revealed only after lengthy *erosion of their cover, but occasionally a new pulse of magma on its way to the surface breaks off fragments that emerge as xenoliths included in lava flows or ash falls.

There are many forms of igneous intrusions, and their classification is generally according to size, shape and their relationship with the country rock around them. A *concordant* intrusion is one whose shape corresponds to the structures of the country rock (for example, following the bedding of strata) whereas a *discordant* intrusion cuts across pre-existing structures. When its thickness is small compared with its other dimensions an intrusion is described as *tabular*; all other types are described as *massive*.

Concordant Intrusions. The commonest concordant tabular intrusion is the sill. Although usually fairly flat-lying, like the filling of a sandwich, sills may be vertical, inclined or undulating depending on the structure, which they follow, of the country rock. Fine examples of sills are the Carboniferous *dolerite sill that forms Salisbury Crags in Edinburgh, Scotland, and the Palisades sill, up to 1000ft (350m) thick, along the west bank of the Hudson River near New York. The Palisades gets its name from the prominent prismatic cooling joints – a common characteristic of large sills – which resemble vertical pillars.

Palisades sill, up to 1000ft (350m) thick, emplaced in the crests and troughs of folded rocks. Much larger in size are lopoliths and laccoliths. The lopolith is shaped like a saucer, concave upward: the Duluth Intrusion at the western end of Lake Superior, USA, 150mi (250km) across and 9mi (15km) thick, is an impressive example. A laccolith is a massive blister-shaped concordant intrusion which may arch the overlying rocks upward.

Discordant Intrusions. The best-known type of discordant tabular intrusion is the dike, a wall-like body which has forced its way, perhaps *via* existing fractures, through the country rock. Most dikes are only a few metres wide and a few hundred metres long, but the spectacular Great Dike of Rhodesia measures 330mi (530km) by 3.5mi (5.5km). Dikes often occur in large groups known as *dike swarms*.

Ring dikes are somewhat larger and shaped like hollow cylinders. They are found usually below *volcanoes which have suffered caldera collapse. Often associated with ring dikes is another type of tabular discordant intrusion, the cone-sheet, which is shaped like a hollow cone, apex downward.

Massive discordant intrusions range upward in size from pipes, the filled-in conduits of volcanoes, through plugs, a larger version of the same, bosses and stocks,

Dike swarms intruded during the Tertiary in northwestern Scotland and Northern Ireland. Swarms are composed of dikes radiating from centers of igneous intrusion as shown diagrammatically in B. Centers of such intrusion are Skye (1), Rhum (2), Ardnamurchan (3), Mull (4), Arran (5), Carlingford (6), Mourne (7) and Slieve Gullion (8).

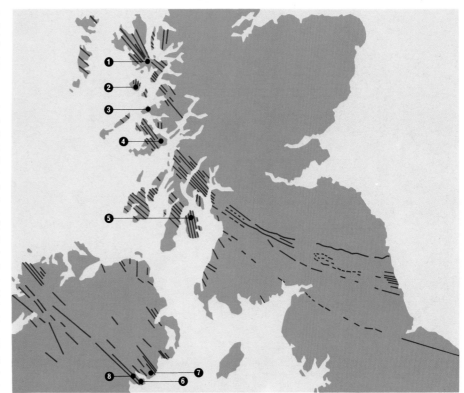

A

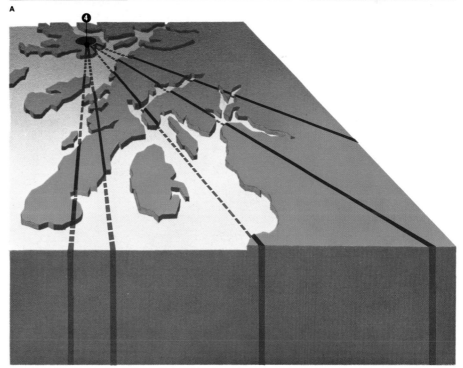

B

which are intrusions having roughly vertical sides and subcircular outcrops, to batholiths. These are plutons with a surface outcrop greater than about 40mi² (100km²): the largest exceed 100,000 square miles (250,000 km²) and form the cores of mountain ranges like the Rockies. Batholiths are multiple intrusions, comprising many separately intruded plutons whose emplacement may have occurred over periods of millions of years. They are complex masses of many different rock types and are generally emplaced above subduction zones (see *plate tectonics). The upper surface is generally irregular, with upwardly projecting stocks and dikes that may be the only surface clue to the much larger body at depth.

Emplacement. Intrusions are emplaced in various ways: for example, by making their way along preexisting faults or fracture zones produced by the upward pressure of the magma; or by *stoping*, a process of gradual movement involving the dislodging of the blocks of country rock and their incorporation – perhaps even assimilation – into the magma. Some intrusions, termed diapirs, appear to have burst through overlying rock like rising bubbles, coming to rest at higher levels.

The upward movement of magma occurs for several reasons. Being a liquid it has a tendency to rise through solid (and therefore probably more dense) country rock, the downward pressure of whose weight also forces the magma into any actual or potential zone of weakness. Magma is also hot, and thus has the ability to melt its way through any material that has a lower melting point: this is limited by the fact that melting of solid rock involves progressive loss of heat energy by the magma, and so a lowering of the magma's temperature.

Mineral Formation. Since it is well insulated by overlying solid rock, a magmatic intrusion cools much more slowly than a lava flow. Although there may be some rapid heat loss at the edges, leading to the formation of a fine-grained or even glassy chilled margin, the rest of the magma usually crystallizes only very slowly within this envelope. Settling of crystals of substances denser than the rest of the magma often occurs, so that layers rich in different minerals are formed, the whole mass then being termed a layered intrusion. During such a process the "volatile" components, such as water and certain elements not incorporated in the minerals common earlier, concentrate as fluids which eventually crystallize either within the intrusion or as injections into the adjacent rock, where they form pegmatites and veins. Pegmatites have very large crystals, usually of only *quartz

and *feldspar, but they sometimes contain rare, economically valuable minerals; while veins may contain also ore minerals, and often show a concentrically zoned structure suggesting several periods of infilling. (See *ore deposits.)

Many geologists, however, regard mineral veins as having been formed by fluids concentrated from the country rock by the heat of an intrusion, rather than as some direct extension of the intrusion itself. Hot, chemically active fluids may diffuse outward from an intrusion to change the

chemical composition of the surrounding rocks, forming new minerals: this process is termed metasomatism. The heat from an intrusion is certainly sufficient to at least harden adjacent rocks, often to recrystallize them and form new minerals in a zone around the intrusion known as a contact metamorphic aureole. Occasionally the heat is great enough to cause partial melting of the country rock – in effect, to produce new magma.

This heat may be of great importance in the future. In many parts of the world solid,

Unusual use made of a volcanic plug in Le Puy, France. Volcanic plugs arise from the erosion of extinct volcanoes, removing the cone but leaving much of the magma that has solidified in the feed channel. They are often termed "puys".

but still extremely hot, intrusions lie sufficiently close to the surface to be reached by drilling. Injecting these with water to produce steam would enable us to harness immensely powerful and long-lived hydrothermal engines, so adding a new energy source for our use at a time when our reserves of gas, oil and coal are dwindling rapidly. JDB

Vulcanicity

A volcanic eruption is perhaps the world's most spectacular way of releasing energy: Krakatoa erupted in 1883 with a force equivalent to the detonation of one thousand million tons of TNT; while the relatively unremarkable eruption of Taal in Luzon, Philippine Islands, in 1965, released an amount of energy equivalent to burning nine million tons of coal. In both cases violent explosions occurred, but a major fraction of the energy expended was in the form of heat: in the Taal eruption the amount of heat energy was eight times greater than the kinetic energy of the explosions.

The Earth is losing heat continuously over its whole surface, but in certain zones this heat flow is concentrated to critical levels. It is in these zones, principally at the

Forms of igneous intrusion: (1) laccolith; (2) sill; (3) batholith; (4) stock; (5) boss; (6) dike; (7) lopolith; (8) phacolith.

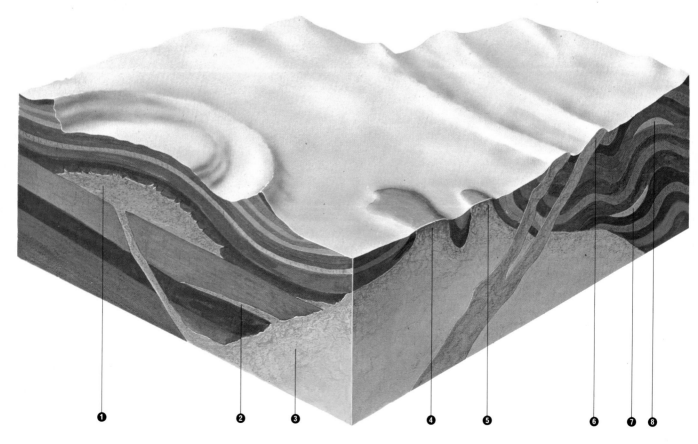

❶   **❷**   **❸**   **❹**   **❺**   **❻**   **❼**   **❽**

margins of tectonic plates (see *plate tectonics), but occasionally within them, that volcanic activity occurs – accompanied by, and closely related to, *earthquake activity.

Generally speaking, volcanic activity is less violently expressed when it occurs within oceanic plates – for example, Hawaii – or at constructive oceanic plate margins, when associated earthquakes are restricted to depths of about 40mi (65km) or less. The 1883 eruption of Krakatoa is an extreme example of the explosive nature characterizing volcanoes located along destructive plate margins, or within continental plates, where earthquakes may occur at any depth down to a maximum of about 450mi (725km). The generally violent release of energy in these areas does not necessarily mean that a greater *total* release of energy occurs there. It may be true that most (in fact, 83%) of the world's known active volcanoes are found along destructive plate margins, but a much greater volume of volcanic material is produced, largely un-

seen; at oceanic constructive plate margins, leading to the formation of entire *ocean floors. Oceanic volcanoes may, of course, have spectacular eruptions, producing impressive clouds of ash and steam – as in the case of Surtsey, Iceland, in 1963 – but this is the result of relatively small volumes of lava exploding when erupted into shallow sea water.

The primary energy source of a volcano, then, is heat contained within magma which has concentrated in sufficient volume to be able to move upward through solid rock. Earthquakes detected some 35mi (55km) below Kilauea volcano in Hawaii are thought to result from this movement of magma batches, although the actual formation of the magmatic liquid before concentration could have occurred, undetected, at greater depths. Subsequent earthquakes at successively shallower depths below Kilauea permit "seismic tracking" of magma on its journey through volcanic conduits until its eventual eruption at the summit caldera and/or along the fracture zones traversing the flanks of the volcano. This now well-observed phenom-

An eruption of Vestmannaeyjar in Iceland. Iceland lies on the Mid-Atlantic Ridge and so straddles a center of sea-floor spreading: this eruption is a consequence of that position.

Spatter cones of Mount Etna, Sicily, the highest volcano still active in Europe: its height varies, with an average of about 10,750ft (3280m). Its lower slopes are fertile and therefore much cultivated, and in places densely populated. The name comes from the Greek *aithō*, "I burn".

Principal regions of volcanic activity. Note the close correlation between vulcanicity and plate margins.

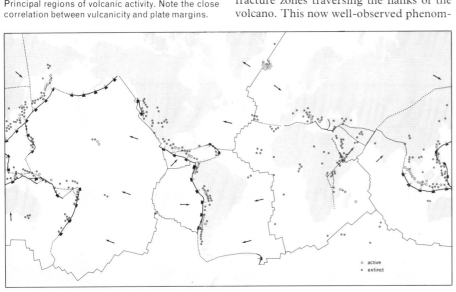

○ active
• extinct

Heimay, Iceland: these houses have collapsed under the weight of recently erupted ash. Volcanic activity takes a high annual toll of property.

Explosive volcanoes disperse their solid material much more widely than do the wholly lava-producing types. Whereas the longest known lava flows, basaltic effusions forming the Columbia River *plateau lavas in the western USA, extend some 125mi (200km), ash from the 1883 eruption of Krakatoa was propelled into the atmosphere round the world, with measurable falls 1500mi (2500km) away in Australia.

Heat may be the primary energy source of volcanism, but gas is the main propellant force behind the high-level eruptive mechanisms of volcanoes. Yet our ideas of the precise compositions and origin of volcanic gas are curiously uncertain. A great deal of water is given off as steam in most eruptions – 15,000 tons a day by Paricutin Volcano, Mexico, in 1945 – but how much of this is groundwater sucked into the volcanic system and how much came from the mantle, dissolved in the magma, is not yet known for sure. The same uncertainty applies to other constituents of volcanic gas, such as carbon dioxide, sulfur dioxide and chlorine, since the elements involved in these could have been derived from crustal rocks as well as being present to some extent in the original magma.

We live in a period when volcanic activity is only moderately intense compared with the great outbursts of early *Tertiary or *Ordovician times. Although its intensity has varied through geological time, volcanic activity has been a major force in the evolution of the Earth since its earliest days. Indeed, we owe our very existence to it since largely by its agency the continents on which we live were constructed and the atmosphere we breathe was first generated; and there is evidence that suggests that vulcanicity may have played a major role in the very *origin of life.   JDB

enon renders Kilauea the only volcano whose eruptive activity can be reliably predicted.

Shallow-focus earthquakes below volcanoes at destructive plate margins may well relate to similar magmatic uprise; but deeper-focus earthquakes, while still possibly recording movement of magma, include some shocks caused by the release of tectonic stress as slabs of lithosphere force their way deep into the mantle. Even then, this form of energy release may contribute to magma formation and hence to volcanic activity. Seismic and volcanic activity thus seem to be inextricably linked.

A volcano is rather like a living thing in some ways. The summit regions of Kilauea and Etna, for example, tilt strongly when magma rises high into the cone; and the volcanoes inflate before an eruption and deflate afterwards – almost as if they were breathing. The internal structure of a volcano contains a complex plumbing system of pipes and passageways, through which magma moves, and cisterns known as magma chambers where the magma may be stored temporarily – sometimes permanently if it solidifies as a high-level intrusion. Deeply eroded volcanoes, such as Piton des Neiges on Reunion Island in the Indian Ocean, reveal this internal substructure as a series of cross-cutting dikes and sills.

The products of volcanic activity are lava, tephra (solid particles of any size from fire ash upward), and gas. When the magma involved is very fluid, gas is easily released and eruptions are nonexplosive effusions, sometimes of great volume and extent. The frequent eruptions of *basalt by Hawaiian volcanoes typifies this style of activity. More viscous magmas impede the release of dissolved gas, which may therefore eventually achieve a vapor pressure high enough to blast out magma – and frequently part of the volcano – as clouds of tephra which may be followed by flows of viscous lava. A higher silica content in a magma increases its viscosity, and thus the andesitic (see *andesite) volcanoes characteristic of destructive plate margins are typically explosive in their activity.

A volcanic bomb from Madeira. Bombs are a variety of pyroclastic rocks, rocks that have had their origins in being thrown into the atmosphere by a volcanic eruption. A volcanic bomb is the result of a body of liquid lava having been thrown spinning through the air.

Geosynclines

A geosyncline is an elongate depression in the Earth's crust that fills with great thicknesses of sediment, beneath which the floor of the geosyncline progressively subsides. Subsequent Earth movements may result in the sediments being deformed into a fold-mountain chain (see *mountain chains).

Two types of geosyncline are recognized. A *eugeosyncline* has a great depth of sediment, of the order of 16,500ft (5000m), and contains a large amount of volcanic rocks: it would appear that the sediments were laid down in deep waters. In a *miogeosyncline* there is a far smaller depth of sediment, of the order of 6500ft (2000m), and an almost complete absence of volcanic rocks: the sediments of a miogeosyncline would appear to have been laid down in comparatively shallow waters.

Associated with geosynclines are geanticlines, uplifted areas which supply the sediments for the infilling of the geosynclines: some geanticlines may represent early stages in the folding of the sediments.   AI

Landscapes

Mountain Chains

The Earth has two great systems of mountain chains in which large areas exceed 6500ft (2000m) in altitude – and the two meet in Indochina.

One is a mainly latitudinal system, oriented west-east and comprising the ranges of the Mediterranean lands (such as the Alps and the Taurus range), of Iran, and the Himalayas. In the east this system branches, thereby enclosing a massive area of high *plateaux culminating in Tibet. The highest elevations on Earth are recorded in the Himalayas (Mount Everest, 29,028ft (8848m)), and much of the Tibetan Plateau lies at around 16,250–19,500ft (5000–6000m). One notable characteristic of this system is that volcanoes, though not absent, are rare.

The second great system of mountain chains is far more longitudinal in pattern and surrounds the Pacific Ocean. It comprises the great western cordillera of the Americas, and associated high plateaux, as in Colorado and Central Mexico, which can be regarded as the counterparts of the Tibetan Plateau. In Colombia and Venezuela there is a forking which gives the discontinuous island arc of the West Indies as one branch; and the chains of Indonesia as well as the island arcs of Formosa, Japan and the Soviet Far East, constitute a more or less symmetrical system that is the other branch. Some of these island arcs may be 1250mi (2000km) or more in length, and they are composed of volcanic materials. Indeed this predominantly longitudinal system is characterized by vigorous volcanic and seismic activity.

Most of these great mountain systems are located on the edges of the main continental areas. This is especially clear in the Americas, but the other continents show it to a considerable degree. Thus in Africa, for example, the Drakensberg, the Guinea highlands, and the Atlas Mountains occur on the perimeter.

Both island arcs and mountain chains tend to lie in close proximity to oceanic trenches. The reasons for this will shortly become clear as we describe their origins in terms of the theory of *plate tectonics.

Composition. The sediments of which these mountain chains are composed show very considerable *folding and overthrusting. The sedimentary rocks characteristically show signs of having been formed rapidly, in deep water, and typically consist of "flysch" (sandstone-shale alternations).

Kang Tega in the Himalayas (the name Himalaya is from Sanskrit and means "abode of snow"). From east to west the range extends some 1550mi (2500km), from north to south 125–250mi (80–155km): the total area of the range is about 230,000mi² (595,000km²).

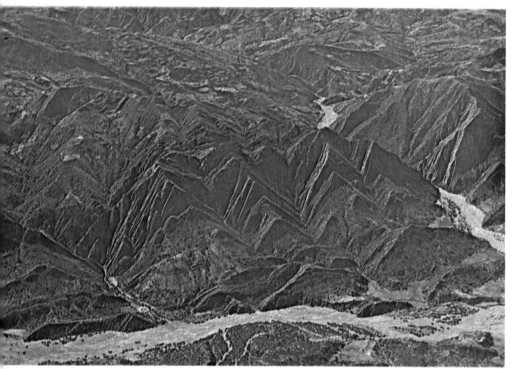

The Andes in Bolivia. The range, which extends from north to south about 5500mi (8900km), contains many of the highest peaks in the world including the highest mountain in the western hemisphere, Aconcagua at 22,834ft (6960m), and a number of active volcanoes, such as Tupungato (22,075ft; 6800m).

There may also be intercalations of submarine pillow lavas or welded tuffs indicative of volcanic islands. All fold mountain ranges develop primarily from exceptionally thick piles of sedimentary strata, commonly 48,750ft (15,000m) or more in thickness. The strata must, therefore, have been developed in a subsiding area, what we sometimes call a *geosyncline, on the continental margin.

The sediments have frequently been metamorphosed by heat and pressure to form *schists. In some areas, such as Japan, there are two parallel belts of metamorphism. One belt, always nearer the ocean than is the other, consists of the so-called "blue schists", containing minerals indicative of formation at high pressure but relatively low temperature. Conversely, the other belt possesses granite and metamorphosed sediments containing minerals indicative of low pressure and high temperature. The blue schist probably formed as a result of the high pressures and low temperatures associated with the ocean trenches, while the inner metamorphic and granitic unit represents uplifted island arcs.

The mountain belts also possess masses of basic or ultrabasic rocks occurring as huge thrust slices or slivers. Their composition and structure strongly suggest oceanic crust or upper mantle which has been sheared from downgoing plates and forced upward under compression into the overlying rock. They probably mark the line of joining of continents which have collided as a result of sea-floor spreading.

Origin. The nature of the sediments and the proximity of mountain chains to continental edges and oceanic trenches clearly indicate that plate movements play a fundamental role in mountain-chain development. Active mountain building (orogeny) occurs where a block of continental crust is carried into collision with another crustal plate.

Most active chains lie on continental plates that are in collision with oceanic crust. For some reason, still imperfectly understood, the lithosphere eventually breaks beneath a geosyncline and starts to plunge into the mantle. The downward-sliding plate of lithosphere butts into the deep water strata, crumples them and rams them against the edge of the continent. The prism of sediment from the geosyncline is compressed into folds and overthrusts. Intensive metamorphism gives schists.

Strata near the bottom of the geosyncline can also be dragged downward by the moving plate. They become heated and the deepest strata may begin to melt. Granitic magma formed by the melting then rises and pushes overlying strata upwards. The melting and stresses associated with the downgoing plate cause the volcanism that produces island arcs in the form of the great Pacific "ring of fire". Their development may be due to the continental plate buckling immediately behind the line of collision where the ocean plate slides beneath it: as the continental plate is lifted and stretched it cracks open and magma bursts through the cracks.

Less common are mountains produced by the collision of two continental plates. When two continents collide they crumple along the colliding edges. However, unlike the situation when a continental plate hits an oceanic plate, a moving continent is too big and its rocks too light for it to be carried down into the mantle with the descending plate of lithosphere. Like a slab of cork the continent bobs up again. This causes marked upward movement, resulting in extremely high mountains. It is this model that explains the development of the Himalayas. Volcanic activity is of little significance in chains formed in this way.

However, some mountain areas are caused by *faulting, pure and simple. A fine example is the Sierra Nevada of the USA. Most mountains formed in this way are less conspicuous than fold mountains – in fact, they are frequently associated with them in a secondary manner, having formed after a prior episode of strong folding.

Ancient and Modern Mountain Chains. In addition to the present great mountain chains, there is also evidence in some areas of ancient orogenic episodes. The areas in question have now been eroded into hills and plains that are no more than mere stubs of former great ranges. In the eastern USA, for example, the contorted rocks of the Appalachians represent the beveled roots of an ancient range. The same applies to the low Aravalli Range of western India, with its greatly denuded schists, gneisses and granites.

What are now high mountain chains are, by contrast, relatively young. They result from orogenies during the Miocene, Pliocene and Pleistone epochs – the last 26 million years or so. Indeed, uplift appears to be progressing with some speed at this very moment. In California, movement operates at a rate of up to 42ft (13m) per thousand years, and in New Zealand rates of 36–39ft (11–12m) per thousand years are known. Given rates of this order, a mountain range with a height of 26,000ft (8000m), like the Himalayas, could develop in less than 800,000 years – though rapid rates of *erosion operative in such high-relief situations would extend the time period required. Nevertheless, it is clear, given evidence of rates of uplift and erosion, that substantial mountain chains can, in terms of the great duration of the Earth's history, be very youthful.

Processes of Mountain Sculpture. Although tectonic events are the primary factor affecting mountain development and form, erosional processes are also of great importance. In the global context, denudation generally proceeds at its highest rate in high-relief areas. The Greater Himalayas and Karakoram are associated with some of the highest recorded rates of large-scale water denudation. The values exceed 3.25ft(1000mm)/1000 years for the Upper Indus and Kosi; and information from Alaskan mountains and the European Alps indicates rates in some cases exceeding 2ft(600mm)/1000 years. For comparison, rates for most lowland rivers are in the range 0.4–4in(10–100mm)/1000 years.

These high rates are produced not only by the large amounts of discharge and sediment carried by the mountain rivers. There are also major mass movements created by a combination of high relief, heavy snow- and rainfall, frequent frosts

Part of the Alaska Range, the northeastern end of a chain that includes also the Aleutian Range and the Aleutian Islands. The chain contains nearly eighty volcanoes, many of which are active, and represents the crest of a midocean ridge. The range includes Mount McKinley, the highest peak in North America (6195m; 20,320ft).

massive scale of the whole Earth, mountain chains are mere wrinkles, but their importance lies not only in the contribution they make to our understanding of Earth history and development, but also in the effect they have on the everyday lives of highlanders and lowlanders alike. (See also Mountain Vegetation, p. 863.)   AG

River Valleys

Like the veins of a leaf or the branches of a tree, river valleys are means by which water moves through a system. The system drained by a particular valley is called the drainage basin or catchment, and the boundary between it and an adjacent valley is called a watershed or drainage divide. (In the USA the drainage basin is sometimes called the watershed, and so the watershed is occasionally referred to as the water parting.)

Whether they are large or small, drainage basins have similar characteristics and comparable patterns. The individual valleys form a branching system, and in general this will be of roughly the same design as are all other such basins. One example of this can be found by ranking streams according to "order". In this system, fingertip tributaries are described as first-order; when two first-order streams combine the result is a second-order stream. Two second-orders give a third-order, and so on. In any particular basin, the number of streams in each order decreases in a regular way as the order increases, much as one would expect. Similar relationships exist between a stream's order and such characteristics as its length, area and gradient; and these relationships hold true for almost all streams.

Although these topological relationships tend to be constant, other aspects of drainage-basin form vary from basin to basin. Thus dissection or *drainage density* (the number of streams per unit area) depends upon both the climate and the physical characteristics of the area: climate exerts a direct influence since it determines the amount of water that the system has to carry, as well as an indirect one by its effects on local vegetation; and rock and soil types are important since they determine the resistance of the surface to *erosion.

The Development of a Drainage System. It is very unlikely that the surface of an area of land that has just emerged from the sea, and whose structure is complicated by harder and softer beds and by *faults, will be smooth. So one would expect that in the early stages streams would quite naturally follow the initial irregularities. We call such streams *consequents*. Gradually, however, structure and rock character become more important, and rivers are guided by zones of weakness in the rock. Such streams are termed *subsequents*. Another class of streams, those that flow in a direction opposite to that of the geological dip of the beds, are called *obsequents*. Streams which appear to depend neither

and occasional earthquakes. Avalanche activity appears to be able to create and maintain high slope angles. In the Karakoram, for example, perennial slopes and ice slopes above 16,575ft (5100m) have more than 40% of their area lying at gradients between 55° and 60°.

High mountains have been shaped also by glacial erosion, which digs deep U-shaped valleys and creates knife-edged ridges (arêtes), scalloped by corries. Glaciers, unlike rivers, can sometimes "overdeepen" their valleys, creating basins which, after glacial retreat, may give deep lakes like those of the Swiss Alps.

Importance. Mountain chains have a considerable impact on other parts of the environment – and on Man. Their size and location with respect to surface and upper winds affect climate: for instance, the western mountain barrier in North America is responsible for a vast extension of semi-arid climates in the west-central part of the continent, and appears also to cause the development of great waves in the upper westerly circulation of the whole northern

hemisphere, thereby influencing the location of the high and low pressure cells that dominate the weather of western Europe. Likewise, the Tibetan Plateau and Himalayas are instrumental in the establishment of the monsoon, and are sufficiently high to affect the trajectories of the jet streams, the high-speed westerlies at the junction of troposphere and stratosphere.

The peripheral location of the ranges with respect to land masses tends to hinder the drainage of the central parts of continents, and so basins of inland drainage often occur there.

They pose certain problems for Man: steep gradients, rarified air, high precipitation, avalanches, earthquakes and volcanoes. Conversely, they also offer protection, recreation, water power, timber, minerals and climatic variety over short distances. Many of the great life-giving rivers of the world, the Indus, the Ganges, the Tigris and Euphrates, the Orange and the Amazon, owe the bulk of their water to the rain and snow of the high mountains.

In terms of their size in relation to the

upon initial irregularities nor upon weaknesses in the rocks are called *insequents*.

As a river system evolves, one stream, flowing along a more easily erodible course, may capture a stream whose course happens to be more resistant. This process of river capture favors the development of subsequent streams. River capture may also be a result of the relative length of the streams: a stream following a long and circuitous course to the sea will be at a disadvantage compared to one whose course is more direct. Possible signs of river capture that can often be detected in the landscape include windgaps and elbows of capture, incision of the capturing stream below the capture, and the evident misfit nature of the beheaded stream.

Not all valley systems, however, show complete conformity with the local geological structure. Some rivers may, for example, cut across *folds. One possible explanation for this is antecedence, whereby a rapidly eroding stream manages to keep on cutting down through a fold rising only

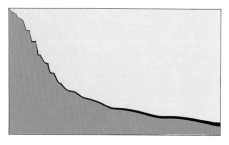

An idealized river long-profile. Close to the source are abrupt changes of gradient: with increasing distance from the source the profile smooths out and the gradient decreases until, in the river's maturity, the direction of flow is horizontal.

slowly across its path. This is known as antecedent drainage. Alternatively, in superimposed drainage, the river courses may have initially developed on a cover of rocks whose structure was different to that of the rocks beneath, the upper beds having since disappeared through erosion.

But nevertheless the effects of lithology and rock structure are important. On an absolutely flat surface of relatively homogeneous rock, a drainage net would probably develop a dendritic, branched pattern, with no great linear control apparent. Where the influences of rock resistance and structure are more significant, where streams find it easier to erode channels along lines of weakness, these streams subsequently become dominant, giving rise to a trellised drainage pattern.

Valleys in Plan. When seen from above, valleys, and the channels within them, present a course which is either straight or meandering or braided. Straight valleys and channels are rare, however, both because water flow tends to be turbulent and because there are inevitably obstructions.

Most rivers show a tendency to meander. This seems to be a characteristic of fluid motion – for example, the jet streams of the atmosphere and the Gulf Stream of the North Atlantic show a similar phenomenon. It is not necessary to involve irregularities in valley materials to explain meandering – the most perfect meanders occur in homogeneous alluvium. Another factor which favors meander development is a cohesive bank material. With less cohesive material the river is less constrained by its bank so that it undergoes frequent changes in position, and branching (braiding) may develop. Indeed, braiding streams seem to

A striking example of river meanders near Golden, British Columbia. Meanders are characteristic of a river's mature stage: their net effect is a reduction in the gradient of the river and therefore of the flow velocity. This can result in a near-perfect balance between erosion and deposition.

be characterized by highly variable discharge, abundant bedload and easily erodible banks. Even meandering streams, however, show considerable movement, for they tend to migrate downstream and also to cut off sharp bends to give ox-bow lakes.

If a winding channel should for any reason cut down deeply, it may become what is known as an incised meander. A change in base-level may mean that a pattern of meandering that was developed on floodplain alluvium becomes superimposed on the underlying bedrock.

River Long Profiles. When we talk of a river's "long profile" we mean the direction, in terms of the vertical, of the flow of the water in it, and hence the direction also of its bed.

Most river long profiles are steeper near the source than they are near the sea – exceptions occur, and they include particularly certain streams in arid regions which suffer a decrease in discharge downstream. There are various reasons for this general feature. Perhaps the most important is that grain-size of riverbed material and load tends to be smaller with increasing distances downstream. Thus the gradient of a stream must be steep in its upper reaches, so that the water has a sufficient velocity to move the coarse debris which is supplied to it there. Downstream, because of attrition, material is much finer, which means that the velocity required to carry it is much lower, and so the river can reduce its slope and still successfully carry its load.

A second reason is that discharge increases downstream. This makes the stream more efficient, for one large stream will have less bed friction than the smaller tributary streams which join together to make it up. Moreover, it will suffer less turbulence and thus less loss of energy.

However, certain stream long profiles tend to show irregularities: cataracts, waterfalls, and points of locally increased slope – kinchpoints. One cause of this may be the presence of hard bands of rock. Many waterfalls, for example, result from the river flowing on a bed of flat-lying strata which is underlain by weaker beds: the stream gradient is very low on the resistant layer, but when it breaks through the gradient can become very steep. Alternatively, breaks in the regularity of the long profile can be caused by changes in the level to which erosion proceeds – this level is often sea-level. A fall in sea-level can lead to the formation of a steep slope over which the river cascades. Headward erosion would be rapid at this point and the river would attempt to obtain a newly-graded and regular concave profile by cutting back upstream.

Valley Cross Profile. River valleys show considerable differences in their cross-sectional form. Some may be scarcely modified glacial features with a characteristic U-shape; others may be the product of great

Kinchpoints (or knick points) are most generally the result of rejuvenation – that is, the relative rise of the land with respect to sea level. Because of this fall of base level, the river downcuts rapidly towards its previous equilibrium long-profile. The kinchpoint represents the intersection of the new, adjusted long-profile with the old, maladjusted profile; and regresses upstream as adjustment continues.

and rapid vertical incision by powerful streams, possessing a prominent V-shape; while others may owe more to lateral cutting processes and possess a broad, flat bottom.

The form of some cross-profiles may be greatly influenced by differences in rock resistance. Similarly, river valleys cut into unconsolidated sands and gravels will tend to be V-shaped because the loose sandy material tends to fall from the valley sides. In silts and muds, on the other hand, sidewalls are maintained at a steep angle because of the cohesiveness of the materials.

Part of the form of the cross-profile may be depositional in origin: this particularly applies to alluvial floodplains. When a river overtops its channel banks and spreads out, its velocity is reduced and so its ability to transport materials is lessened. Thus deposition takes place, with coarse material being deposited near to the channel as levees, and finer material being carried further away and laid down as backswamp deposits. Also, as rivers meander across the floodplain they alternately scour and deposit.

The flood plain of the Paoshan (or Baoshan) River in Yunnan Province, China. Flood plains, which consist of alluvium deposited by the river, are formed by the downstream migration of meanders. As is evident from this photograph, the alluvium provides fertile soil, and many flood plains are extensively cultivated: particularly famous for its size and richness of soil is that of the Mississippi River.

Sometimes a floodplain may be eroded into by a river so that terraces result. Following a fall in the base level of erosion such as that which results in the creation of kinchpoints, the river will tend to cease deposition and will start to cut down into its floodplain alluvium.

Again, some terraces result from a change in climate. Changing climate results in changes of discharge of streams and in the nature of the *weathering and erosion of the valley systems. The latter may well cause the amount and caliber of the load to alter. During the Ice Ages, the advent of a colder phase near an ice sheet often resulted in an increase in frost weathering, glacial deposition and mass movement so that stream load was increased in amount and caliber. Aggradation (see *deposition) took place. Subsequently, however, with a change back to more temperate conditions, incision again predominated, and this resulted in the formation of terraces.

In some rivers the situation may be more complex still. At some point in the past, perhaps because of different climatic or sea-level conditions, rivers may have cut down very low only to be choked by a return to conditions favoring deposition. In such circumstances buried channels may be identified by borehole studies.   AG

Rift Valleys

A rift valley, or graben, is a structural trough formed when an elongated and relatively narrow strip of the Earth's crust sinks between two roughly parallel faults. The valleys so formed are generally fairly straight, and may be hundreds of miles in length, although they are characterized by a fairly constant width, of the order of

20–40mi (30–60km), a measurement that probably relates to the local thickness of the crust. The boundary faults generally dip steeply toward the trough, forming steep-sided slopes called scarps; one or other side of the trough may die out in some places to leave a series of fault blocks. An important feature of rift valleys is that they follow the crests of long, low upwarps of the Earth's crust. Volcanic activity is locally associated with them.

The Origin of Rift Valleys. Perhaps the most closely studied rift system is the Rhinegraben, traced by the River Rhine for 190mi (300km) between Basle and Frankfurt. Its average width is 22mi (36km) and it cuts through an elongated dome 120mi (190km) wide and upwarped 1–2mi (2–3km). The floor of the rift began to subside 45 million years ago as the shoulders rose, and the total throw of the fault is some 2.7mi (4.4km).

Many boreholes through the sedimentary fill have enabled a reconstruction to be made showing that the maximum widening during this period has been only 2.8mi (4.5km). A notable feature is that the steep enclosing scarps remain parallel although the valley itself curves. Geophysical observations of the Earth's crust in the Rhinegraben area have been of great importance in attempts to understand the origin of rift valleys, still very much a subject of debate.

The situation of rift valleys at the crests of domes led early to the concept of the dropped keystone of an arch, and experiments showed that downfaulted rift valleys could be produced by upwarping domes in clay models. However, the advent of *plate tectonic theory has led to a considerable clarification.

Geological and geophysical investigation has shown that rift valleys are related to

The East African rift system: triangles on the map indicate positions of recently active volcanoes; arrows the direction of separation. A simplified history of the rift valley shows initial downfaulting in Kenya some 13 million years ago (1), the deposition of sediment in the resulting valley (2), and the complex pattern of faults that has developed over the last million years (3).

anomalous features deep in the lithosphere and upper mantle which resemble those beneath mid-ocean ridges (see *ocean floor); and the projection of continental rift lines into the ancestral oceanic rifts, as reconstructed by fitting the continents together in their past positions, has indicated a close genetic relationship between the continental and oceanic features. It was therefore proposed that the continental rift valleys were zones where active crustal separation was beginning.

However, evidence has since shown that widening, even over long periods of time, has been only minimal – as in the case of the Rhinegraben. Gravimetric, seismal and geothermal investigations of several rift zones indicate the presence about 12mi (20km) beneath the rift valleys of intrusions of what are presumed to be molten or plastic mantle rocks from the seismic low-velocity zone (see *geophysics). These intrusions constitute a heat source which is probably the prime agent of rift-valley formation: the heating of the rocks beneath the rift zone causes expansion, and this accounts both for the updoming and for the limited horizontal expansion as the rift floor subsides.

The characteristic normal rift faults and the local tension indicated by *earthquake records can thus be explained – but other factors may also be involved. Although the *Cenozoic phases of rift faulting are well documented, geological mapping in older rocks has shown that the rift faults fre-

quently coincide with ancient tectonic dislocations, extending beyond the present active rifts, for which dates far back into the *Precambrian have been posited. It has therefore been suggested that a worldwide system of lineaments originated at an early stage of the Earth's history and has periodically been reactivated. Certain segments of these lineaments were suited to become centers of sea-floor spreading, whereas others remained locked in the continents. The East African rifts, for instance, may be unable to open because the continental plate is being compressed by spreading in the Atlantic and Indian oceans.

The East African Rift Valley. The term rift valley was first introduced to designate what is now known as the Great Rift Valley, the East African rift system which forms a complicated pattern extending 2500mi (4000km) south-southwest from the junction of the Red Sea and the Gulf of Aden, in the north, to the Zambesi River, in the south.

It comprises two systems, the eastern and western. The eastern system, from north to south, consists of the Ethiopian Rift Valley and the Gregory Rift Valley, Kenya, with outlying branches. South of latitude 4°S it passes into a series of east-facing fault blocks curving around central Tanzania as far as the Rungwe volcanic massif (9°S), where it is cut across by the western system. A continuation is provided in Zambia by the low scarps of the Luangwa Rift Valley.

The western system sweeps around Uganda and Tanzania in a great curve containing several fjord-like lakes, including Lake Tanganyika. Here its direction becomes southeasterly, cutting across the eastern system before turning southward, by way of Lake Malawi, to meet the coast near Beira.

The downthrow of the rift faults in the northern sector is 2mi (3km) at Lake Mobutu, and the neighboring horst block of Ruwenzori has been uplifted a similar distance relative to the African *plateau. The floor of Lake Tanganyika is 2300ft (700m) below sea level and a minimum downthrow of 2.2mi (3.5km) is indicated, whereas the marginal horst of Mt Kungwe has been uplifted 3250ft (1000m). It is notable that the greatest uplift and subsidence lie in the same sector. The total length of overlapping rifts in this system is 4200mi (6800km), of which the northern 950mi (1500km), in Ethiopia and Kenya, is accompanied by a profuse belt of volcanoes, mostly extinct. The other, major portion cuts through ancient Precambrian rocks with some local volcanic centers where fault systems intersect each other.   RBM

Plateaux

The term plateau is used more as a description than as a definition since it is applied to any fairly flat high-level region – a tableland or elevated tract of comparatively flat or level land – the surface of which may be uniformly level or have broad summit heights of fairly uniform elevation. There are no scientifically defined lower limits to the height above sea level – although about 300m (1000ft) has been suggested – and, similarly, one or more of the sides may be steep, but not necessarily so.

Like the other physical attributes the geological structure of plateaux is ill-defined. The strata may be in horizontal or

A view of the East African Rift Valley near Ol Doinyo Lengai. This rift system contains active volcanoes that bear testimony to the fact that much of East Africa (Somali Republic and parts of Kenya, Ethiopia, Tanzania and Mozambique) is splitting away from the rest of the continent.

nearly horizontal beds or be gently or severely displaced, in which case the original summits will have been planed down by *erosion to form high-lying plains.

Classification. Because plateaux are elevated they are usually associated with mountain systems. In this respect three varieties are commonly distinguished:

(*i*) Marginal plateaux are found where the mountain folds subside into level and almost level areas on their lower flanks. Examples occur in the Appalachians, where the folds die away westward in the Cumberland and Alleghany plateaux, and in the Jura, where the Jura *plié* is distinguished from the Jura *tabulaire*.

(*ii*) Intermontaine plateaux, which are confined between mountain chains. These are common in mountain cordilleras, famous examples being the Alti Plano of the Andes in Ecuador and Bolivia, the Columbia plateau between the Cascade Range and Rocky Mountains in northwest USA, and the vast plateau of Tibet between the Himalayas and Kumlun mountain chains.

(*iii*) Steep-sided plateaux formed by the wearing down of ancient mountains into high-level tablelands ringed about, more or less completely, by escarpments. A fine example is the High Karroo in South Africa.

On the deep ocean floor there seems to be a fourth variety of plateaux, upstanding submarine tablelands which are distinct from the continental shelf and the continental masses on it.

Modes of Formation.

Modes of Formation. Plateaux may also be classified according to their genesis or mode of formation (which includes elevation to a height that precludes the possibility of the plateau being called a plain). The chief genetic categories are as follows:

(*i*) Tectonically uplifted horizontal or gently undulating strata that remain approximately level after uplift. A supreme example is the Colorado plateau in the southwest of the USA.

(*ii*) Plateaux of accumulation of volcanic outflows, especially of *basalt. These are of two main varieties: folds in mountain chains may be overwhelmed locally by outpourings of basalt and under erosion become a series of plateaux; or, secondly, successive outpourings of sheets of lava may form a large plateau, such as occurs on a vast scale in the Columbia plateau, USA, and in the northwest Deccan of India.

(*iii*) Plateaux formed by the wearing down of mountains by erosional agencies. Weathering and other common erosional agents work fastest on steep slopes and tend to lower and eat back into the mountainsides, leaving at their feet a pediment or plateau. Eventually the upstanding areas decrease in size and stand above a plateau sometimes called a peneplain though today more usually regarded as a series of pediments or a pediplain.

These plateaux cut in ancient, contorted strata are often fractured by mountain-building movements and their main fractures or faults are eroded into steep scarps. Sometimes parallel fractures form *rift valleys – as in the plateaux of East Africa and on the middle Rhine between the Vosges and Black Forest. The popular concept of a plateau – as an isolated tableland with steep sides rising above the surrounding countryside – is often due to steep fault scarps, as for example the southern edge of

The edge of Mount Roraima. This plateau, lying on the borders of Venezuela, Brazil and Guyana, is 9220ft (2810m) high and is the source of many rivers, including particularly the Orinoco and Amazon river systems. It was Mount Roraima that inspired Sir Arthur Conan Doyle's famous novel, *The Lost World* (1912).

the Scottish Highlands and the eastern edge of the Massif Central in France. If a plateau has strong fault scarps on most sides it is in Europe called a *horst*.

However, the comparative flatness of all plateaux of this type is due to erosion, mostly subaerial and in some instances marine: a platform caused by marine abrasion or wave action can be uplifted by tectonic forces to form a plateau. More commonly, a mountain system is worn down to its stumps, mainly by subaerial denudation.

Associated Features. The most ancient plateaux – as in Africa, Brazil, the Deccan, Australia, the Canadian Shield and various

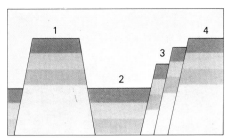

A horst (1), a plateau with steep scarps formed by faulting and later erosion. On the far side of a rift valley (2), step faults (3) lead up to another plateau (4).

shields, massifs, or tablelands in Eurasia – have remnants of former mountains still standing upon their flattened surfaces. Because of the dominance of rainwash over other erosional forces, these features are most common in warmer climates, but they survive in fragmental forms elsewhere, as for example in the granitic tors of Dartmoor.

The term *monadnock*, from the mountain of that name in New England, is used to describe an isolated mountain peak standing above a pediplain or plateau. A monadnock represents the residual mountain peak left upstanding by the reduction of its surroundings by erosion to form a plateau. Such survivals are more common in drier climates and are given special names. *Mesas* are flat-topped, steep-sided tablelands, beyond the edge of which, detached from the main plateau by erosion, may be similar but smaller flat-topped uplands called *buttes*. Combinations and examples of these landforms are common in Spain on the Meseta, itself a large plateau dominated in places by fault blocks.

On tropical tablelands where conditions are humid and arid, residual mountains rising in isolation above surrounding plateaux (pediments or pediplains) are called *inselbergs* or *bornhardts*. Inselbergs (island mountains) vary widely in shape and size and in degree of destruction, their common feature being the abrupt rise above the flat or gently-sloping pediment at their base. Some are large uplands while others are small steep-sided hill-masses: Ayers Rock, Central Australia, and numerous mountains in West Africa are examples. Many inselbergs are dome-shaped and have a granitic structure. They survive for a long time before their eventual diminution, when they may well degenerate into what are called in South Africa *kopjes* and *castle kopjes*. These fantastic collections of massive boulders are reminiscent of the smaller features known as tors in Britain.   R & DB

Karst Landscapes

The word *karst* is the German form of the Slovene word *Krs*, meaning barren stony ground, and refers to the area behind Trieste. Karst landscapes are most noteworthy for their spectacular and distinctive landforms, as is seen by their influence on the art of southern China, the largest area of karst

A butte in the Mesa Verde National Park, Colorado, an eroded remnant of a continuation of the mesa visible in the background. Mesas are isolated plateaux formed where a capping of hard strata has resisted erosion and protected the softer strata beneath : on the small scale this same process results in the formation of earth pillars. Continued erosion of the sides of a mesa may reduce it to a butte, or may lead to the appearance of buttes adjacent to the main body of the mesa.

in the world. They develop on massive soluble rocks, usually limestones or dolomites, in which the dissolving action of water plays a major role in the origin of the landforms.

Limestones are the most commonly occurring soluble rocks on the Earth's surface and comprise about 15% of the *sedimentary rocks. The ideal conditions for karst landscapes occur when the limestones are massive, well jointed and impermeable, to allow the development of secondary permeability; when the relief is high, to permit rapid vertical drainage; and when the rainfall is heavy, to give abundant water to act as a solvent. Not all limestones give rise to karst relief.

Limestones are formed of calcium carbonate, which is only very slightly soluble in pure water; but when the water contains carbon dioxide, as does rainwater, the calcium carbonate is converted into calcium bicarbonate, which *is* soluble – this reaction is reversible, loss of carbon dioxide leading to reprecipitation of calcium carbonate. Carbon dioxide dissolved in water is therefore the most important agent in the solution of limestones: it is derived either from the atmosphere or from biological sources.

Surface solution features are common in all karst landscapes. They include rills, runnels and pits cut into the rock, up to about 6.5–10ft (2–3m) long, called *karren* or *lapies*, terms originated in the Alps where these features were first described and where they are abundant. Karren formed by water containing atmospheric carbon dioxide are sharp-edged and razor-like; those formed by water with biologically-derived carbon dioxide are rounded and smoothed.

Solution penetrates the rock along joints and cracks, and is accelerated under soil and vegetation. At the intersections of fractures, increased solution forms funnel-like hol-lows which, once formed, are self-perpetuating as they form foci for rain waters, growing to over 325ft (100m) deep and over 1000ft (300m) in diameter. Closed depressions such as these are characteristic of soil-covered karst lands in temperate climates, as in Istria and the Jura, and in Indiana, where they basically replace river valleys. They are known as dolines in Europe and as sinks (or sink-holes) in North America.

The enlargement of bedding-planes and joints by solution enables relatively large streams of water to disappear underground into swallow holes: one of the largest rivers to disappear into the ground is the Trebinjčica in Yugoslavia, which drains over 350mi² (900km²). Where streams disappear along vertical fractures, deep chasms or shafts can be formed: these are known as potholes, one of the best known being in northern England; Gaping Gill, on the side of Ingleborough, which is over 390ft (120m) deep. Rivers which cut right through a karst area, like the Tarn and the Dordogne, are allogenic – that is, they deposit sediments brought from elsewhere.

Once underground, water dissolves and erodes the limestones to form cave passages. Many passages formed by streams resemble streambeds of the surface, and contain meanders, ox-bows and river deposits: they are known as *vadose* caves, and are normally controlled in detail by the lithology and the structure of the limestones. There is much evidence that solution also takes place at

Karst landforms develop through the solution of limestone by rainwater. Limestone is composed primarily of calcium carbonate ($CaCO_3$), which does not readily dissolve in water. However, rainwater contains dissolved carbon dioxide (CO_2), part of which reacts with the water to give hydrogen and bicarbonate ions (H^+ and HCO_3^-). The presence of these ions permits the $CaCO_3$ to be converted to $CaHCO_3$, calcium bicarbonate, which, being soluble, dissolves in the unreacted water.

in the form of a submarine spring, and this is common in the Adriatic sea and off the coast of Florida.

Karst springs are among the largest springs in the world, because there is a tendency for water to collect into master conduits. There are two main types of karst spring, one where the water issues by means of free flow, the other where the water issues under forced or artesian flow: the latter type is sometimes known as a vauclusian spring after the Fontaine de Vaucluse in southern France, which has at times a discharge as high as that of the Seine at Paris. Since underground water usually has a high calcium bicarbonate content, its emergence to the outside world is frequently accompanied by tufa deposition, mainly the result of loss of carbon dioxide. Such deposition can be assisted by the presence of algae and mosses, which extract lime from the waters and on a large scale may indicate a significant climatic change.

When karst areas occur in climates with marked wet and dry seasons, as in Mediterranean Europe, the limestones may not be able to absorb all the rainfall which floods the surface in the wet season. Such flooding is intensified by the presence of less permeable beds in the limestones or of impermeable unconsolidated rocks like boulder clay. Acidic flood waters can cause planation of the limestones by solution, and this gives

depth, where underground water is under considerable pressure. Caves formed under these conditions are called *phreatic* and are controlled more by the hydrological gradient than by geology. Most large cave systems consist of vadose and phreatic elements, together with large chambers caused by collapse. Cave temperatures normally approximate to the mean annual temperatures of the surrounding area: in caves in mountainous areas where cold air can accumulate, large bodies of ice exist, as for example in the Eisriesenwelt, Austria.

Water not only flows through limestones in defined channels, but also percolates. Percolation water takes up carbon dioxide and dissolves a great deal of calcium carbonate. When percolation water emerges from a crack into a cave passage, carbon

dioxide is lost to the atmosphere and there may also be evaporation, both processes resulting in the precipitation of calcium carbonate. If such deposition is onto the floor of the cave, *stalagmites* are built up; if from the roof, hanging *stalactites* are formed. The shapes and forms of stalagmites and stalactites are controlled by the quantities of carbon dioxide, water and calcium bicarbonate available, and can be indicators of environmental change. Precipitation can also take place from cave streams, forming layers of crystalline travertine or barriers of soft amorphous tufa known as *gours*.

Water which has circulated through the limestones by means of swallow holes and caves is thrown out in springs at the foot of the limestone outcrop. Where the limestone base is below sea-level, the water may issue

Features of karst landscapes: (1) phreatic zone; (2) sinkhole or doline; (3) polje; (4) vadose region; (5) swallow holes; (6) vauclusian spring; (7) limestone pavement; (8) kamenitza.

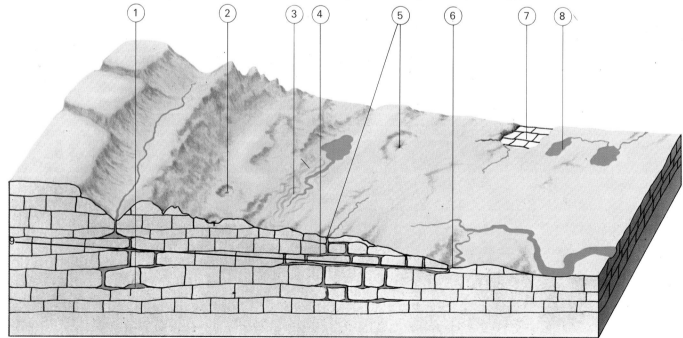

rise to flat-floored, solution-planed areas known as *poljes*: the polje of Popovo in Hercegovina is over 25mi (40km) long.

Though solution is important in all karst landscapes, other *erosion processes occur. Where limestones are only a relatively small part of the total area, fluvial (running-water) erosion is important, forming a fluvial karst with a mixture of karstic and river-eroded features: the limestone areas of the Peak District in England and of Dinant in Belgium are examples. Porous limestones tend also to have fluvial karstic relief, like the Cotswold Hills in England. Glaciated limestones possess abraded surfaces and also shafts formed by melt waters.

Karst landforms develop most slowly in dry areas and in warm or polar deserts, because of lack of water; superficial solution rills and pits are often the only karstic features. Karst develops most rapidly and most fully in the humid tropics, due to the presence of much biogenic carbon dioxide: intensive rainstorms also mean that fluvial activity is added to the solution process in tropical karst. A combination of solution and fluvial erosion produces star-shaped hollows (or *cockpits*) which dissect the limestones into innumerable small drainage basins: such relief, which has often been called cellular or polygonal karst, occurs in Jamaica and New Guinea. Surface repre-

cipitation makes limestone a strong rock in tropical conditions, and so hillslopes in limestone are steeper than in other rock types: hills with slopes of 70° and more occur, the relief being called tower karst.

Much work has been done on the calcium content of karst waters with a view to estimating rates of solutional loss in different areas. The dissolution of the rock depends not only upon the solution rate of calcium carbonate but also upon the volume of water available and its type of flow. Results show that the pattern of limestone removal is similar to the pattern of chemical *weathering in general, and is highest in areas of heaviest rainfall.

Because of relatively rapid solution and collapse of the rock, the underground hydrology of karst areas is continually changing. The behavior of the underground water is different from that exhibited in a porous medium, and the traditional concept of the water table has to be modified. Karst limestones are able to store large quantities of water, but their location and development for human use requires highly specialized study, involving a detailed knowledge of karst terrains. In many areas the actual pattern of underground water flow is unknown; but new methods of water tracing have been introduced, which include dyes and radioisotopes, and these are help-

The interior of Kačna Cave, Yugoslavia, showing spectacular formations of stalactites and stalagmites. These result from the evaporation of water containing dissolved limestone in the form of calcium bicarbonate ($Ca(HCO_3)_2$), which precipitates as calcium carbonate ($CaCO_3$).

ing the piecing-together of the story.

The most obvious application of the study of karst landforms is to the use of underground water, but caves also act as traps for sediments of economic value and the weathering products of karst areas, such as bauxite, the ore of *aluminum, can also be of great importance.   MMS

Arid Landscapes

Arid areas, or hot deserts, are those where annual rainfall is greatly exceeded by water loss through evaporation from the land and transpiration from plants. Because of the severe water deficit, desert vegetation is limited in its development and desert soils are characterized by soil horizons, clay content and organic matter rather different to those of more humid areas. These two factors, vegetation and soil, combined with the sporadic, limited nature of the rainfall, are reflected in distinctive geomorphic processes – and so, distinctive landscapes.

The effects of *weathering are limited:

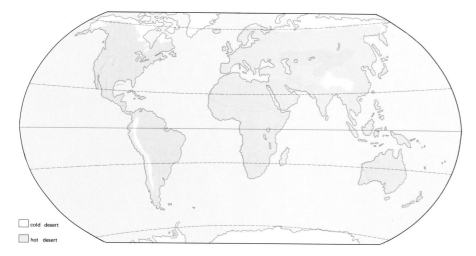

The world's hot and cold desert regions.

cold desert
hot desert

there is insufficient water available to lead to thorough leaching of rocks and soils. Thus, while solutional *denudation is of minor importance, there is, especially where there are no rivers flowing away from the desert area, a tendency for soluble salts, such as gypsum and sodium chloride, to accumulate as salt crusts. Similarly, whereas in humid areas limestone tends to be sculptured to give karstic landforms (see *karst landscapes), in arid areas lime tends to be accumulated rather than flushed out, giving rise to lime crusts (or *calcrete*). Where coastal fogs and night dew are of frequent occurrence, enough moisture may be present to produce some chemical weathering: indeed, weathering in arid areas seems to be greatly accelerated when moisture is present, as in shaded areas or near springs. However, much of the weathering in deserts seems to involve the splitting of rock through mechanical or physical processes (see *erosion). Early workers considered that high daily variations in ground surface temperatures (up to 135F°, 74C°) resulted in sufficient expansion and contraction of rock masses to cause disintegration (*insolation weathering*), but laboratory experiments suggest this process is relatively impotent. Recently it has been suggested that rock can be disrupted by salt, for when a solution of salt accumulates in a rock and evaporates, crystals develop which set up considerable forces (*salt crystallization weathering*). Some salt crystals also expand with changes in temperature and humidity (*salt hydration weathering*).

The wind is another important agent of geomorphologic development. The lack of vegetation, together with the rather loose nature of most desert soils, enables wind to be a substantial factor in soil erosion. Satellite- and air-photographs of areas like the Central Sahara show great grooves aligned with the prevailing trade winds; as well as closed depressions with distinctive orientations, on the lee sides of which the wind-eroded materials have accumulated to give a crescentic dune called a *lunette*. Similarly, when wind operates on an unprotected alluvial surface, the fine silt and sand may be blown away, leaving a lag of coarse fragments called a *stone pavement*.

Dunes. Dunes are one of the clearest manifestations of wind action in the desert environment. The wind molds, shifts and deposits sand into a series of distinctive forms, often large enough to show up on satellite photographs. There are great linear sand ridges parallel to the wind (*seifs*), crescentic dunes with horns facing both upwind (*parabolics*) and downwind (*barchans*), star-shaped dunes (*rhourds*), and many others. Some types may reach 1000ft

Desert landscape in Algeria, with buttes visible in the background. About 18% of the Earth's land surface is covered by deserts of dryness, of which this, the Sahara, is the largest, with an area in the region of 2.7–3.1 million mi² (7–8 million km²), though estimates vary owing to disagreement over its exact boundaries.

(300m) in height and stretch for tens or hundreds of miles. On a continental scale, great sand fields (*ergs*) may be aligned parallel to the wind belts in massive anticlockwise whorls.

Water. However, despite the low rainfall, the power of water action is important in shaping arid landscapes. When rain does fall it may do so torrentially – in one short storm more rain may fall than, on average, the region receives annually. Because of the lack of vegetation and the poorly structured and ill-developed soils, runoff may take place quickly along ephemeral channels (wadis) as *flash floods* or over shallow-gradient surfaces as *sheet floods*. Such rivers may not, however, always form an integrated system, and there are many examples where they do not flow through to the oceans, but end up in closed depressions (*playas*), where salt crusts develop through the evaporation of the water. Where streams leave their hilly tracts and enter playas, they tend to spread out and give a fan-like plain of ill-sorted debris (an *alluvial fan*).

Desert slope forms owe much to the combined action of weathering and water action. They are little masked by vegetation and soil so that they often appear more angular than those of less arid areas. Frequently there are abrupt breaks of shape, especially between mountain fronts and the plains at their bases: it appears that the basal plains gradually extend as the mountain front, maintaining its steepness, retreats. From these plains (pediplains) may rise isolated residual remnants of the mountain front called *inselbergs* (see *plateaux).

The low-angle (generally less than about 8°) concave surfaces which coalesce to form the pediplains are called *pediments*. They are peculiar because they are essentially bare rock-cut surfaces with only a very thin veneer of detritus, separated from the mountain front by an abrupt change in gradient. The reasons for their development are the cause of much controversy. Some early workers thought they were the result of high-velocity sheetfloods which pared down the surface to give a relatively undissected gentle slope. Other workers have envisaged them as being shaped by streams leaving the mountain front, their courses swinging from side to side and thereby gradually eroding and smoothing the surface (lateral planation). More recently it has been argued that pediments develop through surface and subsurface weathering. At the junction between mountain front and plain there is a natural concentration of water through percolation (see *hydrogeology): this leads to pre-

Sand dunes. In this photograph one can see the difference in gradient between the (steeper) lee side and the (gentler) windward side, as well as the striking differences in their superficial appearance (as shown on either side of the crest in the foreground).

ferential weathering at the break in slope, the weathering products being removed by sheetflow, wind and other processes, so that the mountain front retreats backward and the pediment extends.

However, one cannot interpret all arid landscapes solely in terms of present-day processes. During the Ice Ages of the Pleistocene, when high latitudes were subjected to alternations of glacial expansion and contraction, arid areas also suffered changes in precipitation. At times precipitation was even lower than at present (interpluvials) so that the ergs extended into areas that are today vegetated and too moist

for their development (e.g., northern Nigeria or southern Sudan). At other times (pluvials), average rainfall may have been markedly greater so that wadi systems were more extensive, water levels in playa basins were higher, sand dunes became gullied and weathered, and bedrock became deeply weathered to give striking weathering crusts (*duricrusts*) composed of iron and aluminum oxides (in the case of *ferricretes*) or silica (in the case of *silcretes*). Thus many features of a modern arid landscape may be reflections of climatic conditions of the past.

Man. Notably on desert margins, Man himself may cause geomorphologic

Desert roses (or rock roses) display one of the more unusual modes of occurrence of evaporitic minerals (in the broadest sense of the term). Found, as the name suggests, only in arid areas, these clusters of platy crystals are typically of barite or gypsum, and frequently include also sand grains. Their unusual form caused wonder to early explorers, many of whom suggested that desert roses were genuine flowers that had in some way been petrified.

A characteristic V-shaped river valley in the process of invasion by a glacier. U-shaped valleys are characteristic of landscapes that have been at one time glaciated: they represent river valleys that have been invaded by the ice which, during its passage, erodes the walls and floor to produce a round-bottomed form.

changes. Removal of vegetation for firewood or by the grazing of domesticated animals exposes the soil to wind erosion, resulting in dune development and encroachment, and to the erosive action of the infrequent high intensity storms, which produce gully systems (arroyos) with alarming rapidity. These phenomena are known collectively as desertization.

The effect of Man on the landscape of the desert interior is less than that on the margins, for water and vegetation are generally inadequate to support much in the way of agriculture or herding. Only at oases, where groundwater comes sufficiently close to the surface to be exploitable, or on the banks of rivers such as the Nile and the Indus, can farming activities be maintained. Less traditional activities, like mineral exploitation, have slightly modified the situation in some regions, notably in the oil-producing states of the Middle East.

The great variety of desert landscapes must be stressed. Climate is only one control: local tectonic action, for instance, may have had at least as important an impact on landforms. Two contrasting examples are provided by the deserts of the South West United States, where dunes cover less than 1% of the area and alluvial fans and aprons over 31%, and the Sahara, where the situation is almost reversed, well over 25% of the total area being covered by sand dunes and only about 1% by alluvial fans and aprons. (See also Desert, p. 844.)   AG

Glacial Landscapes

The deep imprint which glaciers may leave on the landscape is illustrated by the fact that, in southeastern England alone, glaciers eroded and subsequently redeposited a minimum of 70mi³ (300km³) of debris during the last glaciation of the area.

The most obvious signs of glacial activity are produced in highland areas. In these, ice accumulates on the highest peaks and flows away as glaciers which may be long, deep valley glaciers, or short cirque glaciers. A deep crack, called a *bergschrund*, often occurs at the point where the glacier tears itself away from the mountainside, and the glacier may cascade down the flanks of the mountain, exhibiting crevasses where it has flowed over obstacles on its bed, and icefalls – which are equivalent to waterfalls.

In high mountain areas, the mountainsides which flank the glacier are subject to processes of disintegration. In summer, as the sun strikes them in the morning, many such slopes resound to a noise like gunfire, as boulders and rock fragments, firmly frozen during the night, are released from the grip of ice and sweep down the mountainside. Where there is no glacier at the foot of the slope, a scree cone forms at the natural angle of rest of the boulders (about 35°). When this builds up high enough to mask the cliffs from which boulders are falling, there is no further degradation and the slope is stabilized at a much shallower angle than the original mountainside.

Where a valley glacier runs along the foot of the mountainside, the falling boulders accumulate on its surface as a *lateral moraine*, which is transported away. Thus the flanking mountain walls continue to collapse and recede, and may be progressively steepened. Where glaciers occur in adjacent valleys, the intervening ridge may be sharpened to form a knife-edged ridge (arête) due to retreat and coalescence of the mountainsides on both sides. Where valley glaciers meet and coalesce, the two marginal moraines at the point of junction also coalesce to form *medial moraines*.

In the many upland areas of Britain, northern Europe and America which have been glaciated during the last few million years, there are, though these regions are no longer cold enough to support glaciers, abundant signs of glaciers having bitten deeply into the landscape, leaving their own characteristic signature. Not only are there sharp and fractured arêtes and steep glacier headwalls, but many valleys are very deeply incised, with U-shaped cross-profiles and floors composed of smoothed, striated and streamlined rock hummocks (called roches moutonnées – see *erosion).

Some insight into the way in which glaciers produce these features can be found by direct observation of the situation beneath glaciers of today. In recent years, mining and hydroelectricity companies have had cause to construct tunnels which penetrate into the rocks under glaciers. In one such tunnel, beneath the *glacier d'Argentière* in the French Alps, it is possible to make one's way into natural cavities, 600ft (185m) below the surface of the ice, which exist on the down-glacier side of rock hummocks on the glacier bed. In the roofs

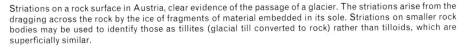

Striations on a rock surface in Austria, clear evidence of the passage of a glacier. The striations arise from the dragging across the rock by the ice of fragments of material embedded in its sole. Striations on smaller rock bodies may be used to identify those as tillites (glacial till converted to rock) rather than tilloids, which are superficially similar.

of these cavities we see the rock-studded glacier sole (the bottom surface of the ice): it is these rock fragments, eroded from its bed by the glacier and then carried along, which are the cutting tools by which rough hillocks are ground down and fine striations are cut into their surfaces.

The debris fragments move less quickly than the ice in which they are contained because of the frictional drag between them and the glacier bed. If the pressure between the glacier and its bed increases, the frictional drag increases and so the debris is retarded even more: however, because of the increased pressure the rate of erosion of the bed increases. If, however, the pressure increases beyond a critical value the increased frictional drag slows down the rate of movement of debris particles sufficiently to cause the erosion rate to begin to slow down. With even higher pressures, the particles no longer move over the bed, erosion has ceased and deposition of the typical glacial material, *glacial till*, has commenced.

Thus, with increasing pressure, erosion

rate increases to a maximum at a critical pressure, and then declines to zero at the second critical pressure, where deposition commences. If a glacier flows for the first time through a typical V-shaped valley in a mountain region, the gradual increase in pressure, from zero at the point where the glacier surface touches the valley wall to a maximum in the valley floor, will tend to widen the valley near to the apex of the V, so that it becomes the typically U-shaped glacial valley.

As we have seen, material eroded from

Five chapters in the story of glacial erratics. *Top*, glacial meltwater splashes round a boulder embedded in the upper surface of the ice, causing local melting. *Upper center*, further melting near the edge of a retreating glacier leaves a boulder straddling an empty channel. *Center*, the ice retreats, leaving this boulder perched on a layer of ice but separated from the main body of the glacier. *Lower center*, the retreat has progressed still further and the ice beneath this boulder has melted away completely, so that it is now stranded on a mass of smaller drift particles. *Bottom*, the end result, boulders lying on terrain of Carboniferous limestones. Study of erratics is important since tracing of them back to source may provide information on past glaciations.

the bed of the glacier is transported in the base of the ice, eroding as it moves, and finally deposited as till. Some boulders eroded by glaciers may be carried many hundreds of miles before being deposited. For instance, rocks from the region of Oslo have been found on the east coast of England, transported there by the great ice sheets which have covered northwest Europe several times in the last half million years. Such rocks are known as glacial erratics.

Although it is the highland landscapes that are dominantly scarred by the evidence of glacial erosion, most of the world's glaciated plains are deeply mantled by glacial deposits which mask pre-existing landscapes. Much of this material is till deposited directly by the glacier. These till surfaces may also be built up into streamlined forms, such as *drumlins*, which occur when the moving debris jams against obstructions on the glacier bed; *crag and tail* features, where till squeezes into the cavities left on the down-glacier flanks of rock obstructions; or *flutes*, where till is squeezed into ridges on the down-glacier sides of boulders on the till surface.

Other characteristic depositional features are *terminal moraines*. Many of these are formed when the ice advances and pushes into the till or other soft sediments lying in front of the glacier, thereby pushing up a ridge which lies along the glacier margin – rather as a bulldozer can push up a ridge of earth. Many of these ridges are to be found on the plains of Europe and North America and represent the positions of the front edges of the large ice sheets which have advanced into these areas during the geologically recent past.

The other potent agent in molding glacial landscapes is the water released when the glacier melts. Some of the most powerful and active streams on the Earth's surface are those fed by glaciers. The meltwater from glaciers is generated in two ways: some is produced beneath the ice from the heat generated by friction between the glacier and its bed, and some is produced largely during summer by melting of the glacier's surface, much of it finding its way down to the bed of the glacier *via* crevasses in the surface. Thus, beneath the glacier, we find great torrents of water which erode the dramatically deep gorges often to be seen in mountainous valleys once ice-covered. These streams transport a great deal of debris which they tend to deposit beyond the glacier as *outwash plains*, often dimpled by depressions known as *kettle holes*, the hollows left when ice blocks carried by the streams and deposited with the other sediments finally melt out.

A dramatic example of the enormous power locked up in glaciers is provided by certain glaciers in Iceland which are subject to glacier bursts: large quantities of water, built up beneath the glacier, are suddenly and catastrophically released, giving measured discharges of water up to 0.5mi³ (2km³) per day.

GSB

Tundra Landscapes

Much of the circumpolar zone of the northern hemisphere is characterized by vast, nearly flat regions with arctic climates and vegetation, in which most physical and biological processes are dominated by the effects of low temperature. This is *arctic tundra*; and it has an equivalent lying above the timberline in mountain areas, *alpine tundra*. (See also p. 850.)

The single most important reason for the particular character of arctic tundra is that the subsoil is permanently frozen, often to some considerable depth. For instance, in many parts of Siberia this frozen earth extends to a depth of up to 325ft (100m). This is not a rare phenomenon: up to one fifth of the Earth's land area is underlain by such permanently frozen ground.

If the climate changes so as to cause the mean annual air temperature to fall below 32°F, the depth of frost penetration in the ground may well exceed the depth of summer thawing, so that there forms a thin layer of frozen ground which does not thaw during summer. This is called *permafrost*. It thickens progressively year by year until a balance is struck between heat flow from the Earth's interior and heat loss from the ground into the atmosphere.

Although air temperature is the principal control on permafrost development, other factors are also important. The high thermal capacity of lakes and rivers tends to inhibit permafrost development, which is also affected by the vegetation cover and the nature of subsurface soil or rock because of their different heat conductivities. In practice we find that the zone of continuous permafrost is limited to those areas where the mean annual temperature is 5°F (−15°C), and this also roughly coincides with the timberline, the northernmost point where trees exist, which marks the southern boundary of the arctic tundra. To the south of this line we find zones of discontinuous and sporadic permafrost, and the boreal forests or *taiga* with their spruce, larch, pine, fir and birch trees as well as abundant tree lichens.

During winter on the tundra the ground is completely frozen to some depth; but in summer the surface layer thaws, to a depth of between 8in (20cm) and 3.25ft (1m). This surface layer is called the *active layer*.

Tundra, landscape characteristic of nearly one tenth of the Earth's land surface, is found at high latitudes and on high mountains. Vegetation is generally of low shrubs, mosses, lichens, grasses and similar herbs, and cushion plants. The faunas are similarly restricted in diversity, though seas in tundra regions are rich in aquatic mammals. The term is derived from the Finnish and means "hostile country".

Polygonal patterns on the ground, resulting from cooling and contraction, can be diagnostic of tundra conditions, past or present.

many places in what are now temperate latitudes have experienced an arctic tundra environment for most of the last 70,000 years. Indeed, one might regard arctic rather than temperate climates to be typical of these latitudes: although we have been free from these conditions for about 10,000 years, there is every reason to believe that they will return. (See also p. 850.)   GSB

Coastal Plains

The olde sea wall (he cried) is down
The rising tide comes on apace,
The boats adrift in yonder towne
Go sailing uppe the market place.
Jean Ingelow's verse draws attention to several features characteristic of coastal plains: they are of shallow gradient and vulnerable to damage by flooding – on the other hand, they are often densely populated and of great economic importance.

We can define a coastal plain as an area of gentle slope, lying inland from the sea, and adjacent to the coastline. The plain is of either depositional or erosional origin, although the former is more common. An important control on the formation of coastal plains is the movement of sea-level relative to the land, because it is only during a period when sea-level remains more or less stable that the land adjacent to the coast can be reduced to a low slope.

As the shallow gradient can result from a variety of processes, coastal plains can be classified in terms of the differing processes that created them.

Erosional coastal plains. These can be formed by the action of rivers, glacial processes or the sea itself.

River erosion of solid rock is normally confined to the steeper reaches of the river channel toward the source, and is primarily downward; it is, therefore, unusual for a wide coastal plain to be cut by river *erosion. By the time a river has started lateral (sideways) erosion it is normally flowing over deposits on an alluvial plain.

Glacial erosion can produce extensive surfaces of relatively low relief. The best known example of a coastal plain formed in this way is the *strandflat* of western Norway. This wide coastal strip is of generally low relief, rock outcrops occurring widely on the low glacially-smoothed rocky islands and adjacent low-lying coastal zone. Considerable argument has been aroused by this geomorphological feature, but it is generally believed to be of glacial origin, formed by the erosive activity of ice flowing vigorously from the Norwegian highlands to the Atlantic Ocean.

Marine processes can also erode low-gradient surfaces under conditions of slowly rising sea-level. Waves can smooth even the hardest rocks to a slope of about 1 in 100, but they cannot erode effectively in depths greater than about 30–65ft

Because of the lack of downward drainage through the underlying permafrost, and because of the water produced by melting of snow and interstitial ice, the active layer is often saturated with water, and therefore small surface pools of water unable to penetrate into the ground provide a common feature of the tundra.

The permafrost surface is in a state of delicate thermal balance, a balance which is easily upset. The growth of trees above the permafrost locally upsets this balance because of their insulating effect. As a result the depth of the active layer varies locally, and there are patches which are much wetter and more unstable than others. The instability of the ground often results in the tree falling over, and trees rarely survive to any great age. Similarly, man-made structures such as houses or pipelines tend to warm the permafrost surface and accelerate melting, so that the structure is liable to sink into the water-saturated subsoil. Large structures in tundra regions are therefore often built on piles, which are held firmly at depth within the permafrost.

Annual freezing and thawing in the active layer causes expansion of the soil, followed by contraction. The forces generated by freezing and thawing tend to segregate particles of different grain size in the soil to produce *sorted polygons*, whose margins are outlined by the coarser soil fragments. Polygons tend to form in the water-saturated active layer, which in summer is extremely unstable and tends to flow down even the gentlest slopes over the underlying frozen surface. Because of this flow, many sorted polygons are streaked out to produce *sorted-stripes* which run down the line of steepest slope.

The churning of the active layer by freezing and thawing prevents the development of a stable soil structure, and its water-saturated state prevents circulation of air so

that the soil becomes acid and sterile. Because of these factors, wet tundra does not allow a rich vegetation to become established. Polar desert soils with a low organic content and low productivity develop, and, when their nature is considered together with the short growing season (during which perhaps just a couple of months may have mean temperatures above freezing), it is easy to see why only a sparse flora is maintained. In soils which are particularly susceptible to churning by frost, organic growth is almost completely inhibited and primitive *ahumic soils* (i.e., without humus, organic material) occur. But on well-drained areas which thaw early in the spring, lush tundra grasslands may develop, becoming a favorite nesting ground for birds and grazing area for musk-ox and reindeer.

Flying over the tundra, one frequently sees a large-scale polygonal pattern outlined on the ground beneath. Closer investigation shows this to be composed of large cracks in the ground surface. These are produced by cooling of the ground to temperatures below $21°F (-6°C)$, at which it begins to contract. Cracking due to contraction, as in the dried-up bed of a lake, typically produces a polygonal (generally hexagonal) structure, which may be several hundred metres across.

It is a mistake to assume that tundra conditions have always been restricted to a narrow circumpolar zone. During the coldest parts of the last ice age (see *glaciation), about 20,000 years ago, much of the landscape of the unglaciated parts of Britain, northern Europe and north America was probably very similar to that of modern tundra areas. Even today, low-level flight by airplane over parts of southeast England can reveal the remains of large-scale tundra polygons and striped patterns on slopes. These serve to remind us that

Coastal plain bisected by the meandering Tailings River, Bougainville, Solomon Islands: a fine oxbow lake is clearly visible. The sediment being deposited under the sea surface at the estuary is in fact effluent carried down by the river from copper mines further up stream.

Lagoons, in which salt marsh development is often active, occur on the landward side of the barrier islands, while sand dunes grow on the barrier crest. When lagoons are absent, dunes may stretch far inland: they often form linear ridges, based on beach-ridge foundations, especially in areas of slowly falling sea-level, as for example along parts of the Tasmanian coast.

Raised and submerged coastal plains. Sea-level has fluctuated widely and rapidly in the 25,000 years since ice sheets were last extensive. A rapid rise since 15,000 years ago has submerged some coastal plains, which can be identified by drowned barriers on the continental shelf: examples occur off northern Australia. Raised coastal plains are widespread in those flat, high-latitude areas that have recently risen rapidly as the weight of the ice sheets has been removed by melting: southwest Baffin Island illustrates this type well.

Conclusions. Their low gradient and proximity to the sea make coastal plains desirable areas for development. Many are densely populated, but, because they are so low-lying, they are liable to damage by the sea under surge or hurricane conditions. Sand dunes form the natural defence of many coastal barrier islands, but these are liable to breaching with consequent flooding. For the protection of these densely peopled coasts, it is of paramount importance that we have an adequate knowledge of their character and the processes that operate upon them. (See also Coastal Vegetation, p. 885.)   CAMK

Deltas

The deltas of the world's great rivers have historically been sites of important civilizations and are still centers of population. The early civilizations of the Tigris–Euphrates, Indus and Nile deltas depended upon the irrigation and soil fertility provided by the rivers. Today, the population of Bangladesh relies on the rich soil deposited by the Ganges and Brahmaputra.

It is ironic that the Nile delta, the site of such magnificent early civilization, should presently be retreating as a result of modern civilization. Since the building of the Aswan Dam, much of the sediment which previously fed the delta is now trapped in the man-made lake behind the dam, and marine erosion is, in consequence, winning the battle at the coast. This problem illustrates the delicate balance between the constructive forces of the river and the destructive forces of the sea, as well as the economic importance of understanding deltaic processes. The balance between construction and destruction is not everywhere the same and the variety of shapes of present day deltas, diverging as they often do from the triangular shape implicit in the name, delta (∆), reflect this varying balance.

Delta Processes. The processes which influence delta morphology can be divided into two classes, those associated with the

(10–20m). For this reason, when the sea-level is stationary, only a narrow platform can be created by the waves. But when sea-level is rising slowly, a much wider marine-cut surface can be formed. The best examples of such surfaces are found at the base of extensive marine transgressions, such as that at the base of the *Cretaceous rocks in western Europe.

Depositional coastal plains. The commonest type of coastal plain is depositional: these can owe their origins to rivers, glaciers or the sea.

Fluvial coastal plains are those areas where the coastline bounds an area of recent river deposition. The coast of the southeast USA provides a good example of such a plain. The area has undergone a series of depositional phases in which wedges of river-derived sediment were laid down and later tilted down toward the sea, producing an area of low relief for some distance inland. Many fluvial coastal plains are deltaic in character, such as the Mississippi delta area.

Glacial deposits can form extensive low areas that, where they meet the sea, constitute coastal plains. The south coast of Iceland, where glacial outwash from the glaciers draining Vatnajökull has formed a wide and very flat sandy plain, locally called a *sandur*, provides a good example. The sandy plain is crossed by rapidly-flowing glacial meltwater streams that deposit their load to build up the coastal plain. It is bordered along much of its length by a coastal barrier, often separated from the dry part of the plain by a shallow lagoon.

A slight fall of sea-level can expose a marine-formed coastal plain, while in some areas marine deposits overlie glacial or river sediments. The coast of Lincolnshire (UK) provides an example of a coastal plain of marine silts overlying glacial *tills and bordered by sand dunes. Part of this coast is building actively seawards, thus providing a truly marine coastal plain of low relief. Such accretional coasts are usually characterized by coastal dunes and often by salt marshes and barrier beaches.

Barrier islands are characteristic of coastal plain seaward margins, and they occur around an estimated 13% of the world's coastlines, being especially well developed along the eastern coast of the USA, parts of southeast South America, Africa and Australia, as well as India. The barriers are mostly sandy, and are best developed in areas of low to moderate tidal range where constructive swell waves predominate.

An unusual photograph of a arcuate (or fan-shaped) delta in East Greenland, with icebergs out to sea. The structure in the left foreground is an earth pillar. The term "delta" derives from the resemblance of arcuate deltas to the fourth letter of the Greek alphabet, delta: Δ.

river itself and those associated with the body of water, the basin, into which the delta is being built and which may be the sea or a lake.

River Input Factors. Three properties of river input seem important: the density of the inflowing water and the amount and type of sediment carried. When a river flows into fresh water, temperature determines how the river- and basin-water mix. Cold dense river water may flow under the basin water while warm river water will float. In the sea, river water is always lighter (because of the sea's salt content) and floats out at the surface.

The amount of sediment discharged determines the delta's ability to build forward: the Nile shows how critical this factor is. Rivers move sediment in suspension and as bedload and the ratio between the amounts carried in these two ways influences the sediment distribution over the delta. Large rivers, particularly in warm climates, carry virtually all their loads in suspension, while smaller streams have more important bedload.

Basinal Factors. We have seen how salinity and temperature of basinal water may influence the flow pattern over a delta, but other basinal factors are also important. First, the depth of the basin determines how thick a pile of sediment must be deposited for the delta to advance. Second, the "energy" of the basin is important: by "energy" we mean the levels of activity of waves and tidal currents. If these are high, they will be more likely to redistribute sediment brought to the basin by the river.

Major Types of Delta. Many present-day deltas depart from the classical triangular shape, where there is an upstream apex and a system of diverging distributary channels fanning out to the shore. While this delta type exists, it is only a single example of a number of patterns which can only be arbitrarily classified. The classification given here involves morphological and process criteria.

Bedload-dominated, Low-energy Deltas. An

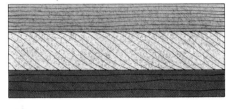

topset

foreset

bottomset

The grading of beds in a deltaic deposit, according to Gilbert. The topset consists of sand and gravel in horizontal layers, the foreset of cross-bedded coarser material; and the bottomset of silt in horizontal layers.

American geologist, G. K. ★Gilbert, at the end of the last century recognized ancient deltas around the shores of now-drained lakes in Utah. As well as describing the morphology of the deltas, Gilbert recorded their internal structure as exposed in gullies. These small lake deltas, similar to many seen in reservoirs during drought, were flat-topped lobes of sand and gravel with steeply inclined surfaces in their downstream ends. The top surfaces corresponded to assumed lake-water level. Gilbert recorded three distinct internal un-

its, each having characteristic grain-size and bedding.

The lowest was horizontally bedded fine sediment. This was overlain by inclined layers of coarse sediment; and this in turn was overlain by horizontally bedded sands and gravels. These units, the so-called "bottomset", "foreset" and "topset" beds, represented respectively the sediment carried out in suspension, the delta slope deposits produced by avalanching during delta advance, and the bedload deposits of the stream which fed the slope.

This simple "Gilbert Delta" dominated thinking for some time and only in the last thirty years have geologists appreciated how restrictive this sequence is. Inclined bedding (cross-bedding) is no longer thought diagnostic of deltaic sediments as it is known to form in other ways also. Our broader understanding of large marine deltas shows that the processes, morphologies and sediment sequences are more varied and complex.

Highly Constructive Marine Deltas. Major rivers tend to have suspended loads and, because of the greater density of seawater, river water almost always floats out over the sea. The plume of turbid river water may extend many miles off-shore and as it widens and decelerates it drops its load, which accumulates on the sea floor: the finest material travels furthest while the coarsest sediment is dropped rapidly near the river mouth. In consequence, the sea floor away from a river mouth shows a progressive diminution in grain-size of sediment. The slope of this surface of accumulation, the delta slope, is usually very low – of the order of a degree or two – in contrast to the steep avalanche slope of the Gilbert Delta. These large deltas build forward, therefore, depositing a sheet of sediment which coarsens vertically upwards. Most rivers discharge their sediment from several distributary channels and their patterns on the tops of constructive deltas are variable. Two main types are recognized, elongate and lobate.

The present-day Mississippi Delta is the classic example of the elongate or "bird-

The growth of the Mississippi Delta: (1) about 1890; (2) about 1940.

1

2

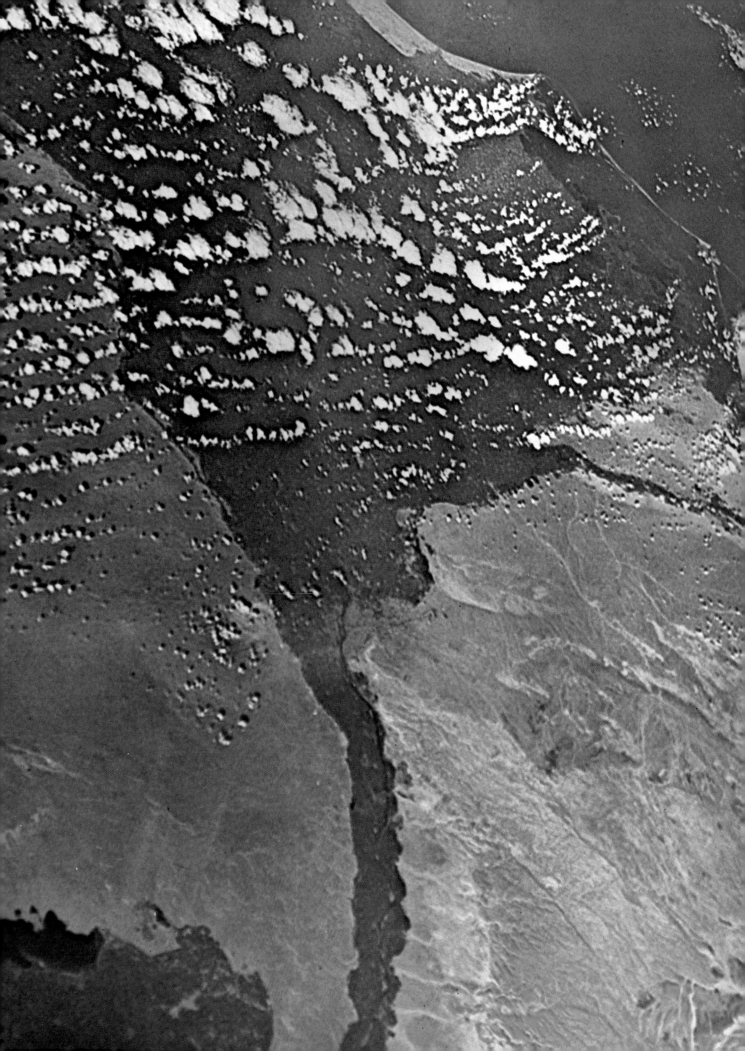

foot" delta. The distributary channels are straight and build out well in advance of the rest of the shore, so that sheltered bays are formed between them. The channels are flanked by levees which accumulate during flood overspill and which extend offshore. At the mouth of each channel is a pronounced shallowing caused by the rapid dumping of sediment at a "mouth bar". As each distributary advances it produces an elongate sand unit with a lens-shaped cross-section, a so-called "bar-finger sand".

Other constructive deltas, lobate deltas, have a pattern of distributaries which fan out from an apex and migrate with time. Each distributary has its own mouth bar, but, because of migration and switching of the distributaries, sheet sands rather than elongate bodies are deposited above the coarsening-upwards unit. The present birdfoot delta of the Mississippi is the seventh to grow there since the post-glacial rise of sea-level, but its six predecessors were all lobate with much less indented shorelines.

Destructive Marine Deltas. While highly constructive deltas are influenced by basinal processes, river processes dominate and determine the delta-top morphology. But this is often not the case; as for example, where input is reduced or where basinal energy is high. Both waves and tidal currents rework river-borne sediment into characteristic morphologies.

Maps or aerial photographs of the Rhône or Ebro deltas in the Mediterranean, or of the western part of the Niger Delta, show how the shore has built forward as a series of ridges accreted on to a beach. Waves have swept material sideways from the river mouths to accumulate as beaches and spits. In the sheltered areas behind these have developed swamps and marshes through which cut the distributary channels. These are typical wave-dominated deltas.

The Brahmaputra/Ganges Delta is a typical example of a tide-dominated delta. The shoreline is primarily influenced by wide-mouthed channels kept open by tidal ebb and flow. Some channels are linked to river distributaries while others are purely tidal. Similarly, the southern part of the Niger Delta has tidal channels as the dominant feature, resulting in a complex pattern of sands at the top of the deltaic sequence.

Rivers Without Deltas. Many of the world's major rivers have deltas which seem small in relation to the size of the river. Sediment – which is undoubtedly delivered by the rivers – seems to disappear. It is often found that submarine canyons occur off these river mouths and traverse the continental shelf and slope. At their lower ends, fans of sediment build out over the *ocean floor. A large proportion of the sediment, therefore, is being transferred direct to the ocean floor, probably by turbidity currents.

The most spectacular example is the River Congo, which has no delta to speak

A photograph from space of the arcuate delta of the Nile, whose fertile soils were cultivated by the forerunners of the Ancient Egyptian civilization.

The coast on Saint Abb's Head, Berwickshire, Scotland, displaying many of the typical features of a coastline retreating under the effects of wave attack, most obviously the steep cliffs. Retreat of a coastline may be due to erosion (as in this case) or submergence of the land, retreat being fastest when both are operative. Conversely, advance may be due to deposition at a rivermouth or emergence of the land. When opposing processes operate (e.g., deposition and submergence), the advance or retreat is considerably slower.

of. Here a canyon extends right into the river mouth and accumulated sediment is flushed out during floods. The situation is quite common with marine deltas, but is even more common in lakes, where density differences favor the development of underflows, so allowing the river to effectively flow out over the lake floor. The Rhône, entering Lake Geneva, is a well described example of this.

Conclusion. Deltas are shoreline areas with complex and variable sediment dynamics, the understanding of which is important to many human activities such as navigation and agriculture. Such understanding is also important for the oil geologist, as many of the world's major oil fields are located in sands laid down by ancient deltas. The ability to predict the extents and shapes of these can be vitally important, and a detailed understanding of delta processes may often increase the ability. (See also pp. 888–91.)   JDC

Coastlines

The sea has a great fascination for most people, particularly along the coast where its action on the land has produced such a wealth of varied forms. The coast can be an area of great natural beauty, but too often it

has been spoilt by ruthless economic exploitation: in order for us to make the best use of the coast and to preserve it properly for the future, the processes at work on it must be fully understood.

One of the major influences on the coastlines of the world has been the great rise in the world's sea-level, starting about 15,000 years ago and lasting until only a few thousand years ago, since when it has remained fairly static in most areas. Thus the world's coastlines are almost universally young, and the many features of coastal erosion and deposition are still developing rapidly.

Classification. Coasts can be classified using a number of different criteria. One classification is concerned with the broad structure related to *plate tectonic theory; another is based on the dynamic processes operating at the coast, the waves and tides; a third is based on the degree of modification the coast has undergone by reason of the influences of the sea or other agents; and the fourth is related to the advance or retreat of the sea.

Structural classification. There are three main types of coast arising from plate tectonic action. One is found at the trailing edge of separating plates; coasts along the Atlantic Ocean, which is a widening rift, are examples of this. Collision coasts comprise another category: meeting plates create stresses that result in the island arcs and *ocean trenches that border the northwest and southeast Pacific. A third type is the conservative plate boundary, where plates slide laterally past each other, as exemplified by the coast of California alongside the San Andreas *Fault.

Dynamic classification. Different regions are characterized by different wave types. In high latitudes storm waves are common and exert a generally destructive effect on the coast, while in lower latitudes long, low constructive swells are usual. A third major category is the low-energy coastal type of wave, which occurs where protection from large waves is offered by the narrow coastal stretch ("fetch") of open water across which wind blows, so reducing the height of the waves. Neighboring land, offshore ice (in polar regions) or coral reefs (in tropical regions) can limit the extent of the fetch. Such coasts are dominated by short, variable waves, generated by the local winds.

Coasts can also be described as macrotidal, where the difference between high and low tides is large; mesotidal, where the range is moderate; and microtidal, where the range is small.

Process classification. Coasts can be subdivided according to the process that plays most part in determining their form. Marine processes can be dominantly erosional or depositional, the latter producing extensive beaches and other accretional forms. Subaerially dominated coasts show the influence of fluvial, glacial, volcanic or other processes in their form. For example, drowned river valleys of the ria coasts, such as those of southwest Ireland, can be differentiated from glacially eroded drown-

ed coasts, exemplified by the fjords of Norway and southwest New Zealand. (See also *coastal plains.)

Spatial classification. For many practical purposes it is useful to know whether the coast is advancing or retreating. A coast may advance seaward either through *deposition or because sea-level is falling; the latter situation occurs where recovery from glacial unloading is still continuing (see *glaciation): such coasts (e.g., the shores of the Hudson Bay), are characterized by raised shorelines. Retreating coasts result from either *erosion or rising sea-level: the coast of Holderness is a good example of the former and coasts along parts of the southern North Sea, where rising sea-level more than compensates for coastal deposition, are typical of the latter.

High Coasts. Two basic coastal types can be differentiated in terms of coastal form. These are high, usually intricate coasts, and low, often smooth coasts. The action of marine processes on a high, complicated coast usually produces a straightening of the coastline as a result of both erosion and deposition.

Erosional features include various cliff forms, which are determined both by the rock type or drift and by its degree of exposure to wave attack. *Vertical cliffs* occur in resistant rocks along exposed coasts, where the marine attack is vigorous. The 650ft (200m) high cliffs of Moher in western Ireland and the chalk cliffs of Beachy Head are examples. *Drift cliffs* are usually less steep and liable to slumping and landsliding, such as those at the Warren at Folkestone, southern England. *Wave-cut platforms* may extend seaward from the foot of the cliffs, with a typical slope around 1 in 100. Their extent depends on a number of factors: the time that sea-level has remained stable, the resistance of the rock, the vigor of wave attack, and the amount of beach material.

Details of the coastal scene include *blowholes*, *geos* (narrow clefts along joints), *arches* and *stacks*, all of which develop, mainly by hydraulic action, in suitably jointed rocks as the sea attacks the cliffs. In fact, these features often form progressively in the order given, until the stack is finally eroded by the waves to leave a platform below the cliffs.

The straightening of the coastline is aided by wave refraction, which concentrates the wave energy on the headlands, material eroded from them drifting into the bays. The coastal system consists of a number of cells within which movement of material is restricted; these are the bays between adjacent headlands.

Depositional forms are built up wherever more material reaches the coast from offshore or alongshore than leaves it: usually the alongshore movement of material is more important. On an intricate coastline its direction is dependent on both the coastal outline and on the nature of wave attack. Beaches accumulate in the sheltered bays, while spits prolong the coastal direc-

tion where this changes abruptly, or where rivers interrupt the alongshore movement of material. Barriers may be formed across bays, and islands may be tied to the mainland by sand or shingle bars called tombolos. In high-latitude, previously glaciated areas, tombolos are often formed of shingle, the commonest beach material in such regions. Sand is the dominant beach material in low and middle latitudes, where swell waves predominate. Where material can move into an area from two directions, or where shelter is provided offshore, a cuspate foreland (such as Dungeness, the point of which is protected from wave action from the southeast by the proximity of France), may be formed.

Depositional forms tend to be more complex where the fetch is small and the direction of longshore drift is variable owing to changing wave conditions and coastal orientation.

Low coasts. Flat, gently sloping coasts usually consist of relatively unresistant material, generally depositional in character. For this reason, the waves can relatively easily modify the coastal outline to form a fairly straight coast: alongshore movement of material can operate over long stretches of coastline, producing extensive cells within which material can move.

Low coasts are usually sandy in nature, and their commonest features are wave-built sandy barriers with sand dunes, lagoons and salt marshes. The sand forming the extensive barriers is derived partly from inshore (*via* the rivers), sometimes from the erosion of sandy cliffs, but often predominantly from the continental shelf, across which the rising sea has swept sandy deposits which are built into barriers by the long, constructive swells. The southeast coast of the United States exemplifies a typical low-barrier coast, with dunes on the barrier islands and lagoons behind, separating an intricate, low mainland coast from the smooth, open-ocean beaches on the seaward side of the barrier.

Organic coastlines. In areas of very low wave energy, as in deep embayments such as the Wash (England), salt-marsh coasts occur in middle and high latitudes; while in similar circumstances in low latitudes, where fine material is available, mangrove coasts are more characteristic. The nature of the vegetation, in particular its ability to trap silt and fine sediment brought in by the tide, plays a major part in the formation of such coasts. (See also pp. 888–91.)

Another form of organic coast is provided by the reef-building *corals of the tropical seas. Fringing reefs built up by these animals become barrier reefs as their volcanic foundation subsides. When it has disappeared, a more or less circular atoll remains.

Conclusion. We are living in a time of great geological activity, and so our coastlines are in the process of rapid change. For this reason also we are lucky enough to be able to see a huge diversity of coastal forms, only a few of which, for reasons of space, have been described here.   CAMK

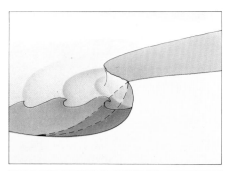
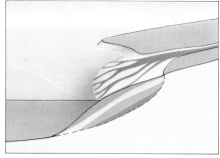

Advancing and retreating coastlines. *Above*, a retreating coastline with steep cliffs carved out by the erosive action of waves; *below*, a coastline advancing as sediment is washed into the sea by a river.

A row of craters testifies to the dominance of vulcanicity as a shaper of Icelandic landscapes. Note the lava plateaux on either side of the craters: such plateaux are characteristic of fissure eruptions. Lavas from such eruptions are generally of basalt and highly fluid.

Volcanic Landscapes

An erupting volcano is a flashback to Earth's primeval dawn, for volcanic landscapes, the most primitive landscapes of all, display the Earth's crust in the very process of formation. The type of landform produced by volcanic activity depends largely upon the style of eruption, which in turn is controlled to a large extent by the chemical and physical properties of the magma involved as well as by the structural nature of the region.

The mountains, hills, plateaux, plains and depressions resulting from volcanic activity are constructional landforms; that is, they are actively built rather than carved out by the forces of *erosion. Of course, erosion is at work – even as the volcanic products pile up – and nowhere was the contest between these opposing forces better displayed than in the eruption of Surtsey volcano off the south coast of Iceland during 1963–66. In its early stages, the volcano kept piling up ash and cinders but at the same time its crater was continually being flooded by the sea and its material washed away. Eventually a barrier of solid lava excluded the sea, and the volcano became a permanent island.

The term "volcano" embraces both the aperture in the Earth's surface from which volcanic materials – lava, tephra, and gas – emerge and the hill which forms from their accumulation. The hole in the ground may be a lengthy fissure if the crust is under tension, as, for example, in central Iceland, and in this case a *fissure volcano* is formed. If the volcanic activity is centered on a more or less circular vent or cluster of vents, a *central volcano* is the result.

Fissure volcanoes emit large volumes of very fluid material, either lava flows which are usually basaltic, or ash flows which have been described as aerosols of incandescent solid fragments suspended in hot gas. On coming to rest these solidify into ignimbrites which commonly have the composition of *rhyolite. In both cases, large areas are rapidly covered with flat-lying sheets of volcanic material, and repeated emissions build up great plains or *plateaux. The *basalt plateau of the Parana basin in southern Brazil and Uruguay is some 380,000mi² (1,000,000km²) in area, the lava having a probable volume of 200,000mi³ (850,000km³). Outcrops of ignimbrite now occurring in Nevada and Utah indicate that the original plain constructed there some 30 million years ago must have had an area of about 50,000mi² (130,000km²).

Lava plateaux are composed of overlapping broad flat cones of lava which have slopes of not much more than 1°. This *shield* structure is more obvious in the case of some Icelandic volcanoes, which have diameters up to about ten miles (about 15km) and slopes up to about 8°, and which have usually been built up by one lengthy eruption; but the largest shield volcanoes, such as those of Hawaii and the Galapagos Islands, are formed by innumerable fluid outpourings of basalt. Mauna Loa, a Hawaiian shield volcano, is effectively the Earth's largest mountain, rising more than 30,000ft (nearly 10,000m) from the sea floor, but with slopes nowhere steeper than 12°.

The Hawaiian shield volcanoes erupt both from a large summit caldera which may be occupied by a lava lake and from fissure or rift zones along the flanks: in this respect they are transitional between central and fissure volcanoes. Their basalt eruptions are voluminous but rarely explosive – although the projection of red-hot lava to heights up to 1500ft (450m) forming a "curtain of fire" along the rifts is spectacular enough. Older Hawaiian volcanoes display numerous parasitic cones of tephra and lava along the flanks, marring the original symmetry of the shield.

Volcanoes which erupt both lava and tephra build up a layered cone shape and are termed *composite volcanoes* or *stratovolcanoes*. This graceful shape, conforming to the popular image of a volcano, is produced by concentration of activity at the central summit crater, from which short flows may emerge and away from which tephra layers thin out in all directions. Fuji-san in Japan

is a well known example, having rather a large proportion of lava, but the most symmetrical of all is Mayon in the Philippines.

Eruptions from central volcanoes are generally classified according to their scale

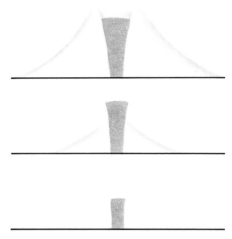

The formation of a volcanic plug. The cone of the extinct volcano is less resistant to erosion than the solidified magma within.

Hot springs at Kerlingarfjoll, Iceland, contrast oddly with the glaciated hillside behind. Such springs are typical of volcanic landscapes: they arise from contact between groundwater and volcanic gases, etc., underground. In several countries, underground hot water is being exploited as a source of heating and electricity.

of violence, the name of each category being for a typical example – e.g., Peléean for Mont Pelée in Martinique. Any volcano, however, is capable of erupting in several different ways, even during a single episode of activity.

The eruptive activity may change a volcano's morphology continuously over a long period or very rapidly in the space of a few weeks or less. In the first case, flank activity involving explosions of viscous magma may erect numerous ash or cinder cones, which have steeper slopes than lava cones (because the natural angle of rest of particulate material is greater). Spatter cones and spatter ramparts form around parasitic vents and fissures when eruptions are less violent and the magma more fluid. Very viscous magma such as *dacite or rhyolite may be extruded as *domes*. Rapid changes in morphology may ensue from landslide collapse of a whole sector of the volcano, initiating rubble and mud flows and leaving gaping depressions. More frequently documented than this is caldera collapse.

A caldera is a large, open depression at or near the summit of a volcano: older calderas may be almost totally obscured by erosion or later infillings. Steep and sometimes terraced walls suggest periodic downfaulting, which may be caused by withdrawal of magma beneath. Catastrophic collapse has occurred in many cases after rapid emission of great volumes of ash flows – the 1883 Krakatoa eruption was of this type. Crater Lake in Oregon, USA, is a waterfilled caldera some 5mi (8km) across and about 2000ft (600m) deep which formed after the collapse of a 12,000ft (3700m) andesitic stratovolcano, known as Mount Mazama, about 6000 years ago. The violence of the event may be judged from the fact that ash flows spread over 30mi (about 50km) from the volcano and ash falls occurred over 500mi (800km) away in Canada.

A great deal of volcanic activity occurs under water. If the load pressure of the water exceeds the gas pressure of the magma, there is no formation of tephra and piles of pillow lavas are produced. Eruptions in shallower water lead to the formation of ash or tuff cones in which glass fragments are very common. By the nature of things these only rarely become land forms, but similar volcanic forms are pro-

duced when eruptions occur under ice sheets, as in Iceland. Ridges or cones of granular glassy rocks and pillow lavas result from subglacial eruption through fissures or vents respectively. Occasionally these are topped by massive lava bodies, erupted subaerially when the overlying ice was melted through, producing volcanic table mountains.

Hot springs, geysers and fumaroles are generally regarded as typifying the waning stages of volcanoes. The heated water and gas cause strong chemical alteration of surrounding rocks and minerals, and the relatively soluble products weather easily to form rounded slopes with characteristically bleached soil and rock colors. Bitter experience, provided, for example, by Vesuvius in AD 79, has shown that it is dangerous to regard a volcano as extinct, and it is by no means certain that this "solfatara" stage of a volcano need be its last, as was shown in the case of the original Solfatara in the Phlegraean Fields, near Pozzuoli, Italy: nearby, in 1538, there was a massive cinder-cone eruption resulting in the formation of Monte Nuovo – the "new mountain".   JDB

A beautiful example of a ropy (pahoehoe) lava formation is provided by part of a recent basalt flow on the island of Jebel At Tair in the Red Sea. Lava that is instead blocky in form is called aa.

Types of Volcanic Eruption

		Eruption Type	Characteristic Activity	Other Features	Example
No magma involved	Eruption increases in violence	Fumarolic	generally long-lived weak to moderate escape of gas producing mineral encrustations	minor amounts of ash and boiling mud pools	Solfatara, Italy
		Gas eruption	continuous or rhythmic discharge of gas	may precede more violent eruption involving magma discharge	Hekla, Iceland, 1947
		Ultravulcanian	weak/violent ejection of old solid lava blocks		Kilauea, Hawaii, 1924
Magma increases in viscosity	Eruption increases in violence	Basaltic flood	lava fountains; voluminous, widespread flows of very fluid lava	spatter cones and ramparts; flat shields forming lava	Lakagigar, Iceland, 1783
		Hawaiian	lava fountains; thin, widespread flows of fluid lava from craters or fissures	spatter cones and ramparts; broad shield volcanoes	Mauna Loa, Hawaiian Islands
		Strombolian	moderate explosions of pasty lava as bombs and cinders; short flows	cinder cones	Stromboli, Italy. Paricutin, Mexico, 1943–52
		Vulcanian	moderate/violent explosions of lava blocks and ash; rare thick short flows	ash and block cones	Vulcano, Italy, 19th Century
		Peléean	moderate/violent explosions of lava blocks and ash and glowing avalanches (nuées ardentes)	ash and pumice deposits; viscous domes extruded	Mt. Pelée, Martinique, 1902
		Plinian	extremely violent ejection of ash to great heights; ash flows of varying size. May be associated with caldera collapse	beds of ash and pumice	Vesuvius, AD 79; Krakatoa, 1883
		Rhyolitic flood	rapid voluminous effusion of hot ash flows from fissures or calderas	ash flows variously welded into ignimbrite plains	Katmai, Alaska, 1912
		Subaquatic	steam and ash explosions in shallow water	ash and cinder cones, pillow lavas below	Capelhinos, Azores, 1957
		Subglacial	lava erupts below or into ice and snow causing floods	mudflows, pillow lavas, glassy fragments	Katla, Iceland

The Ocean Floor

The Ocean Floor and Sea-Floor Spreading

It is well known that the oceans cover some two-thirds of our planet's surface; what is perhaps less well known is that the floors of the ocean basins provide as great a variety of relief as any of the continents. Mount Everest could be completely submerged in many parts of the Pacific Ocean; the grandeur of the Alps is repeated on a global scale by the world-encircling mid-ocean ridge system.

In geological terms, the sea floor is ephemeral. It is being continuously created and destroyed by the sea-floor spreading process (see *plate tectonics), and from initial creation to eventual destruction a given piece of it may last no more than 200 million years – a small fraction of the age of the Earth. However, as it moves like a conveyor-belt across the globe, the sea floor develops a fascinating variety of topographic forms.

The Shaping of the Sea Floor. The sea floor is formed at the mid-ocean ridges by the cooling and solidification of magma and lava welling up from deep within the Earth. Because the newly-formed sea-floor mat-

erial is hot, it has a low density and rises high above the average level of the sea floor. It is then carried away from the ridge-crest at a rate of an inch or so a year, gradually sinking deeper as the newly-formed material cools and shrinks. From an initial average depth of some 8775ft (2700m), it may sink to about 13,000ft (4000m) after 20 million years, and by a further 4875ft (1500m) in the next 50 million years.

During the first few million years the rocks of the sea floor are subjected to strong forces which break them and uplift some relative to others to produce a rugged morphology. As time goes on, the ocean bottom gradually accumulates a cover of sediment derived from the remains of dead marine organisms or washed off the land by rain. This mutes the topographic forms as snow blankets a landscape, until eventually all the undulations, peaks and crevices are entirely covered by a smooth plain of sediment.

Mid-Ocean Ridges. Each of the world's oceans contains a mid-ocean ridge, the site of the spreading center at which all the sea floor in that ocean is produced. There is a virtually continuous system of such ridges around the world, almost completely circling the globe. Starting near the northern

coast of Siberia, the mid-ocean ridge system crosses the Arctic Ocean, then descends through Iceland and down the North and South Atlantic as the Mid-Atlantic Ridge, curving south of Africa into the Indian Ocean. There it branches, the Carlsberg Ridge running north between India and Africa before curving westward into the Gulf of Aden; and the other branch running south of Australia as the Indian–Antarctic Ridge and the Pacific–Antarctic Ridge. Thence the East Pacific Rise goes north toward Southern California, and finally the Gorda and Juan de Fuca Ridges run northward off the west coast of Canada.

A typical mid-ocean ridge may be 650 or more miles across, and rise to at least 1.9mi (3km) above its base. The mean depth below the water surface of the world's ridge crests is 8775ft (2700m), but in Iceland and at the western end of the Gulf of Aden ridges emerge above sea-level.

The ocean floor near the northern edge of the Madeira abyssal plain at a depth 15,320ft (4670m). The level bottom is of globigerina ooze, the small mounds being produced by bottom-dwelling animals. Note the starfish imprints on the right.

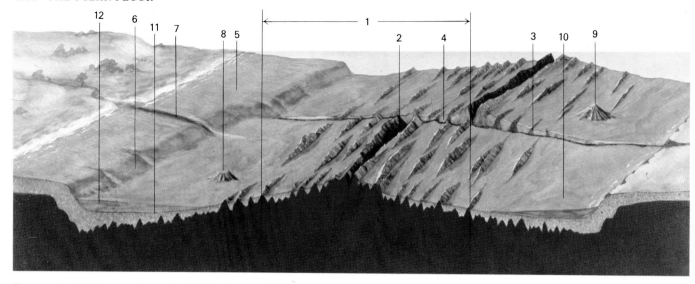

The ocean basin between passive continental plates (not to scale). Occupying a central position is a mid-ocean ridge (1) on whose slopes are abyssal hills and along whose crest runs a median valley (2). At right angles to the line of the ridge is a fracture zone, or transform fault (3), motion along which has resulted in an offset in the ridge (4). Also shown are the continental shelf (5), the continental rise (6), a submarine canyon (7), a guyot (8), a seamount (9) and the abyssal plain (10). Near to the ridge, which is a center of sea-floor spreading, basaltic rocks are found: closer to the continents, pelagic sediments (11) are overlain by turbidites (12).

The detailed form of a mid-ocean ridge depends on the rate at which it is spreading. "Slow" ridges such as the Mid-Atlantic Ridge (separating at 1.2in (3cm) per year) exhibit extremely rough topography, comprising row upon row of individual ridges and valleys, all parallel to the main ridge crest. These minor ridges are about 12.5mi (20km) apart, may be up to 30mi (50km) long, and are 3 to 6mi (5–10km) across. They are usually several hundreds of metres high, and their sides, which are formed by *faulting, are very steep, perhaps almost vertical in places. Near the crest of a slow-spreading ridge these long blocks form what are called the *crestal mountains.*

At the precise center of most slow-spreading ridges is an especially deep valley, known as the *median valley.* This may be over 0.6mi (1km) deep from its floor to

the summits of the crestal mountains. The main part of the valley is about 6mi (10km) across, but the tops of the crestal mountains on either side may be 30mi (50km) apart. The median valley is roughly V-shaped, with a floor only a mile or two across. Within this floor is the actual site of the generation of new sea floor, and recent studies using manned submersibles have shown that the lavas forming the new material erupt into long, low volcanic ridges. As the newly-created sea floor moves away, it is fractured into enormous blocks which are subsequently uplifted to form the crestal mountains.

Fast-spreading ridges such as the East Pacific Rise (up to about 8in (20cm) per year separation rate) are generally much less rugged than slow-spreading ridges, although they still exhibit a subdued ridge-

and-valley topography which is the result of faulting near the site of sea-floor generation. They usually have no median valley, and new lavas pile up directly on the crest of the ridge before being spread apart.

Because they consist of newly-formed volcanic rock, the central portions of mid-ocean ridges are completely devoid of sediment, though this begins to accumulate immediately at a rate of a hundred feet or so every million years. Because the lavas are extruded under water, they cool rapidly and soon become very viscous. This gives rise to weird-shaped formations, called *pillow lavas* but often resembling, not pillows, but short sections of squeezed toothpaste. These rocks are all *basalts (dark-colored lavas with relatively low silica content). The feet of the scarps formed by faulting are usually littered with scree made up of broken pillow lavas, completing the chaotic aspect of these regions.

Fracture Zones. The crests of the mid-ocean ridges are not continuous over distances of more than a few hundreds of miles, but are offset by enormous fractures called transform faults (see *plate tectonics). On either side of a transform fault the sea floor is moving in opposite directions. As the sea floor moves past the end of a transform fault the relative motion ceases, but any topographic forms created within the zone of the transform will be preserved. In this way long features known as *fracture zones* are created which extend, at right angles to the mid-ocean ridge system, across entire ocean basins.

Within the active (i.e., transform fault) part of a fracture zone, the opposite motion on either side of the fault breaks the sea floor into small fragments. Often there is additional volcanic activity within this area, and recent studies have shown that transform faults are the sites of hydrothermal activity, where seawater, circulating within the fractures in the crust, carries minerals such as chromium from the interior and deposits them on the sea floor.

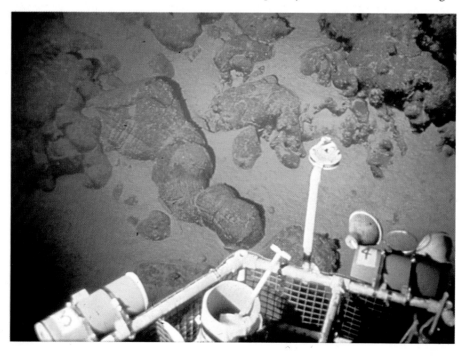

Pillow lavas of the deep ocean floor on the slopes of Mount Pluto in the mid-Atlantic, as photographed from the submersible Alvin. These globular forms are typical of lavas extruded under water.

At the junction between a transform fault and a median valley the sea floor is usually particularly deep. This phenomenon is not well understood, but it does contribute to the shaping of fracture zones, which usually have deep valleys associated with them. There must also be strong vertical forces (again, not well understood) operating within the transform fault region, which result in the sides of fracture zones having been uplifted by hundreds of yards.

Fracture zones typically consist of a deep valley perhaps 6mi (10km) across, flanked on one side by a steep scarp and a high ridge. However, the larger fracture zones often have rather complex structures, and there are a great variety of different forms incorporating various combinations of linear ridges, valleys and scarps. Because the sides of the fracture zones have been faulted, they often expose bare rock, some of which has been uplifted from depths of hundreds of yards beneath the sea floor. The bottoms of the valleys, however, are usually filled with sediment; indeed, since the fracture zones cut through the mid-ocean ridges, they often provide channels by which sediments may be carried from one ocean basin to another.

The width and vertical relief of a fracture zone is related to the distance of offset at the ridge crest, which may range from tens to hundreds of miles. The most spectacular fracture zones are found in the north-eastern Pacific where they extend for thousands of miles westward from the west coast of North America.

Abyssal Hills. As the ocean floor ages, it spreads away from the ridge crest where it was formed and gradually sinks. At the same time, as we have seen, sediment begins to cover it, thickening at a rate of a hundred feet or so every million years. By the time the sea floor is a few hundred miles from the ridge crest and approaching the base of the ridge, the sedimentary cover is considerable. Many of the lower sea-floor ridges have already been completely buried by sediment, and others have sediment draped over them, producing more rounded forms than occur near the ridge-crests. Only the steepest and highest parts of what once were crestal mountains are now free of sedimentary cover. These topographical features are referred to as abyssal hills, but of course there is no clearcut dividing line between these and the crestal mountains. The spacing and horizontal dimensions of the abyssal hills are similar to those of the crestal mountains, but naturally their vertical relief is less, usually only a few hundred yards. In general, the spacing increases with age, as more and more hills become buried and the sediment basins between them expand.

The sediments which accumulate on the flanks of mid-ocean ridges and in the abyssal hill regions are called pelagic or deep-sea sediments. They are generally oozes (consisting of the remains of mainly microscopic marine organisms) and clays. The oozes are classified according to the type of organism forming them; e.g., globigerina ooze (the remains of *globigerina), which is made principally of calcium carbonate, and diatomaceous and radiolarian oozes (the remains of *diatoms and *radiolaria, respectively), which are siliceous. The solubility of calcium carbonate in seawater increases with depth, and below about 3mi (5000m) it is so high that all calcareous sediments are dissolved, leaving

A small-scale turbidity current. Such currents, suspensions of silt and mud in water rapidly moving downslope on the bottom of the sea, are responsible for carving out submarine canyons.

the red clays which are generally found in the deepest water. These comprise very fine particles which have been eroded off the continents and carried either in the sea or by wind out into the deep oceans, together with volcanic dust.

The distribution of sediments depends on the action of currents as well as the age and depth of the sea. Faster-flowing currents can pick up and carry along particles of sediment, but if they change direction or slow down they may redeposit them. Also, in the presence of currents, sediments will be deposited more easily on gentle than on steep gradients, so current action will cause preferential accumulation of sediments on the floors of basins and keep steep slopes free.

Topographic forms can greatly influence currents, which may for example be channelled along deep valleys, accelerated by passing over shallow saddles (so that such features may be scoured free of sediment), or diverted round large hills and ridges. Because of the Earth's rotation, currents meeting a sea-mount will not divide but will be preferentially diverted on one side; this may result in a trench being scoured out on one side, whereas sediment will accumulate on the other side where there is little current flowing.

Sometimes sediments will temporarily accumulate on steep slopes, perhaps supported by small ledges, but will eventually become unstable and slump to the bottom of the slope. Often the sediments become fluidized during their fall, and flow freely

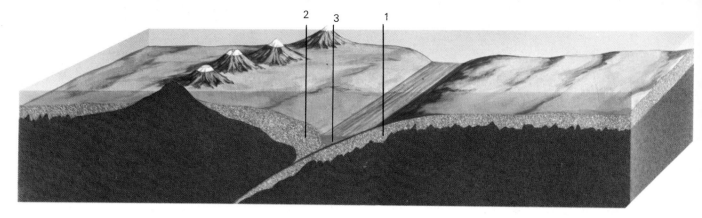

down into basins where they are deposited in almost flat-lying layers.

Abyssal Plains. Gradually the sediment thickness increases until most of the abyssal hills are covered. However, the deepest parts of the oceans are often the sites of large, extremely flat areas whose lack of relief cannot be explained entirely as a result of pelagic sedimentation. These are the abyssal plains, and typically they have slopes of one in a thousand (or less) over hundreds of miles. They are usually located just seaward of the continental margins, for the adjacent continents provide rich sources of sediments for deposition in them.

The extreme flatness of the abyssal plains is explained by the fact that the uppermost sediments on them have been deposited by turbidity currents. These currents are caused by the slumping of great masses of sediments off the continental slopes. As they fall, the sediments carry the surrounding water along with them, and become fluidized. In this condition they flow very easily, and turbidity currents may attain speeds of around 60mph (100km/h), persisting for many hours and flowing for thousands of miles. Because they are so fluid, they generally reach the deepest parts of the basins and deposit their sediments in level beds called turbidites. During the flow, the largest-grained material is deposited first, the finer grains later, so that an individual turbidite bed, a foot or more thick, will vary from silt or clay at the top to sand or gravel at the bottom. This makes these deposits easy to recognize in, for example, a cored section.

Turbidity currents are effective agents of *erosion, and may scour out channels where they flow. They may also "overflow" the edges of these channels, depositing sediment and building up levees like those produced in the flood-plains of terrestrial rivers. These channels may extend for thousands of miles through the ocean basins, and are known as *mid-ocean canyons*.

Fast-flowing currents also leave their mark on the bottom in the form of ripples and dunes in the sediments. Such structures may be associated with the currents of the general oceanic circulation as well as with turbidity currents, and are not, of course, confined to the abyssal plains.

Continental margins. The deep ocean basins are typically 2.5–3mi (four to five kilometres) deep, whereas the average elev-

ation of continents is several hundred yards above sea-level. The transition between these two levels usually occurs over a fairly narrow zone, known as the continental margin. Geologists distinguish two types of continental margin: active and passive.

Passive continental margins are found when new ocean basins open up, which takes place owing to the rifting apart of continents. During this process (see *rift valleys) the Earth's crust is subjected to strong tensional forces which fracture it. At the same time dense magma from the Earth's upper mantle is intruded into the crust, increasing its average density. Great slices of this overweighted crust sink along the tensional fractures, and simultaneously the two sides gradually spread apart. This process continues, with the rift floor gradually getting denser and sinking deeper, until eventually all of the old continental crust has been moved away to either side. At this point the rift floor will have sunk below sea level and attained the composition and structure of oceanic crust. Water can now flood in, and a new ocean has been formed. Subsequently the ocean grows by the normal sea-floor spreading process.

The passive continental margin formed by this process clearly will consist of a series of downthrown steps in the continental crust, and is usually also characterized by a seaward thinning of the crust. The changes which have taken place often cause the edge of the continent to sink slightly so that it becomes flooded: this flooded region then forms the *continental shelf*, which is rarely deeper than about 650ft (200m).

The continental shelf has exactly the same underlying structure as those parts of the continent which are above sea-level, though its surface features may be altered by erosion and deposition of sediment under the influence of strong, mainly tidal, currents. These may cause the formation, and perhaps migration, of great bars and banks of sand and gravel. Deposits of this kind can sometimes be usefully exploited, but may also cause inconvenience and perhaps hazard to shipping.

As time goes on, sediments which have been washed off the land gradually accumulate on the continental shelf, eventually forming deposits many miles thick. The shelf tends to sink under the weight of these sediments, so that its upper surface still remains below sea-level. These thick

A deep-sea trench and its accompanying arc of volcanic islands. The dense oceanic plate (1) is being subducted beneath the lighter continental plate (2), resulting in deep earthquake activity and the formation of the island arc. The basaltic rocks of the oceanic plate are overlain by pelagic sediments, and close to the trench these are in turn overlain by turbidites (3).

sedimentary sequences are excellent sites for the formation of *petroleum, and a great deal of effort is being expended by governments, industry and research institutions around the world to explore the continental shelves for this valuable resource.

Most continental margins have an abrupt edge, usually at about 650ft (200m) depth, where the sea floor falls away quite steeply toward the typical ocean depths of 2.5–3mi (4 to 5km). This steep region is called the *continental slope*. Usually it marks the position of the old rifted continental edge, but in some places, especially opposite the mouths of large rivers, great quantities of sediment are laid down over the continental slope, which consequently grows outward, forming a *sedimentary cone*. An example is the Ganges Cone, which extends from the mouth of the Ganges in the Bay of Bengal far southward into the Indian Ocean.

At the foot of the continental slope is the *continental rise* – a region of gentler slope, marking the final transition to the deep ocean floor.

Continental slopes and rises throughout the world are cut by deep valleys called *submarine canyons*, the largest of which may extend far out to sea to become mid-ocean canyons. They are generally a few hundred yards deep and a few miles wide, usually with a V-shaped cross-section. Submarine canyons are created by the erosional effect of turbidity currents as they sweep off the top of the continental slope down into the basins. These currents are extremely powerful, and are a potential hazard to any man-made structures on the sea floor in these regions. They provide a great deal of trouble for the engineers who lay and maintain submarine telegraph cables.

Arcs, Trenches and Active Margins. Although sea floor is being continuously created at the mid-ocean ridge axes, the surface of the Earth is not, so far as we know, expanding. Therefore there must also be places where sea floor is being destroyed or consumed. This happens at the great trenches, where converging slabs of sea floor, or "plates", meet: one slab dips down under the opposite one, plunging at an angle of about 45° into the interior of the Earth. The deepest and perhaps the most famous of the trenches is the Marianas Trench, south of Japan: it was here that Piccard and Walsh dived in a bathyscaphe in 1960. The bottom of the Marianas Trench, 35,820ft (11,022m) below sea-level, is the deepest point on the surface of the solid Earth.

Most of the deep-sea trenches are found around the borders of the Pacific, stretching from the Kermadec Trench just north of New Zealand in a great arc west, north and finally eastward across the Aleutian Trench between Siberia and Alaska, and also off the west coast of Central and South America. Other trenches occur in the Caribbean, the southernmost Atlantic (the South Sandwich Trench) and south of the East Indies in the Indian Ocean.

A trench always runs parallel to the edge of a continent (e.g., South America) or a line of islands. In the latter case, the islands always lie along a curve which is convex toward the open ocean (e.g., the Aleutian Islands). For this reason they are known as island arcs.

Trenches have an asymmetric V-shaped cross-section. The steep side of the V always borders the continent or island arc, and the gentler slope (perhaps 1 in 5 to 1 in 20) leads out to the open sea. Trenches are typically a few miles deep relative to the surrounding sea floor, which itself is about 3mi (5km) below sea-level. A trench may be a few thousand miles long and about 30–60mi (50 to 100km) wide at the top. Although sediments mantle the sloping sides, there is usually a narrow plain of flat sediments (probably derived from local slumping and turbidity currents), a few miles wide, at the bottom.

The trenches are formed by the down-turning of the sea floor prior to its 45° plunge into the Earth's interior. As one plate is pulled down under the other, some of the sediments from the down-going plate are scraped off and piled up onto the other. Other sediments, however, are carried down into the Earth with the descending slab, and this property of the trenches has led to the suggestion that they be used as sites for dumping various waste materials. Research to investigate the feasibility of such proposals is actively under way at present.

As the descending slab moves down into the Earth it heats up, and eventually part of it melts. The molten material may then rise to the surface behind the trench and erupt through volcanoes. It is in this way that the island arcs are formed, all these islands being volcanic. The curved distribution of the islands is a function of the geometrical relation between the dipping, down-going slab and the curved surface of the Earth.

When the trench borders on a continent, it produces an active continental margin. Such a margin (in common with the island arcs and mid-ocean ridges) is characterized by *earthquakes and volcanic activity, in contrast to the quiet sedimentation and erosion which are the only activity on the passive margins.

Seamounts, Guyots and Atolls. Strictly speaking, any large, isolated peak on the sea floor – for example, an especially high peak in the crestal mountains – may be called a seamount. More often, however, seamounts are formed by volcanic activity on sea floor which is shallow enough for volcanoes to rise above sea-level. This may occur where a mid-ocean ridge is particularly shallow (the volcanoes of Surtsey, which first appeared off Iceland in 1963, and Tristan da Cunha in the South Atlantic, are examples), in island arcs, or at "hot-spots". The latter are areas of uplift and local volcanic activity in the Earth's crust situated away from the main active plate boundaries. They apparently lie above particularly hot zones in the Earth's mantle, which some scientists believe to be the sites of rising convection currents of plastic rock. During sea-floor spreading the ocean floor may be carried over a hot spot, which will cause uplift and

An aerial view of Saba Island, Red Sea, part of a chain of recently active volcanoes marking the plate margin where Africa and Arabia are being rifted apart.

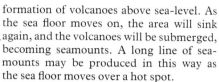

The formation of an atoll as the relative depth of sea around a volcanic island increases (either by a eustatic rise, as here, or as the island sinks beneath the surface while migrating away from a center of sea-floor spreading). Initially coral is growing around the edges of the island: as the sea level rises, so the coral grows upward to stay above the surface. The end result is an atoll surrounding an empty lagoon.

formation of volcanoes above sea-level. As the sea floor moves on, the area will sink again, and the volcanoes will be submerged, becoming seamounts. A long line of seamounts may be produced in this way as the sea floor moves over a hot spot.

A good example of the result of this process is the Hawaiian-Emperor seamount chain in the northwest Pacific. At present, volcanic activity occurs only in the Hawaiian Islands: however, stretching away to the northwest is a long line of submerged volcanoes making up the seamount chain. As would be expected, they become progressively older as one goes farther away from the present hot-spot.

Most oceanic volcanoes tend to sink with time, as the Earth's crust and upper mantle on which they were formed cool and sink. However, some seamounts are so heavy that the Earth bends beneath them, and so they tend to sink under their own weight. In this case a shallow "moat", perhaps a few tens of miles wide, forms on the sea floor around them. Study of this phenomenon can be of interest to marine geologists since it enables the strength of the Earth's lithosphere (the rigid, 50mi (80km) thick outer layer) to be determined.

If a volcano is formed in waters inhabited by reef-building *corals, and subsequently sinks, an atoll may be formed. At first a "fringing reef" grows up around the shore of the volcanic island. As the island sinks, the coral grows upward so that the top of the reef remains at sea-level. Since volcanic islands are generally cone-shaped, the area above sea-level diminishes as the island sinks. Coral thrives best on the outer side of

a reef, where it is adjacent to open water containing plenty of nutrients, and so an outer coral ring forms, containing a shallow lagoon. Eventually the original island may sink entirely, leaving only a ring-shaped atoll surrounding an empty lagoon. This theory of atoll formation was first propounded by Charles *Darwin in the nineteenth century, and after considerable controversy it was finally proved correct when American geologists drilled deep boreholes into some Pacific atolls and found volcanic rocks overlain by great thicknesses of coral.

Some seamounts are shaped like truncated cones, having quite flat tops. These are called guyots. Many guyots are thought to be submerged atolls where coral growth has not kept up with subsidence, either because the island sank too rapidly or because the coral for some reason died. However, some guyots were probably formed by erosion of volcanic islands to a flat *plateau prior to sinking. Around the Azores, for example, in the north Atlantic, are a number of flat-topped seamounts, some of which contain central pinnacles which may be ancient, uneroded volcanic plugs.

Conclusions. In this article we have examined some of the more important topographic forms of the sea floor and seen something of their variety, complexity and origins. The slope of the sea floor varies from the near-vertical cliffs of the mid-ocean ridges and fracture zones to the incredibly flat surfaces of the abyssal plains. Its composition ranges from rough, blocky basalt through shelly sediments to the finest

of clays. The oceans contain mountains and canyons, hills and valleys. We have looked briefly at the important and fascinating mechanisms of sediment deposition and transport, and have seen how currents can modify or sometimes completely change this process.

In the last 20 years, the deep ocean floor has been mapped on a reconnaissance basis, the major features have been identified and many of the processes occurring there are becoming understood. However, much remains to be done. The distribution of sediment types is incompletely mapped. The polar regions are poorly surveyed, and more detailed surveys are needed in many parts of the oceans. We have barely begun to search for minerals in the deep oceans, or even to understand where and how they occur. We are not certain what causes the uplift of crestal mountains or the depression of fracture zone valleys, nor are we sure how stable is the sea floor far from the ridges and trenches. As mankind extends his activities out onto the continental shelves and down into the deep ocean basins, it is becoming increasingly important for us to answer these questions and achieve a detailed knowledge and understanding of all parts of the ocean floor. Perhaps our very survival depends upon it. RCS

Economic Geology

Engineering Geology

On the evening of December 2 1959 the newspaper headlines throughout Europe carried the shattering news of the failure of the Malpasset Dam in southern France and the subsequent loss of over 400 lives in the catastrophic flood wave resulting from the emptying of the reservoir. Less than four years later, on October 9 1963, an even more massive flood wave was formed when part of Mount Toc, in northern Italy, fell into the Vaoint Reservoir causing considerable destruction downstream and the deaths of over 1500 people.

Such events bring sharply to our awareness the hazards inherent in civil-engineering construction, when Man interferes, often unwittingly, with the forces of the natural environment. In both cases the reaction of a rock mass to changed conditions – resulting from the construction of a dam – was not fully appreciated. At Malpasset, a highly stressed arch dam was built on a relatively weak foundation composed of faulted schists; failure occurred in the left foundation as a result of rupture along pre-existing defects within the rock structure. However, at Vaoint, the conditions were different in that flooding by the reservoir of the toe of a very old landslide, forming one side of Mount Toc, resulted in a weakening of the rock mass, followed by movement of about $1060 \times 10^7 \text{ft}^3$ (300 million cubic metres) of rock.

Such dramatic examples illustrate the importance of adequate prediction of geological conditions prior to the construction of engineering works. However, engineering geology, which is concerned with the application of geology in engineering practice, is not directed solely to ensuring that sites are free of natural hazards: it is equally important that the cost estimates for a project are as accurate as possible and that unreasonable delays or cost increase will not occur during construction as a consequence of the late recognition of geological conditions which had not been fully appreciated at the outset.

Rock Properties. Most branches of economic geology are concerned with the extraction of mineral resources and the use of these resources in our industrial society. In distinction, engineering geology is concerned with the engineering properties, behavior and interaction of rocks, soils and water in their natural environment. The main properties which are of relevance to the behavior of rock materials are their strength; deformability and permeability (see *hydrogeology), together with their long-term chemical stability. The strength of a natural rock mass is a function of its ability to withstand imposed loads: the failure of the Malpasset dam foundation and the slope of Mount Toc were both a consequence of rock masses being unable to withstand such loads. Rock failures of this type result from movements along planes of weakness within the rock mass, such as bedding planes, joints and faults, which reduce the bulk strength of the rock.

The deformability of a rock is of direct

Part of the Tarbela Dam on the Indus River in Pakistan under construction: The dam is destined to be the biggest in the world, but flaws due possibly to poor design have delayed completion.

A simple dam being constructed in the hills of China to provide a drinking-water reservoir. Use has been made of the form of the sides of the valley, and most of the stone used for building is local.

relevance to the compression which occurs as a consequence of loading. When a heavy structure such as a power station or multi-storey block is constructed, settlement of the underlying ground takes place. If this settlement is excessive then the building may finish up at a lower level than is required, or it may tilt or even crack.

Many rock types are subjected to chemical and physical changes when exposed to a new environment (see ★weathering), and, when those changes are relatively rapid, the life of an engineering structure can be affected. For example, solution of limestone by groundwater can give rise to the opening of joints, and consequent increase in permeability and progressively greater groundwater flow through the rock mass. Such changes have serious implications on the watertightness of a reservoir when the underlying rocks are composed of limestone.

Apart from these properties, there are two essentially environmental factors which can influence the engineering behaviour of rocks and soils; these are the natural stress state and the groundwater conditions. All rocks in the Earth's crust are confined by the surrounding rock materials and are in consequence subject to stress, which may result from the weight of overlying material and/or the aftereffects of

mountain-building processes (see ★plate tectonics). Artificial excavations, such as tunnels or mines, result in the release of such stresses and this can have adverse effects on the stability of the excavation. Similarly, the deeper an excavation is below the water table the greater is the groundwater pressure, and such a situation can give rise to rupture of the rock by an inrush.

Early Stages of a Project. Any engineering project, whether for construction or extraction purposes, passes through a number of well-defined stages involving investigation, design, construction and operation. Although engineering geology has a role to play throughout this sequence, the subject is possibly of greatest importance during the early stages, as a project is being conceived and passing through phases of investigation and design. Later on, when firm decisions have been made, the role of engineering geology is to confirm that the predictions are correct – or to identify changes in the actual conditions from those predicted, so that appropriate steps can be taken.

The engineering geologist works with experts in the related fields of soil mechanics and rock mechanics. The study of the engineering properties of soft and unconsolidated rocks, such as clays, silts, sands and gravels, is known as soil mechanics (the term soil has in engineering, therefore, a very different meaning from the one it has in geology – see ★soils). Rock mechanics deals with the study of the properties of

rock masses as engineering materials.

The investigation of an engineering project is the vital first stage to the formulation of any scheme, whether it is a major reservoir and hydroelectric complex or a small housing development. Before construction can commence it is necessary to plan the basic layout of the project and then to design each unit in detail. In consequence an investigation is normally phased, customarily moving from the general to the particular as information is accumulated.

The first stage is to review such data as may be available, and this normally takes the form of a desk study supplemented by a walk-over survey of the project area. A clearer idea will be obtained at that stage as to the topography and geology of the region, the technical problems which may be present and, possibly most important, the type of investigation methods which would be most appropriate. The next stage is to prepare geological maps of the complete area, together with more detailed maps of locations where structures are to be built. It is normal practice for aerial photographs to be used during this mapping procedure; and, under appropriate circumstances, remote sensing systems involving special forms of photography (infrared, false-color) or oblique radar housed in aircraft may also be used. One of the purposes of such mapping is to identify and delimit geological conditions which may give rise to engineering problems such as fault zones, unstable ground or shallow groundwater.

The physical exploration of the subsurface is carried out by excavations, boreholes or geophysical surveying.

Excavations permit access into the rocks and soils in which construction is to take place, so that direct observations can be made, samples taken for laboratory testing and *in situ* tests of the engineering properties carried out. Such excavations include trial pits, trenches, shafts, adits and tunnels. Possibly the commonest form of exploration is based upon the drilling of boreholes, in which cylindrical cores of rock or soil are recovered. Rock cores are obtained by drilling a diamond-tipped core barrel into the ground, progressively recovering lengths of rock – if unstable conditions are encountered, steel casing is installed in order to support the borehole walls. Water is added to keep the bit cool and to remove cuttings as drilling proceeds. Boreholes drilled in softer rocks or soils do not require such powerful equipment and tube samples can be obtained by pressing or hammering samplers into the ground. Once the samples of rock or soil have been recovered the materials are described in detail for record purposes and selected samples sent for laboratory testing.

The techniques of geophysical surveying most commonly used in engineering geology are the seismic and resistivity methods (see *geophysics). The seismic technique is most successfully used for determining the contact between rock and overlying superficial materials, and for providing an indication of the relative quality of the rock in engineering terms, higher seismic-wave velocity being generally associated with denser, more massive rocks. The resistivity method relies upon variations in the apparent resistivity (resistance to the flow of electricity) of the rocks, primarily determined by the degree of saturation of the rocks or soil, and the salinity of the groundwater. Thus dry sands have a high resistivity, whereas sands saturated with seawater, or shales, tend to have lower resistivities. By this means it is possible to delimit, in plan or profile, variations in apparent resistivity and hopefully relate such variations to changes in geology or groundwater conditions.

At the close of an investigation the geological information is prepared in the form of plans and sections, and then related to the results of field and laboratory tests and other observations. Only a tiny fraction of the ground has been sampled or tested, so that it is essential to rely to a considerable degree on the extrapolation of known geological conditions in the interpretation of the results of the engineering tests. Very considerable reliance must be placed upon geological judgment at this stage but, where possible, this can be minimized by appropriate design of the investigations: in the case of a major project it is clearly advantageous to phase the investigations so that the explorations can be modified and developed progressively as new information becomes available.

Building a Dam. The application of engineering geology in practice can probably be best illustrated by considering the range of problems which could be associated with the construction of a major dam in connection with a hydroelectric scheme.

The location of a dam is generally governed by a constriction in a valley, which permits use of the smallest possible structure. Such a constriction is commonly geologically controlled, in that the steeper valley-sides are associated with more massive and resistant rocks – a feature which again favors construction of the dam. The reservoir basin upstream of the dam should preferably open out into a broad flat-bottomed area with gently sloping valley sides.

Once one or more alternative dam sites have been located, consideration needs to be given to the type of dam which can be constructed at the site. Concrete dams require rigid rock foundations, the depth of overburden and weathered cover being at a minimum so that limited excavation will be necessary. If the valley sides are moderately steep it is practicable to construct a curved arch dam, which transmits the loads from the weight of concrete in the dam and of water in the reservoir into the floor and flanks of the valley. Gravity and buttress dams, which are constructed in more open valleys, transmit stresses directly into the valley floor and generally require less rigid foundations than arch dams.

The Volta Dam in Ghana. Lake Volta, formed by the dam, is the largest manmade lake in the world, with an area of 3275mi² (8482km²). The Volta Dam project supplies hydroelectricity and water for irrigation.

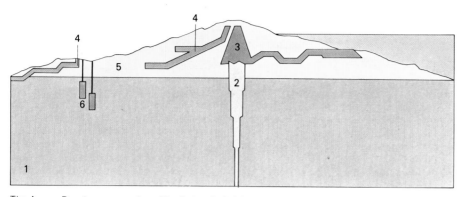

The Aswan Dam in cross-section: (1), alluvium bed; (2), clay and sand grouted with cement; (3), clay; (4), crushed stone and sand; (5), rock and sand; (6), drainage wells.

Various methods can be used to improve, or reinforce, the rock mass or to modify the manner in which the stresses from the dam are transmitted into the rock foundations so that less favorable sites can be adopted. For example, the Kariba Dam has been constructed on massive biotite *gneisses. The upper part of the south bank is composed of fractured, weathered quartzites which include clay seams: it was recognized that the rock was too weak and deformable to withstand the loads from the dam, and so it was decided to construct a series of buttresses underground, carrying the thrust of the uppermost part of the dam into sounder rock at depth.

However, if the foundations are unfavorable for a concrete dam it is more common practice to construct an embankment dam, composed of placed and compacted soil and rock materials. Embankment dams can be built in a wide variety of geological and topographical situations, including relatively weak and deformable conditions, which occur when the valley floor is underlain by thick alluvium composed of clays, silts and sands. An essential feature of any embankment dam is its impermeable membrane, commonly composed of low-permeability soils which contain a significant proportion of clay and silt; artificial membranes can be provided by concrete or bitumen. The membrane is supported by shoulders composed of more free-draining material such as sand or gravel. In order to ensure that groundwater pressures within the dam are controlled, filter and drainage layers composed of aggregates are provided next to the membrane and the foundation. If the membrane is inside the dam (the usual situation) then a protective layer of coarse rock is dumped on the upstream face to minimize *erosion by wave attack.

An additional factor which can influence the type of dam chosen is the availability of construction materials. In the case of concrete dams, coarse and fine aggregates are combined with cement, which must be imported to the site, for the manufacture of concrete. Aggregates can generally be obtained either from existing quarries or by the development of a new source of gravel and sand. If cement is not readily available at the site, or no potential sources of concrete aggregate are present, it may be necessary to construct an embankment dam.

Although more types of construction material are required in the case of an embankment dam it is not uncommon for such a dam to be built upon a site that could equally be used for a concrete dam – the reason is that an embankment dam can be constructed more economically. Although the foundation requirements for embankments are less rigorous than for concrete dams, significant problems can arise if the strength or deformability are suspect. If the foundations are composed of clay, high pore-water pressures will be generated in the foundation as the embankment is heightened. Boreholes drilled in the foundation and back-filled with sand are used to drain the pore-water, thus reducing the pressures and increasing the in situ strength of the clay. Soft clays can deform considerably under imposed load, leading to foundation settlement. This can be controlled by appropriate drainage and compensated for by addition of sufficient fill.

Apart from the questions which arise from the location and foundations of the dam, together with the materials which are to be used in construction, one of the major issues which needs to be assessed is the watertightness of the reservoir and the dam-site. Leakage from a reservoir can result from flow through specific geological defects, such as fractured rocks, or by general seepage through a zone of moderate permeability where the preexisting groundwater pressures are less than those which will be imposed by the reservoir. Special measures need to be adopted at the dam to minimize seepage and these generally involve the construction of a treated zone of rock – usually by injecting a cement-water mix (grouting) from boreholes – across the valley below the dam to an elevation above the top water level.

The water contained in the reservoir must be controlled as it passes through, over or past the dam. Water needs to be discharged from the reservoir in a controlled manner if it is to be used for water supply, irrigation or power generation. Similarly water may overtop the dam if the reservoir is filled and, for this reason, a spillway needs to be provided. These hydraulic works can be incorporated within the dam if it is of concrete construction and adequate size, but, in the case of embankment dams, they are commonly underground or excavated into the adjacent hillside.

Tunnelling is commonly associated with the construction of dams, the method of excavation and support being determined by the rock conditions. In fractured or faulted rocks, or where clay seams are present, instability can develop soon after excavation, so that installation of support is urgently required. In soft or water-bearing ground it is necessary to use carefully controlled excavation methods and rapid support. The prediction of geological and groundwater conditions in advance of tunnelling is possibly one of the more difficult problems in engineering geology.

Apart from the structures associated with the construction of a dam, there can be a number of related matters of engineering geological importance. For example: the construction of large reservoirs can give rise to *earthquakes, probably as a consequence of the imposed load of the reservoir associated with changes in groundwater pressures at depth; the instability of valley sides within the reservoir can give rise to damage to engineering structures, dislocation of communications or, in exceptional cases such as Vaoint, catastrophic flood waves which overtop the dam crest; changes in water-level downstream of the dam can give rise to land sliding; and the release of water from reservoirs can cause major erosion in the valley floor downstream of the dam.

This example, the construction of a dam, demonstrates the diversity of activity within engineering geology. Similar scope occurs in other areas – such as highway engineering, where it is necessary to apply engineering geology in initial route selection, to ensuring the stability of embankments and cuttings, exploring sources of construction materials and controlling groundwater flow into excavations.

Conclusions. The most spectacular consequences of the interaction between engineering and geology are, regrettably, failures which cause damage and loss of life. The more routine interactions are hardly noticed – unless they cause some form of inconvenience, however trivial. The primary purpose of engineering geology is to forestall such inconveniences by ensuring that the geological hazards likely to occur during construction and operation are recognized and minimized, that the cost of a scheme is correctly estimated, and that unforeseen delays do not take place. Such aims must inevitably appear optimistic, particularly in light of the difficulties of predicting geological conditions at depth

The Kariba Dam on the Zambesi River provides hydroelectricity for much of Zambia and Rhodesia. The artificial lake that has been created behind it has a total of more than 2000mi² (5000km²).

and the response of rock and soil materials to engineering operations. Nevertheless, without the essential input of engineering geology, there is little doubt that many engineering projects would be rendered impossible by failures, delays and cost. JK

Hydrogeology

The importance of water to mankind is generally underrated except at times of flood and drought. Yet these are merely localized, extreme events in the *hydrologic cycle*, which embraces the occurrence and mode of circulation of water from the atmosphere to the Earth and back again in perpetuity. Powered by the energy of the Sun, the cycle cannot be halted, though most of its individual components can be modified by Man on a local scale.

The discipline dealing with the distribution of water beneath the Earth's surface from a strictly resources viewpoint is described as groundwater hydrology or geohydrology, while the term hydrogeology is used in a wider, geological context that recognizes the significance of water as an agent of geological processes as well as the most beneficial of all Earth's resources.

Of the total amount of precipitation that falls as rain, snow, hail or dew, some two-thirds is returned to the atmosphere by evaporation and the remainder is disposed of either as direct surface run-off to streams or through infiltration into the soil, the proportion depending on prevailing geological conditions. The water in active circulation in the hydrological cycle is named meteoric water, and a part of this is called connate water when temporarily removed from the cycle by geological circumstances. Those new additions to the circulation system from volcanic or magmatic sources are known as juvenile water and are infinitesimally small in comparison with meteoric water. In order that one may appreciate the full role of underground water in the subsurface regime, it is necessary to realize firstly that the source of such water is precipitation and, secondly, that the water is never "pure" but rather behaves as a solvent.

Distribution and Occurrence. Following the natural sequence of the hydrologic cycle, the water that penetrates into the ground enters the province of subsurface water. The *zone of aeration* is that part of the ground in which spaces are not permanently filled with water: adjacent to streams or lakes it is less than 3.25ft (1m) thick, but elsewhere it can be 330ft (100m) or more in thickness. Any water infiltrating downward through this zone is subject to the forces of molecular attraction that tend to suspend the water against the pull of gravity: this water is termed vadose, from the Latin *vadosus*, shallow. Below the lower limit of the zone of aeration all inter-

The hydrologic cycle. Water from the atmosphere falls as rain, snow, etc., on both land and sea. Some of the water that falls on the land is carried by surface run-off (i.e., streams and rivers) to the ocean; some travels to the ocean by groundwater seepage; while some is returned to the atmosphere either by straightforward evaporation from bodies of water and from the land surface or by the transpiration of plants. The hydrologic cycle, shown schematically on the right, is completed by evaporation of water from the ocean to the atmosphere.

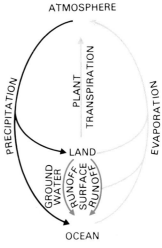

on the other hand, where cementation has significantly reduced the number and size of original pore spaces, the permeability depends largely upon the presence and scale of secondary features such as fractures or solution channels.

To illustrate the point, one may consider clay, chalk, gravel and limestone, which have porosities ranging from more than 50% for clay to less than 10% for limestone. Their permeabilities are, however, in reverse order: clay's is low because its small pores offer great resistance to flow of water in comparison with the large solution channels that produce the very high permeability of some limestone formations. Since permeability is a relative term it follows that a classification of deposits as permeable or impermeable is only meaningful in a particular context since truly impermeable strata are rarely encountered.

Any permeable formation or group of adjacent formations that yields water readily enough to be significant as a source of supply may be designated an *aquifer*. This includes both the zone of aeration, which functions as the intake area, and the zone of saturation from which the groundwater is obtained. The complementary term aquiclude is used to describe strata such as clays and shales which are impermeable in comparison with adjacent aquifers.

Where the top of the zone of saturation of an aquifer is a free-water surface it is known as the *water table* (or phreatic surface) and the condition is described as unconfined. If a well is drilled from the zone of aeration into the zone of saturation, then water will be struck at the level of the water table and will remain standing at that level even if the well is deepened. An aquifer that is saturated up to the base of an overlying aquiclude is said to be confined (or artesian). When a confined aquifer is pierced by a well the groundwater is under sufficient pressure to rise above the top of the aquifer. The pressure (or piezometric) surface is an imaginary plane extrapolated from the static level of the water in such wells: where the level of this surface is above the ground the wells are described as having artesian flow and need no pumping. Should the pressure surface be lower than the ground surface then sub-artesian flow will take place.

Further information can be obtained by geophysical techniques (see *geophysics): these include studies of density, magnetic susceptibility, and electrical potential and conductivity. Gravity methods, like magnetic methods, are not commonly useful in groundwater studies. Electrical methods, on the other hand, have long been used. Measurements of the ability of Earth materials to conduct electrical energy allow the sequence and nature of strata to be iden-

connected void space is fully occupied by water. In this *zone of saturation* occurs *groundwater*. Whereas infiltration is directed essentially vertically downward, groundwater percolates in any direction in response to hydrostatic forces, though it commonly has a dominant sideways component.

Water occurs underground in a variety of void spaces in a wide range of geological strata, and can move *via* pores and cracks from the surface of the soil down through the unweathered rock of depths of 6mi (10km) and more. Nevertheless, it is the uppermost 1600ft (500m) of the Earth's crust that is of most significance for water-supply purposes. Which materials form natural underground reservoirs (aquifers) depends on the size of their voids and the degree to which these are interconnected.

Two important factors govern the amount and availability of water in an aquifer. The first is the *porosity*, which is the proportion of the total volume of the rock or deposit that consists of voids which

can be occupied by water. This gives some indication of the holding/storage capacity of a geological formation. However, so far as water supplies are concerned, the capacity of a material to yield water is of much more importance than its ability to hold water. For example, it is not possible to completely dewater a saturated deposit by drainage because some water is always retained by molecular attraction. The void space actually emptied is described as the effective porosity of the deposit.

The second factor is the *permeability*, and this determines how easily water can move through geological formations. Although sometimes erroneously regarded as synonymous with porosity, it is time-related and has dimensions of velocity. Permeability depends on the lithology and geological history of the formation. In an unconsolidated deposit, it is a function of the size-distribution, shape and packing of the grains of the aquifer material and depends more particularly on the geometry of primary void spaces. In a consolidated rock,

tified. Seismic methods also have great value in hydrogeological investigations. In both electrical resistivity and seismic refraction surveying it is important to recognize that in most cases corroboratory evidence of a more direct nature is required.

Confirmation of the geophysical interpretation is best obtained by drilling wells and collecting representative samples of the strata and water penetrated. The nature of the samples depends on the type of tool used to drill the hole. Percussion and rotary methods are both in common use and each has advantages and disadvantages in specific cases. The only wholly satisfactory sampling method is continuous coring, but this is time-consuming and expensive.

Unless the hydrogeological conditions are particularly simple no single exploration technique will be sufficient, but a combination of several techniques should at least ensure that the conditions are sufficiently well understood to allow predictions to be made of groundwater occurrence, well locations, design, yield and performance, water quality, and especially the effects on the immediate hydrological environment that development of the groundwater resources must inevitably introduce.

Hydrogeology Today. The steadily increasing demand for water in all countries of the world is the result of expanded industrial production, improved domestic conditions and intensive agricultural programs sustained by irrigation practice.

These demands are still being met in conventional fashion from natural reservoirs or wells, and the same sources are likely to be sufficient for many years to come. Nonetheless, the groundwater reservoir is finite; and the serious, sometimes catastrophic, effects of local overdevelopment give plain warning of the larger scale consequences of ill-conceived development.

Understandably, Man has in the past been primarily interested in drinking-water but, by definition, groundwaters include both drinkable and non-drinkable waters. It follows that, in the future, use must be made of brackish and saline groundwaters, either by mixing with drinkable water or by desalination.

One of the newer applications of hydrology is to the study of geothermal energy potential and its beneficial use. Heat is conducted from the interior of the Earth through the agency of *vulcanicity. Groundwater can be trapped in particular geological conditions and become superheated to form steam: wells drilled into such reservoirs tap the steam and conduct it to the surface where it may be used as a source of energy. Despite its apparent wide potential, relatively little power is produced from geothermal sources outside the USA and Italy.

Of more widespread and immediate benefit is geothermal water too low in temperature to be used for the steam-generation of electricity, but which can readily be used for space heating for domestic and agricul-

tural purposes. Rapid progress is being made in this respect in Iceland, Japan, the USSR, Europe and the USA. In many other parts of the world geothermal sources of energy are never likely to reach major proportions.

Because groundwater is an integral part of the hydrologic cycle, any form of development must affect the related components to some degree. The modern approach to hydrogeology emphasizes study of those quantitative aspects that allow predictions to be made of the consequences of Man's utilization of groundwater and subsequent modification of the cycle.   GPJ

Mining Geology

Every year the mines of the free world produce around three thousand million tonnes of ore ready to be processed for metals and minerals – quite apart from coal production and ignoring the necessary waste rock and overburden which accompanies mining. This amount of rock would be yielded by a tunnel 10ft (3m) in diameter drive $3\frac{1}{2}$ times round the world at the equator, and reflects an average demand of about one ton of ore per annum for every man, woman and child in the free world.

The primary industry of mining must meet the escalating world demand for min-

Chuquicamata copper mine, Chile. Copper dominates the Chilean economy; its control has played a major part in the political history of the country.

erals in ever-wider variety and in ever-greater quantities. In two major facets of the mining industry, mining geology plays an essential role. First, there is the engineering task of extracting the valuable content of a mineral deposit (the ore) economically, efficiently and safely, and with minimum disturbance to the environment. Second, since every ore deposit has a limited life, the future of the industry depends on prospecting and exploration to discover and evaluate new deposits to replace dying mines and to meet increasing demands.

Mining Operations and Methods. ★Ore deposits exist in a huge variety of physical sizes, shapes, attitudes and geological environments, and for each ore body these factors must be accurately defined so that the optimum mining method can be designed. Alluvial mining of unconsolidated sediments is by dredging or hydraulic jets. For hard rock the choice lies between open-cut and underground methods. Steeply dipping and narrow tabular ore bodies are best exploited by underground "stoping" with access to the working faces from horizontal tunnels driven at intervals from a vertical or inclined shaft. Horizontally orientated tabular ore bodies close to the surface are most efficiently exploited by open-cast mining, where the waste stripped from above the ore is cast back into the excavation behind the working face.

Moderately dipping tabular ore bodies and those of irregular, massive or pipelike form are most economically worked by open pits from the surface, the successive "benches" forming an inverted cone. Waste rock must be mined from outside the ore limits to form a stable pit slope; when the ratio of waste to ore reaches a critical figure (which varies for each individual ore body) the economic pit limit is reached, and mining to further depth may be found to be more economic by underground methods. Underground mining methods are relatively labor-intensive and more complex and expensive than the machine-intensive and generally larger-scale open-pit meth-

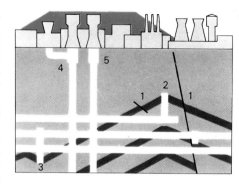

Simplified diagram of the workings of an underground coal mine. Folded coal seams are displaced by faults (1). Shafts are built upward (2) or downward (3) from the horizontal corridors. Access is gained *via* a vertical pit shaft (4), and coal brought to the surface via another (5).

ods which are so well suited to the modern technology of bulk mining and treatment.

For relatively large and massive ore bodies with suitable rock-strength characteristics, underground mass-mining methods, such as block caving, where the ore is induced to collapse in controlled fashion and withdrawn through workings below, are used. For relatively small ore bodies, the variants of numerous stoping methods are classified as either open stopes, where the strength of the rocks of the excavation walls permits safe working in open excavations with little artificial support, or as filled stopes, where the excavations must be backfilled with rock or sand.

Whatever the working method, the overall economics and engineering efficiency of any mine depend upon the accuracy and timeliness of the observations and predictions of the mining geologist. The following are typical examples:

(*i*) Estimation of ore reserves, in categories such as "proved", "probable" and "possible", according to the relative certainty of the figures, forms the basis of engineering and financial control and planning throughout the life of the mine. A typical simplified ore reserve statement such as "10.50 million tons of proved ore at an average in-situ grade of 2.65% copper" summarizes two related quantitative investigations. The tonnage reflects the geologist's prediction of the detailed three-dimensional shape of the minable ore body. The average grade or content of the valuable metal or mineral in the ore can be calculated from mathematical weighting procedures or statistical treatment of sample data taken.

(*ii*) The profitability of mining operations depends on clean mining practice, which is enhanced by accurate and timely forecasts of potentially hazardous geological conditions. For example, faults and shear zones cause displacement of the ore body, and underground waters under high pressure can cause disasters.

Smashing pieces of coal on a muck tipple in the Mount Isa coalmines, Queensland, Australia. Much Australian coal, the bulk of which comes from New South Wales and Queensland, is exported to Europe.

Loading ore at Chuquicamata copper mine, Chile. Much of what we can see being loaded is in fact gangue – that is, unwanted parts of the ore – that will be removed during processing.

(*iii*) Most mines require closely coordinated geological and engineering advance planning and operational practice in grade control (or quality control). The blending of heterogeneous ores from various parts of the mine achieves a uniform feed which ensures optimum efficiency in the treatment plant and a uniform quality of product.

(*iv*) It is the responsibility of the mining geologist to discover and explore any extensions of the known ore body which affect the continuity and life of operations. This task draws upon applied geological science and technology, including a working theory of ore deposition and an understanding of the physical limitations to ore.

Prospecting and Exploration. Prospecting is the science of discovering new mineral fields and mining prospects. Exploration is the work of investigating and evaluating the physical characteristics and economic viability of prospects, very few of which, in the end, become mines.

Mineral deposits are geological anomalies, and those few with economic ore grade and deposit size are not only rare but also, usually, well concealed by nature. Modern prospecting is essentially the application of geology to finding the most favorable target areas, assisted by a variety of techniques designed to detect the geophysical, geochemical and/or mineralogical anomalies within the geological environment that betray the presence of an ore body.

The primary guides to potential mineral fields are global or large-scale geological features or rock associations. For instance, for porphyry copper deposits one would search the calc-alkaline intrusives of the volcanic belts above subduction zones such as the Andes.

At successively finer scales, geological indications of many kinds are sought and integrated with the results of the following main prospecting techniques:

(*i*) Photogeological interpretation assists rapid production of geological maps from aerial photographs, and similar interpretations are based on images from "remote sensing" surveys from artificial satellites.

(*ii*) Geophysical methods are designed to detect anomalies in the Earth's physical properties associated with certain rock types, structures and mineralization patterns, and these must then be geologically interpreted. The most useful geophysical surveys for mineral deposits are magnetic (relatively cheap, fast and very helpful in geological mapping as well as for detecting magnetic iron ores, etc.), radiometric (the main prospecting tool for uranium deposits, using Geiger counters, scintillometers and gamma-ray spectrometers), electromagnetic, electrical, gravitometric, and

seismic (of limited use in mineral exploration as contrasted with *petroleum exploration surveys). Magnetic, electromagnetic and radiometric techniques are commonly adapted to airborne surveys in helicopters or fixed-wing aircraft and so afford rapid systematic coverage of large areas. (See *geophysics.)

(*iii*) Geochemical methods are based upon chemical analysis – in the parts-per-million (ppm) range – to detect the anomalous primary or secondary dispersion patterns of the constituent elements around ore deposits. A copper sulfide ore body being weathered in mountainous tropical rain forest can, though invisible to the eye, be detected by the few ppm of copper in the stream sediment and by sampling the residual soil, which may be similarly enriched to a few hundred ppm of copper, above the ore body. Besides stream sediment and soil surveys, geochemical methods are being developed to detect trace amounts of gases such as sulfur dioxide or radon released into the soil or atmosphere from ore bodies that are being weathered. Geobotanical meth-

ods make use of vegetational patterns, which may reflect anomalous soil chemistry over mineralized ground.

(*iv*) Mineralogical methods include the still-important prospector's pan for gold, diamonds and other heavy minerals dispersed downstream from the source ore body. Trains of mineralized boulders give similar evidence in glaciated countries. More sophisticated is the use of patterns of mineralogical alterations such as the potassic alteration of volcanic rocks associated with porphyry *copper deposits.

Once a mineralized area or prospect has been discovered, the more detailed and expensive work of exploration begins. It continues until the prospect has been either abandoned as uneconomic or promoted through a feasibility study for development and capitalization as a new mine. Drilling methods of various kinds, but especially percussion drilling and diamond-core drilling, play an essential part in providing not only geological information concerning the three-dimensional shape and size of the ore body but also samples of its valuable content, on which an estimate of ore reserves can be based. Exploratory underground workings may also be used to provide bulk samples for metallurgical testing, and to determine geological and geotechnical engineering data necessary to design the future mine and forecast its operating costs and mineral output.

Conclusion. Food and clothing excepted, most of Man's essential raw materials are dug from the crust of the Earth. Fossil fuels, construction materials, industrial minerals, metals – all are produced in vast quantities. The continuously improving knowledge and application of geology to the mining industry adds confidence to the view that Man will not waste his planet's precious mineral resources, and that through his understanding he will be able to discover enough to meet his future needs – at an acceptable cost.   GRD

Ore Deposits

In 1964 Ken Philips, a geologist working for Conzinc Riotinto of Australia Exploration, Ltd., led an exploration team over to the southwest of the Crown Prince Range, which runs down the spine of Bougainville Island, Papua/New Guinea. In the unpopulated and mountainous Panguna region, an area where gold had been worked between 1933 and 1951, the team discovered anomalously high copper concentrations in stream sediments. Subsequent drilling of over 200 holes to obtain 50mi (80km) of core proved the existence of one of the biggest porphyry copper ore deposits in the world.

The story is not altogether an unusual one: ore deposits can be found through scientific exploration or just plain luck – and often a combination of the two. The term "ore deposit" is as much a commercial as a geological one, referring as it does to economically workable natural concentrations of elements and minerals.

The total cost per ton of ore, mined and processed, must be less than the income derived from the element or mineral contained in each of those tons. This means that the principal factors which determine the economic feasibility of working a particular deposit are the concentrations of the element of interest (grades), the size of the deposit, its location and the market values of the products.

The concentrations of elements in ore deposits are, typically, a thousand times greater than the average throughout the crust as a whole. But the concentration factors are quite variable and range from as little as 10 (iron deposits) to as much as 30,000 (chromium deposits).

Ore deposits must be large in order to provide a reasonable return on capital investment. Reserve tonnages are variable, but few deposits contain less than one million tons of ore, and the largest contain around 15,000 million tons.

The depth of the deposit beneath the land

Fluid inclusions (here in sphalerite) are samples of the fluid from which hydrothermal ore deposits were precipitated: each comprises saline water and a gas bubble. The bulk composition of the fluid can be deduced from its freezing point, the temperature of formation of the deposit from the temperature at which the gas bubble disappears.

surface is critically important because it determines whether a mine is worked by open-cast or underground techniques (see *mining geology).

Geographical location determines transport costs as well as the type of government which controls mining activity. Metal prices are clearly critical when considering the commercial viability of the deposit. Fluctuations in the price, whether caused by changing economic or political conditions, can make and break mines.

When the natural processes which can lead to the formation of ore deposits are considered, diversity is the theme: practically all natural processes can generate elemental concentrations. There are three major generic groupings: magmatic, hydrothermal and sedimentary.

Magmatic Deposits. In deposits of this kind, the minerals have typically crystallized from a silicate melt (magma) and accumulated selectively in layered basic intrusions as magmatic sediments. The chromite seams of the Bushveld igneous complex of southern Africa are the prime examples of magmatic deposits.

Hydrothermal Deposits. As the name suggests, hydrothermal ore deposits are formed by minerals dissolved in hot water (at temperatures of the order of 200–1300°F, 100–700°C) crystallizing out. The minerals contain small inclusions of the solution from which they crystallized.

Modern geochemical work, in particular that based on the use of radioisotopes as tracers, has shown that the natural fluids in hydrothermal ore deposits had diverse origins: magmatically derived water, meteoric water (rainwater), sea water and water contained in deep sedimentary formations have all been found in the cores of porphyry copper deposits, whereas in the surrounding layers evidence of the presence of rainwater has been obtained.

Sedimentary Deposits. Chemical precipitates can also form in the sedimentary environment, being in some, but not all,

Banded iron formations are generally of early Precambrian age. They are made up of alternating laminae of chert on the one hand and a variety of iron minerals including siderite, hematite, magnetite, pyrite and greenalite on the other. The texture is usually fine-grained but sometimes hematite occurs as ooliths.

cases a result of evaporation increasing the concentration of a solution. Crystal accumulations (*evaporites) which formed in response to evaporative concentration of enclosed water bodies in hot climates are particularly important sources of *salt, potassium minerals for the fertilizer industry, and such uncommon elements as boron and strontium.

A good example of straightforward accretion at work is provided by the manganese nodules which cover large areas of the deep *ocean floor. The *Precambrian banded iron formations are also thought to be straightforward chemical precipitates.

There are two main exceptions to this theme of chemical precipitation – residual deposits and placers. The former are the surface residues, similar to soils, which remain after being deeply leached by percolating groundwater in hot, wet climates. Examples include *bauxites, as a source of aluminum, and nickeliferous laterites. Where leaching of sulfide ore deposits occurs, residual red and brown iron hydroxyoxide cappings (gossans) are left, and other elements can be carried down and precipitated in a zone of "supergene" enrichment near the water table. Placer deposits were formed where moving water mechanically sorted heavy and physically resistant minerals in river gravels and beach sands.

Formation Today. As can be seen, most geological processes play a part in the formation of ore deposits. Most of the processes involved in the formation of sedimentary ores can be observed taking place at the moment: for example, on the continental shelf off southwest Africa phosphatization of sediment is actually occurring today. Magmatic and hydrothermal deposits, however, are less commonly observed in the process of active formation for the obvious reason that they generally occur within the Earth.

A striking exception is provided by a hydrothermal exhalite type of deposit ac-

Manganese nodules form on the sea floor by straight forward accretion: they comprise an important mineral resource of the future since manganese ore deposits are relatively scarce on dry land. Ore deposits from the ocean floor (copper, cobalt and nickel nodules are also forming) are today the focus of much research.

A core of sediments from the Atlantis II Deep, Red Sea: the most recent sediments are at the top left, the oldest (i.e., deepest) at the bottom right. Metalliferous sediments have been accumulating on the floor of the Deep for the last 12,900 years, and this sedimentary ore deposit is still today in the process of formation.

tively forming today in the Atlantis II deep at the bottom of the Red Sea. At a depth of about 1.25mi (2km) there is a depression in which are found layered hot metalliferous brines. The lower layer has increased in temperature from 133°F (56°C) in 1966 to 138°F (59°C) in 1971, and the upper layer is at 120°F (49°C). For the past 12,900 years metalliferous sediments have been accumulating on the floor of the depression, and there now exists an ore deposit of about 200 million tons (on a dry basis) which contains 0.34% copper, 1.58% zinc and smaller quantities of silver, gold and lead. ETCS

Crystals

The outer surfaces of nearly all natural objects in the world about us are more or less curved. The bodies of plants and animals, the slopes of hillsides, the horizon itself and the heavenly bodies, all are characterized by regular or irregular curvature. Only in the Man-made environment are the flat plane and the straight line familiar sights – except in the case of crystals.

Man's interest in crystals began with the observation that there exists one unique class of natural objects which, in many instances, do possess plane surfaces and straight, even parallel edges. Well-formed crystals have a geometric regularity which cries out for explanation and understanding. The study of crystals, crystallography, in its classical pre-20th-century sense, was concerned with the description and classification of crystals and attempted to explain the origin of crystal shapes in terms of regular geometric patterns in the fine-scale structure of crystal-building substances. Powerful modern techniques involving the use of X-rays, electron microscopes and nuclear reactors, have enabled the 20th-century crystallographer to explore this fine-scale structure down to the atomic level. Crystallography today is a highly technical and complex subject with appli-

cations in chemistry, metallurgy and biology: it was X-ray crystallography which eventually revealed the double-helical nature of the deoxyribonucleic acid (DNA) molecule, and showed how the mechanism whereby the living cell replicates itself is based essentially on the atomic structure of that molecule. To the geologist who seeks to understand the rocks of the Earth, some knowledge of crystallography is essential, since rocks consist of minerals and *minerals are crystalline substances.

For a substance to be crystalline, and hence potentially capable of forming regular crystals with plane surfaces (faces), it must of course be solid. It must, in addition, be more or less homogeneous and have a definite chemical composition expressible as a formula. Most importantly, it must possess an orderly arrangement of its constituent particles (ions). The best-known example of a non-crystalline solid is glass, which can vary widely in composition and whose ions are more or less randomly arranged.

It is important to realize that crystalline substances, including minerals, do not always form well-shaped crystals with regular faces, although they continually aspire to this condition during growth. For instance, competition for space between minerals crystallizing from a magma usually produces a final mosaic in which the majority of crystal boundaries are uneven, irregular and curved. Nevertheless the rarer well-shaped crystals, formed without constraint (often in cavities), provided the first clues concerning the nature of the crystalline state.

One of the most important concepts in crystallography, although hinted at by earlier workers, was fully formulated by the Frenchman René-Just *Haüy in 1784. The mineral calcite (calcium carbonate) often forms well-shaped crystals, and these are produced in a bewildering, apparently haphazard variety of shapes (called crystal habits). After accidentally breaking a speci-

men of calcite and noting that the plane of fracture was flat and smooth, Haüy succeeded, after several trials, in cleaving the damaged piece along two further sets of planes. Extending the experiment, he found that calcite crystals of all habits produced six-sided rhombohedral cleavage fragments with identical angles between corresponding sides. Each cleavage fragment could be further subdivided into smaller identically shaped fragments down to the limit at which the fragments could be observed. Haüy proposed therefore that all crystals of calcite are built of large numbers of minutely small, identically shaped and identically oriented "*molécules constituantes*", which he conceived as solid objects.

Haüy went on to demonstrate how different crystal faces and crystal habits of a mineral could all be generated from the same "*molécule*" by appropriate stacking procedures. In one of his original diagrams he showed how the pointed "dog-tooth" habit of calcite is constructed. This early work was extended to many other minerals: he showed also how a fluorite crystal, a cube with bevelled edges, can be built from "*molécules*" which in this case are perfect cubes. The "*molécule*" (now called the unit cell) is in reality so small compared with the complete crystal that surfaces resembling flights of steps when represented diagrammatically are, in the developed crystal, smooth and planar – i.e., they are genuine faces.

Unlike Haüy, we now know the absolute sizes, measurable in Angstroms, of the unit cells of most crystalline substances. In the case of fluorite, for example, a crystal having a volume of one cubic millimetre is built of approximately 6×10^{18} (six million million million) unit cells.

It is now realized that, although Haüy's concept explains the development of crystal

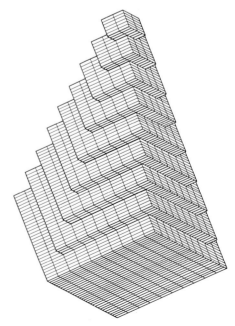

Haüy's diagram to show how a crystal of "dog-tooth" calcite can be considered as constructed of a large number of very small rhombohedral units.

A normal and a "swallowtail" crystal of gypsum. The latter is an example of twinning, which can be of great value in mineral identification. A crystal is said to be twinned when it comprises two or more parts in which the crystal lattices are differently oriented: such disorientation, which leads to the development of complex crystals, is never random; the parts of a twinned crystal of a given substance are related to one another according to certain crystallographic rules. In simplest terms, twinning is in some cases the result of a type of "defect" or "error" that occurs during nucleation (the very earliest stages in the formation of a crystal): this is somewhat analogous to biological twinning. In other cases twinning results from readjustment of the lattice of a completely formed crystal in response to exterior physical stresses.

faces, it oversimplifies in some respects the true nature of the crystalline state. In particular, we now know that most of the volume occupied by "solid" matter is empty space, and we envisage the fine-scale structure of crystalline materials in terms of an orderly, three-dimensional array or pattern of atoms. The unit cell, which replaces the solid "*molécule constituante*" of Haüy, is the geometrical block-like outline of the unit of pattern which, by repetition, builds up the entire structure.

Rigorous geometrical analysis shows that there are seven and only seven essentially different types of unit cell. All are six-sided block-like objects having opposite pairs of faces parallel to one another (parallelepipeds). All crystalline substances have lattices built of one of these types of unit cell and, according to the type, we recognize seven different crystal systems, namely the triclinic, monoclinic, orthorhombic, tetragonal, trigonal, hexagonal and cubic systems.

Crystal symmetry. Fortunately, it is of-

Below: Crystals in the cubic system are referred to three crystallographic axes which are at right angles to each other (A). An axis of symmetry is an axis about which a crystal can be rotated so that it comes to occupy two or more indistinguishable positions in space in the course of a complete turn. A cube has three axes of 4-fold symmetry, or tetrads (B), four axes of 3-fold symmetry, or triads (C) and six axes of 2-fold symmetry, or diads (D).

Bottom: A cube has nine planes of symmetry that divide it into sections that are mirror images of each other: three (1) plus two (2) plus two (3) plus two (4). The three planes shown in (1) contain the crystallographic axes and are called axial planes.

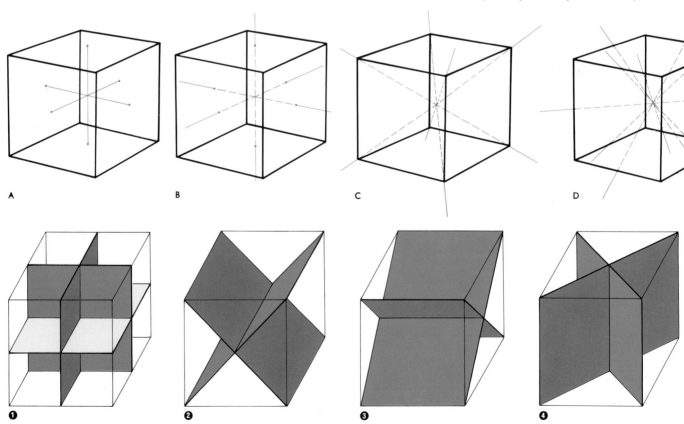

A   B   C   D

❶   ❷   ❸   ❹

Crystal system			
Cubic		Cube	All edges the same length; edges meet at right angles.
Tetragonal		Square prism	Edges meet at right angles; base and top are square, but vertical edges are longer (or shorter) than horizontal edges.
Orthorhombic		Rectangular parallelepiped	Edges meet at right angles; the three edges meeting at any one corner are of unequal lengths.
Monoclinic		Right prism on a parallelogram as base	Base and top are parallelograms, not rectangles, and are horizontal; sides are vertical; the three edges meeting at any one corner are of unequal lengths.
Triclinic		General parallelepiped	The three edges meeting at any one corner are of unequal lengths; none of the angles formed by edges meeting at corners are right angles.
Hexagonal		Prism on 60°/120° base	A special case of the monoclinic cell, in which the parallelogram base and top have angles of 60° and 120°, and in which all parallelogram sides are of equal length.
Trigonal		Rhombohedron	A cube deformed along one diagonal; all edges are of equal length.

ten possible, given well-formed crystals of a substance, to assign it to its correct crystal system without first determining the details of its atomic structure, and hence its unit-cell type. This procedure involves a simple study of the gross morphology of the crystals, and specifically the identification of types of symmetry (called symmetry elements) in the crystals. These symmetry elements are now described.

Plane of symmetry. If a crystal is (theoretically) divided into two equal halves along a plane, such that the two halves are, without displacement, mirror images of one another, the plane is called a plane of symmetry.

Axis of symmetry. If any object is rotated 360° about any imaginary line passing through it, it will of course present its original appearance to an observer in any fixed position. It may, however, also present its original appearance from time to time *during* rotation through 360°. According to whether this occurs every 180°, 120°, 90° or 60°, we recognize respectively two-fold, three-fold, four-fold, or six-fold rotation symmetry, and the line about which rotation produces these results is called a two-fold (or diad), three-fold (or triad), four-fold (or tetrad) or six-fold (or hexad) axis of symmetry. No other axes of rotation symmetry are possible in crystals, except for the trivial case of the one-fold (or monad) axis, of which any object possesses an infinite

number.

Inversion-rotation axis of symmetry. Certain groups of crystals possess a more complex form of symmetry element, involving rotation about an axis coupled with inversion of the crystal about its center for the crystal to present its original appearance. For our purposes it is sufficient to note that, for each rotation axis of symmetry, there is an equivalent inversion-rotation axis. These are designated the inverse monad, inverse diad, inverse triad, inverse tetrad, and inverse hexad axes. (An example of an inversion-rotation axis is described under ★tetragonal system.)

According to the number and types of symmetry elements present in a crystal, it is assigned to a particular crystal system. The crystal systems are arranged approximately in order of decreasing symmetry, the cubic system being the most symmetrical: a crystal must be assigned to a system as near to the top of the list as is compatible with its symmetry.

Let us take a simple example. Inspection of a box-shaped crystal would quickly reveal the presence of a diad (two-fold) axis passing through the centers of the two largest faces, suggesting that it may belong to the monoclinic system. Further examination, however, would reveal that there are, also, diad axes passing through the centers of the other pairs of faces – that is, three diads in all – and hence the crystal is

The seven types of unit cell, giving rise to the seven crystal systems.

correctly assigned to the orthorhombic system. (In addition it should be noted that this crystal also possesses three planes of symmetry. These are insufficient to promote it to a more symmetrical crystal system, say the tetragonal.)

Nevertheless, comparison with a crystal of, for instance, epsomite, which is also orthorhombic (3 diad axes) but lacks mirror planes, suggests that subdivision of each crystal system into smaller categories according to the presence or absence of additional, systematically superfluous symmetry elements may be possible. In fact, as long ago as 1830, J. F. C. Hessel correctly predicted on theoretical grounds that, on the basis of the symmetry elements so far considered, the seven crystal systems could be subdivided into a total of 32 (and *only* 32) crystal classes.

It is worth noting that, when crystalline structures are studied at the atomic or crystal-lattice level of detail, two new kinds of symmetry elements, not observable in complete crystals, may be recognized. A detailed analysis of all possible combinations of symmetry elements and types of lattice produces a total of 230 categories called the 230 space groups. In the same way as an animal belongs to a phylum, an order, a family, a genus, and so on, so a crystalline substance belongs hierarchically to a system, a class and a space group. Unlike the divisions and subdivisions of the animal kingdom, however, which may be added to as new forms are discovered, the divisions and subdivisions of the crystalline state, being prescribed by the laws of mathematics, are precisely known. Although each year sees the discovery of a few new minerals and of many synthetic compounds, each belongs to an already established category of crystal structure.

Examples of real crystals having the geometrical perfection of our idealized examples are very rare. A number of external and often variable factors influence crystal growth, and these normally lead to the unequal development of symmetrically related faces, so that the full symmetry of a natural crystal is partly obscured and appears less than that of its idealized counterpart. In practice, for purposes of classifying a crystal, the crystallographer pays no regard to either the absolute or the relative sizes of faces: instead, he is concerned only with the angular relationships between faces.

A valuable aid in recognizing symmetry elements in even highly distorted crystals is

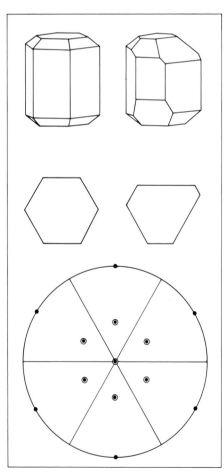

Above left, a "perfectly formed" crystal of apatite, with a cross-section in the shape of a regular hexagon. *Above right*, a "misshapen" apatite crystal, whose cross-section is an irregular hexagon. Angles between corresponding faces are the same in each case. Although the crystals are evidently of different shape, representation of either by a stereographic projection produces the same result (*below*).

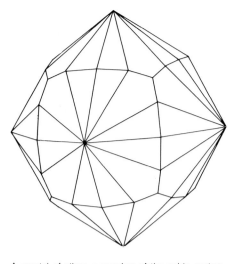

A crystal of silver, a member of the cubic system, having the form of a hexoctahedron.

the device known as the stereographic projection. The angles between perpendiculars to faces are first measured, preferably on an optical instrument called a goniometer, and the perpendiculars are then projected as points or (in the case of faces situated on the underside of the crystal) as small rings on or inside a circular diagram. A full account of the construction of the stereographic projection (stereogram) is beyond the scope of this book, but we can note in passing that, since the projection ignores the shapes and sizes of faces and represents only angular relationships between faces, it simplifies the recognition of crystallographic symmetry elements in the misshapen crystal.

Modern crystallography. The discovery in 1912 by M. von Laue that X-rays are scattered or diffracted in an orderly way when passed through crystalline material proved that such material has a regular internal structure – as had been proposed by Haüy. The physicists W. H. Bragg and his son, W. L. Bragg, quickly realized that the X-ray diffraction patterns produced on photographic plates indirectly represented layers of atoms or ions in the crystal structure, and in 1913, using this new and elegant technique, they were able to determine the detailed atomic structure of the simple substance sodium chloride (*halite).

From these early beginnings, structural crystallography has made great progress, and the precise atomic arrangements of thousands of substances, including most minerals, have now been elucidated. Even newer techniques, involving the diffraction behavior of neutrons and electrons and the use of modern computational methods, have extended the amount of information obtainable from crystalline substances.

A more or less routine geological application of X-ray crystallography is the rapid identification of a mineral from an X-ray diffraction photograph of a small amount of powdered sample. The positions and intensities of the curved diffraction lines seen in such a photograph provide in most cases a unique "fingerprint" for a particular crystalline substance, and its identity is

thus found from files of "fingerprints" using an established search procedure.

Cubic System

The unit cell of this system is a cube, in which all sides are equal and all faces and edges meet at right-angles. Clearly such a unit cell is capable of building a crystal that is itself a cube, and this object contains the maximum number of symmetry elements possible in a plane-sided three-dimensional object, namely 4 triad axes, 3 tetrad axes, 9 mirror planes, 6 diad axes, and an inversion center. Other crystal forms possessing all these symmetry elements, and thus belonging to the highest symmetry class (called the holosymmetric class) of the system, include the octahedron, the dodecahedron and the trapezohedron. Common minerals belonging to this class and crystallizing in these forms or combinations of them are *halite, *galena, *fluorite, *spinels (including *magnetite), *garnet, and the metals *gold, *silver and *copper.

The cubic unit cell may, however, be used to construct other crystal shapes which, while preserving the four triad axes (by definition essential to the cubic system), do not contain all the other symmetry elements of the cube itself. Two examples of crystal forms illustrating this point are the tetrahedron and the pyritohedron. The tetrahedron has four triad axes, but only diads are found in directions corresponding to the three tetrads of the cube, and the number of mirror planes is reduced from nine to six. The pyritohedron, named after the mineral *pyrite, is also less than holosymmetric, possessing four triads, three diads (strictly these are inverse tetrads) and only three mirror planes. Although the symmetry and hence the class of pyrite can be readily determined when it forms pyritohedra, the same mineral frequently crystallizes in the form of cubes, and may thus appear at first sight to belong to the holosymmetric class. However, examination of the faces of such cubes reveals the presence of striations which reduce the symmetry from that of the perfect cube to that of the pyritohedron.

Altogether there are five separate classes in the cubic system. Most common cubic minerals belong to the holosymmetric class: notable examples of minerals belonging to lower symmetry classes are *sphalerite, pyrite and *cobaltite.

Tetragonal System

The unit cell of this system is a square prism which may be envisaged as a cube that has been either stretched or compressed in the vertical direction. The holosymmetric class of the tetragonal system contains a single tetrad axis, 4 diad axes and 5 mirror planes. Although there are no fewer than six less symmetrical classes in this system, only one common mineral, *chalcopyrite, is represented among them. It is worth considering a simplified chalcopyrite crystal since it may be used to illustrate the concept of an inversion-rotation axis of symmetry. Such a crystal, called a sphenoid, possesses no tetrad axis, but passing along its length is an

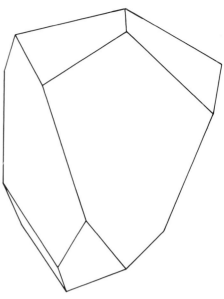

A sphenoidal crystal of chalcopyrite, representative of the tetragonal system.

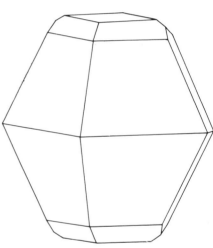

A crystal of sulfur, a member of the holosymmetric class of the orthorhombic system.

Both halite (*top*) and spinel (*above*) are members of the highest symmetry class (holosymmetric class) of the cubic system since they possess six diad axes, four triad axes, three tetrad axes, nine mirror planes and an inversion center. Members of this class of the cubic system display the maximum possible number of symmetry elements of a crystal.

axis of symmetry that appears to be a diad (that is, it produces a position of congruence after rotation through 180°). In fact this axis is rather more than a diad: if the crystal is rotated through only 90° and then inverted (i.e., turned upside down), a position of congruence is achieved. This is an example of a four-fold inversion-rotation axis (or inverse tetrad) and its presence is characteristic of two of the lower symmetry classes of

the tetragonal system.

Apart from chalcopyrite, the only common tetragonal minerals, *cassiterite, *rutile, *zircon and *idocrase, all belong to the holosymmetric class.

Orthorhombic System
The unit cell of this system is a rectangular parallelepiped, which may be visualized as a brick- or matchbox-shaped block.

The holosymmetric class of this system

has three mutually perpendicular diad axes and three mirror planes. The class is represented by a large number of minerals, including *barite, *celestine, *sulfur, *stibnite, *topaz and *olivine.

There are two less symmetrical classes in the orthorhombic system: in one of these the three diads are retained but the mirror planes are lost; and in the other a single diad axis is combined with two mirror planes.

Monoclinic System
The monoclinic unit cell is a right prism having a parallelogram for its base. Such a cell, and crystals constructed therefrom, have rather low symmetry. The holosymmetric class has a single diad axis at right angles to a mirror plane, and this class includes many minerals, especially *gypsum and a number of important rock-forming types such as *orthoclase, *augite, *hornblende, *chlorite and *epidote.

Monoclinic minerals belonging to the two lower symmetry classes, which contain a diad axis or a mirror plane alone, are relatively rare.

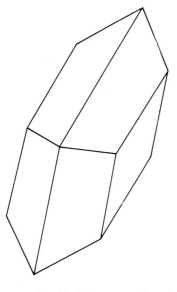

Gypsum, a member of the holosymmetric class of the monoclinic system.

A crystal of corundum, which crystallizes in the holosymmetric class of the trigonal system, having three vertical mirror planes that intersect along an inversion triad axis.

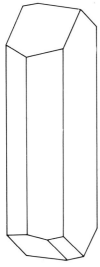

A crystal of albite, one of the plagioclase feldspars, a member of the triclinic system.

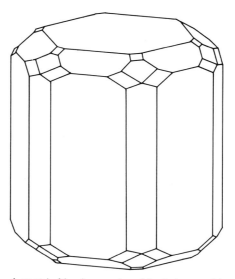

A crystal of beryl, a member of the holosymmetric class of the hexagonal system.

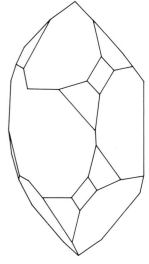

A right-handed crystal of the mineral quartz which, up to around 573°C (1063°F) crystallizes in the trigonal system.

Triclinic System

The triclinic unit cell is the most general type of parallelepiped, in which the three sides meeting at any corner are all of different lengths and in which the angles between edges are not right angles.

Crystals constructed from this type of cell have either no symmetry elements whatsoever or, in the case of the holosymmetric class, possess a single inverse monad. The effect of this axis is that each corner, edge and face of a crystal has an identical counterpart at the opposite extremity of the crystal.

*Kyanite and the important rock-forming silicates, the *plagioclase feldspars, belong to this class.

Hexagonal System

The hexagonal unit cell can be regarded as a monoclinic unit cell in which the parallelogram base has angles of 60° and 120°. The hexagonal holosymmetric class con-

tains a single hexad axis, 6 diad axes and 7 mirror planes, as seen in well-crystallized examples of the mineral *beryl and its varieties *emerald and *aquamarine. Although there are no fewer than six less symmetrical classes in the system, all of which contain at least a hexad or inverse hexad, only two common rock-forming minerals, *apatite and *nepheline, are represented among them.

Trigonal System

The trigonal unit cell is a rhombohedron, which may be visualized as a cube deformed along one diagonal. The holosymmetric class contains an inverse triad axis, 3 diad axes and 3 mirror planes. *Calcite, the three cleavages of which happen to lie parallel to the unit cell sides and which thereby played such an important role in the birth of crystallography as a science, is the best known mineral belonging to this class. Other structurally related carbonate min-

erals, together with *corundum and *hematite, belong here also.

*Dolomite, *tourmaline and *quartz each represent a separate trigonal class of lower symmetry. It may seem surprising to find quartz in this system. Well-formed crystals having six symmetrically disposed prism faces are common, suggesting that quartz belongs to the hexagonal system – as indeed it does above a temperature of 1063°F (573°C). It can be shown, however, that at normal temperatures quartz is trigonal, and this is also indicated by a consideration of some of the smaller inclined faces on a well-shaped crystal.   FBA

Gemstones

Whether or not a mineral is classed as a gemstone, worthy of mining, cutting, polishing and mounting for the purpose of adornment, is ultimately a matter of supply and demand. Although there is no rigorous definition of a gem, it is possible to list the essential attributes common to the precious stones and shared, at least to some extent, by the semiprecious materials.

The first, self-evident quality is beauty. The beauty of a gemstone may depend on its intrinsic color (e.g., the fiery red of ruby or the verdant green of emerald); or on its dispersion, the property of splitting white light entering the stone into tantalizing gleams of color (e.g., the "fire" of diamond); or on special optical effects such as the iridescence of opal. The second quality is durability. Gem material is ideally extremely hard, and able to resist scratching and abrasion by all common substances, including steel. It should be impervious to chemical attack by all common acids, alkalis and other solvents, and it should be able to withstand accidental percussive blows – that is, it should possess no cleavage or cleave only with great difficulty. Finally the status of a gemstone is greatly enhanced if, as a raw material, it is rare. It seems unlikely that diamonds would be highly prized if they were as common as pebbles of flint.

Transparent and translucent gems are usually fashioned into stones with flat facets. It is important to realize that these facets, although resembling natural crystal faces, are artefacts. The arrangement of facets is chosen to enhance the desirable optical characteristics of the material. More or less opaque gem material such as turquoise or moonstone is usually cut and polished in cabochon form; that is, with a curved upper surface.

A few modern compounds unknown in nature are nowadays made into attractive gemstones, and a number of familiar gem materials such as ruby and emerald are successfully synthesized in the laboratory for use in jewelry. FBA

Minerals

With the exception only of the relatively rare natural glasses such as obsidian and pitchstone, all the rocks which form the Earth, the Moon and the inner planets are composed of minerals. Minerals may be broadly defined as naturally formed solid substances made up of atoms arranged in an orderly and regular fashion. The chemical composition of a mineral is fixed or varies only within predictable limits, and is thus expressible – unlike that of a rock – as a chemical formula.

Minerals vary greatly in size, shape, color, beauty, abundance and economic importance. Gold, diamonds and rubies are minerals; so are salt, iron ores, asbestos, and the humble constituents of sand and mud. Despite the large number of known minerals (more than two thousand), nearly all types of rock consist almost entirely of a relatively small number, the so-called rock-forming minerals, although a further small number of economically important ore minerals are locally abundant in particular geological or geochemical environments.

Classification. Minerals are normally classified on a chemical basis. Thus we have groups such as the native (i.e., naturally occurring) elements, including copper, sulfur and diamond; the sulfides, which include galena and pyrite; the carbonates (e.g., calcite and dolomite); the oxides; the halides; and so on. The silicate group, which comprises most of the rock-forming minerals, is so large that it is convenient to subdivide it, and this is done on the basis of differences and similarities in the crystalline structures of members of the group.

In some instances, two or more minerals with different names have an identical chemical composition. These *polymorphs* have, however, different crystal structures and, in consequence, different physical properties; they rarely occur together, forming under different temperature and/or pressure conditions.

Another important concept in mineralogy is that of solid solution. The magnesium silicate, forsterite (Mg_2SiO_4), and the iron silicate, fayalite (Fe_2SiO_4), are rare minerals; they, are, however, the extreme end-members of a whole series of common minerals, the *olivines, which contain both iron and magnesium in all possible ratios between these extremes. Such a series is called a solid solution series, and all members have the same crystalline structure. This phenomenon is common, especially among the silicates.

The Properties of Minerals. Some of the various physical properties of minerals useful for their correct identification in a hand specimen will now be discussed. Many of these depend directly or indirectly on the crystalline structure.

Crystal Shapes. When a crystalline substance is free to grow without constraint, it usually forms individual "bits" – i.e., crystals – bounded by flat faces which are disposed and related to one another in a way

Panning in Borneo for the most valuable mineral of all – diamonds. The techniques of panning are simple, though the work is slow and laborious. The pan is filled with water and loose material from the riverbed: larger lumps are broken by hand and the bigger pebbles discarded. The pan is then given a rotary motion, occasionally being tilted from side to side, so that the heavier particles settle towards the center and the unwanted light gangue material is washed over the rim.

Iron pyrites crystallizes in the cubic system. It is best known as fool's gold – because of its color, which is slightly similar to that of gold. However, pyrites and gold can be readily distinguished even in the field.

A polished slice of "crazy lace" agate. A form of chalcedony, agate is characterized by layers or bands of different color: these are generally irregular, sometimes concentric, and form by the progressive lining of a cavity.

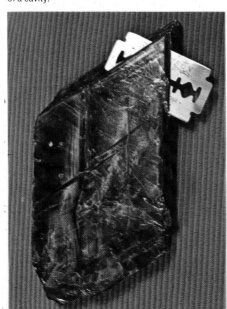

Biotite displays a single perfect cleavage, as shown by the insertion of a razor blade between two "pages" of this biotite "book". Perfect basal cleavage is typical of the mica family, whose members include biotite, phlogopite, muscovite, lepidolite and glauconite.

values within this range. If test minerals are not available, unknowns can be compared with the fingernail and a steel pocketknife blade which have hardness values of about $2\frac{1}{2}$ and $5\frac{1}{2}$ respectively. Minerals of hardness 1 feel soapy or greasy.

Density. The density of a substance is usually expressed in grams per cubic centimetre (g/cm^3). Density can, of course, be measured accurately using suitable equipment, but some minerals are so dense that even hefting a sample in the hand helps to identify them.

Optical Properties. The color of a mineral, its opacity or degree of transparency, and its luster (the way in which light is reflected from its surface) are immediately obvious properties. Unfortunately, however, these properties are not always consistent from one specimen to another of the same min-

determined by the underlying atomic structure. Thus a mineral will usually develop a shape characteristic of the species and called the "crystal habit". In some instances the way in which individual crystals of a mineral are joined or aggregated together is especially characteristic of the species.

Cleavage and Fracture. The atomic structure of many minerals is such that there may be one or more sets of planes within the structure across which the binding forces are weakest. If roughly handled, such minerals will break preferentially along such a plane or planes, giving rise to flat, usually shiny, cleavage surfaces. The number of cleavage directions in a mineral and their angular relationship to one another (if there are more than one) are important diagnostic properties.

Some minerals, having structures of more or less equal strength in all directions, do not exhibit cleavage. When roughly handled these substances fracture rather than cleave. Fracture surfaces are less angular than cleavage surfaces and may occur in any direction since they are not structurally controlled. They may, however, be of value in mineral identification.

Hardness. Different minerals vary greatly in their resistance to scratching and abrasion. This property, hardness, is constant for a particular mineral, and is easily tested by observing whether or not an unknown mineral scratches or is scratched by test minerals. The ten test minerals, originally selected by Friedrich Mohs (1773–1839) in 1812, are arranged in order of increasing hardness and assigned numerical hardness values as follows:

1. talc	6. orthoclase
2. gypsum	7. quartz
3. calcite	8. topaz
4. fluorite	9. corundum
5. apatite	10. diamond

All other minerals have Mohs' hardness

Double refraction displayed by a crystal of Iceland spar (calcite). Certain crystals can split a ray of unpolarized light into two rays plane-polarized at right-angles to each other. One is refracted in the normal way, the other with a refractive index that depends on the original direction of the ray.

eral. Thus, although sulfur is always a distinctive yellow, quartz can occur in a wide range of colors resulting from minute traces of different impurities. But, used with experience and caution, the optical properties of minerals are of great diagnostic value.

Other Properties. Some minerals have distinctive properties which serve to identify them. These include the property of fluorescence, whereby certain substances emit light in the visible part of the spectrum when bathed in ultraviolet light; the property of effervescence with dilute acids, exhibited by many of the carbonate minerals; and the properties of solubility in water and taste. In addition, magnetite has distinctive magnetic properties, and uranium-bearing minerals are radioactive.

Of the greatest importance in mineral identification is a knowledge of likely mineral and rock associations. For example, zinc minerals often occur together with lead minerals; zeolites usually form in cavities within basalt; and gypsum and anhydrite frequently crystallize in *evaporite sequences. Conversely, a knowledge of incompatibilities is also important: for example, chromite is never found in granites.

Conclusion. The study of minerals can be considered on the one hand as a science in its own right – much modern research is concerned with determining the detailed structures of minerals using sophisticated X-ray and electron-microscopic techniques – and on the other as an essential part of the science of petrology – the origin and history of a rock is often deduced from a detailed study of its component minerals. Above all, the importance of minerals to mankind, past, present and future, cannot be overemphasized. As minerals are the raw materials which have given rise to and support our

Iridescence displayed by plagioclase feldspar. This phenomenon, the production of colors of varied hue, is due to the interference of light reflected from either side of faults and boundaries within crystalline solids (or from front or back of thin films).

complex civilization, we require to understand their nature and origin, and to exploit the Earth's not unlimited resources with wisdom and foresight.

Actinolite
Actinolite is a member of the *amphibole group, and may be regarded as *tremolite in which some of the magnesium has been replaced by iron. It forms green blade-like crystals or fibrous aggregates. If the fibers are long, visible to the unaided eye, and separable, then the mineral is a member of the *asbestos family; if they are minute and interlocking to give a fine-grained rock, the material is called *nephrite or *jade.

Actinolite is a metamorphic mineral found typically in low-grade *schists. With increasing temperatures of metamorphism it reacts with other components in the rock to form *hornblende.
Formula: $Ca_2[Mg,Fe'']_5(Si_8O_{22})[OH,F]_2$.

Amethyst, a colored variety of quartz, crystallizes in the trigonal system.

Agate
Agate is perhaps the best known variety of *chalcedony (compact submicroscopic quartz). It forms at low or moderate temperatures in cavities, and is characterized by possessing alternating layers or bands: these are arranged concentrically, paralleling the cavity walls. The bands vary in their color or degree of transparency, or both.

Agates are slightly porous and may be "improved" for use in jewelry by immersion in pigmenting solutions of the desired color. If the bands are plane and parallel the material is known as onyx. Black and white onyx is used for cameos, the piece being so carved that the figure in white stands in relief on a black background. Sardonyx is red onyx.

Moss agate is misleadingly named, for it shows no layering or banding, though the adjective "moss" is well chosen: set in white chalcedony is darker material (manganese and iron oxides), forming patterns much resembling delicate mosses, lichens or ferns.
Formula: SiO_2.

Amber
Amber is fossil resin or gum exuded by coniferous trees. The most celebrated amber, used for necklaces and bracelets, occurs as yellow-brown translucent nodules in *Oligocene deposits on the southern shore of the Baltic Sea, whence it is redistributed by ocean currents and washed up on the beaches of Norway, Denmark and eastern England. Some of this amber entrapped contemporary insects and spiders, preserving even the soft parts of these delicate organisms. There is one remarkable instance of a spider caught while manufacturing threads for its web; under the microscope it is possible to trace each thread back to the corresponding spinneret of the animal.

Amethyst
Amethyst is well crystallized *quartz having a pale violet to rich purple color due to its containing small amounts (up to 0.1%) of ferric *iron. On close examination it can be seen that the color is concentrated in thin sheets lying parallel to particular crystal faces.

Amethyst was known and valued in an-

Moss agate derives its name from the mossy patterns of iron and manganese oxides in white chalcedony.

tiquity. *Exodus* records that amethyst was one of the twelve stones inscribed with the names of the twelve tribes of Israel on the breastplate of the High Priest. It was believed to possess various magical properties, including the capacity to cure or prevent drunkenness (the name is derived from a Greek word meaning "not drunken").

Since amethyst is both attractive and durable (7 on Mohs' scale), its modern status as merely a lesser gemstone can only be ascribed to its relative abundance.

On heating to $1022°F$ ($550°C$), amethyst changes to a yellowish-brown color; and many of the stones marketed as citrine (naturally occurring yellow quartz) are in fact heat-treated amethysts.
Formula: SiO_2.

Amphibole Group

The amphiboles are an important group of rock-forming silicates widely distributed in igneous and metamorphic rocks. They all consist of double chains of silicon and oxygen atoms, the chains being linked by a wide variety of other elements. They form orthorhombic or monoclinic crystals elongated in the direction of the chains and having two cleavages parallel to the chains and at an angle of $120°$ to each other. This important property distinguishes the amphiboles from the *pyroxenes. Amphiboles further differ from pyroxenes in that they are silicate hydroxides, the hydroxide (OH) group being an essential part of the structure.

All amphiboles have nearly identical amounts of silicon, oxygen and water, but are otherwise very variable chemically because of the extensive atomic substitution that takes place. Altogether some thirty amphibole minerals are known, the more important being *actinolite, *glaucophane, *hornblende, *riebeckite, *tremolite, *asbestos and *nephrite.

Andalusite

The minerals andalusite, *kyanite and *sillimanite are aluminum silicates with identical chemical composition, but each has its own individual structure and related physical properties. This is an example of polymorphism, and the minerals are described as polymorphs. All three form in aluminum-rich rock, typically pelites (sediments in which *clay minerals are abundant), during metamorphism, the pressure and temperature conditions controlling which polymorph is formed.

The formation of andalusite is favored by low pressures, and it is thus found typically in contact metamorphic pelites, although it occurs also in some pelites which have been regionally metamorphosed at depths less than 18mi (30km). The crystals are elongate, with square cross-sections, and are usually reddish or green in color. Cross-sections of the variety of andalusite called chiastolite show a black cross formed by the crystallographic arrangement of *carbon inclusions: such sections are sometimes worn as amulets.

Andalusite has been mined as a raw material for refractories and high-grade porcelain. In particular, for many years it was extracted with difficulty in the Inyo Mountains of California at an elevation of 10,000ft (3000m) for use in sparking plugs – until it was realized that aluminum oxide is a superior raw material for this purpose. Transparent green andalusite is occasionally used as a gemstone.
Formula: Al_2SiO_5.

Anhydrite

Anhydrite (calcium sulfate) is produced when a body of sea water is evaporated to about 15% of its original volume (see *evaporites): it has been estimated that the evaporation of a depth of over 2300ft (700m) of sea water is necessary to yield a 1.6ft (0.5m) bed of anhydrite. Large crystals are rare, the mineral usually forming as colorless or white sugary masses which readily break into rectangular cleavage fragments.

The name alludes to the lack of water in the crystal structure. The mineral hydrates easily, however, to form *gypsum. The reverse of this process may also occur, and the extent to which gypsum and anhydrite in evaporite deposits are primary minerals or have been secondarily derived from one another is not always clear.

The major uses of anhydrite are as a soil conditioner and as an additive to Portland cement to delay its setting time.
Formula: $CaSO_4$.

Apatite

Most magmas contain a small amount of phosphorus which, on crystallization, largely combines with calcium and fluorine to produce apatite, which is thus an important accessory mineral in many igneous rocks. It also occurs in a wide range of metamorphic rocks and, as *collophane, in fossil bones and other organic matter.

Crystals are usually elongate with hexagonal cross-sections: although commonly green or brown they may be translucent in a wide range of colors. Magnificent gems have been cut from the purple crystals of Maine, USA, and the yellow-green crystals of Durango, Mexico ("asparagus stone"), but apatite's low hardness (5 on Mohs' scale) makes it an inferior gem.

The mineral weathers rather easily, contributing to soils the phosphorus essential for plant life and necessary for the building of animal bone and tooth material.

The fluorine present in common apatite (fluorapatite) may be replaced partially or entirely by chlorine (chlorapatite) or by oxygen and hydrogen (hydroxyapatite).
Formula: $Ca_5[F,Cl,OH]_3(PO_4)_3$.

Aquamarine

The lovely transparent sky-blue to blue-green gemstone aquamarine is a variety of *beryl, the color being ascribed to minute amounts of iron or possibly to slight defects in the crystal structure.

Aquamarines occur in cavities in granite. Larger crystals – including the largest gemstone ever discovered, a 229lb (104kg) Brazilian crystal – are obtained from granite pegmatites. They are much less costly than *emerald, the green variety of beryl, doubt-

Aragonite crystallizes in the orthorhombic system: heat and pressure can change it to trigonal calcite.

less because of their greater abundance as large, relatively flawless, crystals.
Formula: $Be_3Al_2Si_6O_{18}$.

Aragonite

Aragonite has the same chemical composition as *calcite, but a different crystal structure. Although some of its properties are the same (for instance, reaction with dilute acid), those which depend upon its orthorhombic structure differ from those of trigonal calcite. Thus aragonite has only a poor cleavage and forms very slender pointed crystals; twisted coral-like aggregates known as "flos ferri"; or, when twinned, distinctive stout, six-sided crystals. The best examples of the latter are found in the Aragon district of Spain and in the sulfur deposits of Girgenti, Sicily.

Aragonite is less common and less stable than calcite. It usually forms near or at the surface in hot spring deposits, in beds of clay or *gypsum and in veins and cavities with other carbonates – calcite, *dolomite and *siderite. It has been noted in the upper oxidized zone of ore deposits.

The shells of certain mollusks are made of aragonite, a constituent of both mother-of-pearl and pearl itself. Many fossil shells were probably originally made of aragonite which has, during prolonged burial, gradually become calcite.
Formula: $CaCO_3$.

Arsenopyrite

The mineral arsenopyrite may be regarded as *pyrite (FeS_2) in which half the sulfur atoms have been replaced by arsenic. It forms monoclinic crystals, less symmetrical than the cubes of pyrite, and these may be distinctive. However, it is the color of the mineral, a metallic silvery-gray, which is its most diagnostic feature. It forms as a high-temperature vein mineral, often with *gold and the ores of *tin and tungsten.

It is an important ore of *arsenic.
Formula: $FeAsS$.

Asbestos

It is said that Charlemagne enjoyed impressing guests after a banquet by throwing the tablecloth into the fire, where debris was consumed without the cloth itself being affected. His party trick depended on the incombustible nature of the asbestos fibers making up the fabric.

Asbestos is the name given to a number of natural substances of widely differing composition, all sharing the property of crystallizing as long, thin, more or less easily separated fibers. Most important from a commercial point of view is the *serpentine mineral chrysotile, which accounts for over 90% of the world's asbestos production. Other types of asbestos are fibrous varieties of the amphibole minerals *actinolite, *tremolite and *riebeckite. Of these, the best known is the variety of riebeckite known as *crocidolite or "blue asbestos", which forms long, silky fibers. It is this asbestos which has achieved notoriety as a cause of lung cancer.

Sometimes crocidolite is replaced by *quartz, which mimics the silky fibers of the asbestos; iron originally present in the crocidolite structure is oxidized to give a golden brown color. This material is cut and polished and used in inexpensive je-

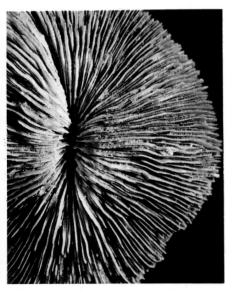

A rose of barite, whose name is derived from the Greek word for "heavy". Barite is found all over the world, fine crystals being known from several countries in Europe and North America.

Tiger-eye is formed when crocidolite, a type of asbestos, is replaced by quartz. The golden brown color is due to the oxidation of iron originally present in the crocidolite.

Top, asbestos mine at Wittenoom, Western Australia. *Above*, chrysotile, a form of asbestos, is fibrous serpentine. Asbestos is most used for fireproofing and for brake linings.

welry under the name "tiger-eye".

Major uses of asbestos are in the building industry, where it is a constituent of wall boards, and in the manufacture of brake linings for automobiles.

Augite

Augite is the most abundant and widely distributed *pyroxene, being an essential component of the basic *igneous rocks basalt, dolerite and gabbro, and a common component of the intermediate rocks andesite and diorite as well as some ultrabasic peridotites. It is also present in some high-grade *metamorphic rocks.

Although so abundant, and familiar to the professional geologist who studies his rocks with the microscope, augite only rarely forms crystals large enough to attract the attention of the amateur. Conspicuous stout black monoclinic crystals with eight-sided cross-sections are found in some porphyritic basalts and andesites, and in

some volcanic tuffs. Usually, however, the rock has to be examined with a hand lens and the right-angled cleavages, characteristic of all pyroxenes, must be sought. Augite in basic igneous rocks of certain types coexists with a second pyroxene, usually orthorhombic *hypersthene.
Formula: $[Ca,Mg,Fe,Al]_2[Si,Al]_2O_6$.

Azurite

The intense azure-blue of azurite makes it one of the more spectacular of minerals, especially when it occurs, as it often does, with bright-green *malachite. Both are copper carbonate hydroxides formed secondarily in the upper zone of copper ore deposits. Azurite may occur as tabular crystals or radiating aggregates, or may be fine-grained and interbanded with malachite. Often malachite completely replaces crystals of azurite, perfectly preserving their original shapes. At one time azurite was ground for use in paint, but the

gradual conversion of the azurite blues to malachite greens proved most unsatisfactory for the artist!

Azurite is a minor ore of copper, and is occasionally used as a decorative material.
Formula: $2CuCO_3 . Cu(OH)_2$.

Barite (Barytes)

Barite (barium sulfate) takes its name from a Greek word meaning "heavy", and its most characteristic property is its density, which is unusually high for a non-metallic mineral. It commonly grows as tabular crystals or as thin, divergent plates forming a "crested" or "cockscomb" aggregate. Barite concretions in some sandstones have a spectacular rosette-like appearance and are called "desert roses". Its crystals are normally colorless to white but may be tinged with a variety of hues.

Barite is a common mineral and occurs in a variety of deposits. It is frequently found with ore minerals in metalliferous veins,

and in cavities in limestones and other sedimentary rocks. Less commonly, it is found in hot-spring deposits and as the petrifying mineral in some *fossils. It is the principal source of *barium for the chemical industry, but its chief use is in the petroleum industry, where more than a million tons a year are used in the search for oil. Mixed with mud it provides a high density slurry which lubricates the drilling bit in deep oil wells, but which has sufficient weight to prevent oil and gas being blown from the hole.
Formula: $BaSO_4$.

Beryl

Beryl's chief claim to our attention is provided by its famous gem varieties, *emerald and *aquamarine.

Beryls typically grow as hard, more or less elongated crystals with hexagonal cross-sections. The ordinary variety is colorless or pale green, but other colors include yellow (heliodor), pink (morganite), blue-green (aquamarine) and deep green (emerald). All types other than emerald are chiefly formed as accessory minerals in granitic rocks, frequently occurring in cavities and pockets in the rock. Beryl crystals in some granite pegmatites grow to very large sizes, up to 6.5ft (2m) in diameter and 19.5ft (6m) in length.
Formula: $Be_3Al_2Si_6O_{18}$.

Biotite

Biotite is one of the most important members of the *mica group of minerals. Chemically complex, it shares with the other micas a sheet-like crystal structure which confers upon them a perfect cleavage, so that individual crystals can be split and opened up, like the pages of a book, by insertion of a knife blade. The cleavage plates thus produced are flexible, elastic and extremely smooth and shiny. Biotite is readily distinguished from *muscovite mica by its color, which is essentially black with sometimes a hint of green or brown.

Biotite is a common rock-forming min-

Bornite, an important ore of copper, is often called "peacock ore" for its iridescent tarnish.

eral. In igneous rocks it is usually associated with *quartz, *feldspars (especially *orthoclase), muscovite and *amphiboles in granites, syenites, diorites and their fine-grained equivalents: very large crystals are found in granite pegmatites. It is also an important constituent of many metamorphic rocks, especially *schists formed at low to medium grades of metamorphism. In contrast with their random arrangement in an igneous rock, the biotites of a micaschist are all aligned parallel, the result of growth under directed pressure.

A somewhat paler-colored mineral, richer in magnesium and poorer in iron than biotite, but in other respects identical to it, is called phlogopite. This occurs in ultrabasic igneous rocks (notably *kimberlite) and in some pegmatites.

Biotite and phlogopite are susceptible to chemical *weathering and are therefore much less common than muscovite in sedi-

ments, unless these are highly immature.
Formula: $K[Mg,Fe'']_3AlSi_3O_{10}[OH,F]_2$.

Bornite

Bornite is an important ore of *copper. A freshly broken surface has a metallic reddish-bronze coloration, but the mineral is usually identified by the purplish iridescent tarnish it develops on exposed surfaces. It is this property which gives rise to its popular name, "peacock ore".
Formula: Cu_5FeS_4.

Bronzite

Bronzite is an orthorhombic magnesium iron *pyroxene. Named for its bronze-like color and luster, it commonly occurs as stubby crystals or fibrous masses in basic and ultrabasic *igneous rocks. It is found in the early-formed rocks of many layered *igneous intrusions where it has accumulated by sinking through the magma; and it is an important constituent of many charnockites and granulites, and of the stony *meteorites called bronzite-chondrites.
Formula: $[Mg,Fe'']_2Si_2O_6$.

Calcite

Of the few non-silicates sufficiently abundant and concentrated to be regarded as rock-forming minerals, calcite is the most important.

Well-formed crystals occur in a bewildering variety of shapes; but all break in the same way along three mutually oblique cleavage directions to yield rhomb-shaped cleavage fragments. It was this observation, first made in 1782 by *Haüy, that led to the concept that all crystals of the same substance are built of identically-shaped minute building blocks.

Calcite is usually milk-white but it may be tinted in a variety of hues due to impu-

Calcite crystallizes in the trigonal system. Twinning is common (below). Though calcite adopts a wide variety of crystal habits – the most common being tabular, scalenohedral (dog-tooth), prismatic and rhombohedral (below left) – all of these display a perfect rhombohedral cleavage. Calcite is a major constituent of the limestones.

rities. When, however, it is clear, transparent and colorless ("Iceland Spar"), calcite exhibits better than any other common mineral the property of double refraction; that is, the splitting of light into two rays so that when an object is viewed through the mineral two images are seen.

Calcite is relatively soft (3 on Mohs' scale) and, like most of the carbonates, effervesces readily in dilute acid, giving off bubbles of carbon dioxide.

*Limestone and chalk are sedimentary rocks whose chief or only constituent is calcite. The mineral may be precipitated directly from seawater, but, as it also forms the shells of many living organisms, these on death may accumulate to form bioclastic limestones. Chalk consists of the calcite shells of the microorganisms *coccoolithophores and *foraminifera. Rainwater which has absorbed carbon dioxide during its descent is capable of dissolving calcite, and spectacular cave systems often develop in limestone country (see *karst landscapes).

If limestones are metamorphosed, the calcite recrystallizes in larger grains and the white granular rock produced is called marble. *Carbonatite is an unusual type of igneous rock rich in calcite and other carbonate minerals, and calcite is common in high, medium and low temperature veins where it may accompany metallic ores.
Formula: $CaCO_3$.

Cassiterite
The Phoenicians satisfied the needs of the ancient world for tin – a component of bronze – by purchasing it from islands "in the Atlantic" known as the Cassiterides. It seems almost certain that the islands were the British Isles, specifically Cornwall, where the mineral cassiterite has been mined intermittently for thousands of years.

Cassiterite forms tetragonal, often twinned, brown crystals in high temperature ore deposits. Some granites, in Cornwall and elsewhere, are surrounded by zones of mineralization, cassiterite together with *wolframite, *topaz, *tourmaline and *arsenopyrite forming in veins in the innermost, highest temperature, zones. It seems very probable that Cornish tin was obtained initially not from the veins themselves but from ancient stream channels where the ore was concentrated in an easily extractable form.
Formula: SnO_2.

Celestine (Celestite)
Celestine is usually found disseminated in limestones, sandstones and shales, or forming thin layers between them. The most spectacular crystals come from cavities in sedimentary and volcanic rocks.

The mineral is difficult to distinguish from *barite, having an identical orthorhombic structure and similar physical properties. The rather rare, delicate sky-blue variety to which the mineral owes its name is distinctive. Celestine is mined for its *strontium.
Formula: $SrSO_4$.

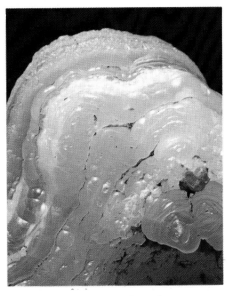

Chalcedony is silica in the form of minute quartz crystals having submicroscopic pores. Here it is seen in its mammillated form.

Chalcopyrite (copper pyrites), a brassy yellow mineral, crystallizes in the tetragonal system, its crystals having a more-or-less tetrahedral appearance.

Cerussite
Cerussite, lead carbonate, often forms well-shaped white or gray orthorhombic crystals in a variety of shapes, the distinctive features being high specific gravity and a brilliant luster. The mineral, which is an ore of lead, is usually of secondary origin, forming in the upper oxidized parts of mineral veins by the action of circulating waters on the primary lead sulfide, *galena.
Formula: $PbCO_3$.

Chalcedony
Chalcedony is the variety of *quartz that lacks all external evidence of crystallinity. Although X-ray and chemical evidences prove that chalcedony consists of quartz grains, these are usually so minute as to be invisible in even the most powerful optical microscope: the word "cryptocrystalline" is applied to this condition.

It is somewhat less dense than ordinary quartz owing to the presence of submicroscopic pore spaces in the material. It is precipitated from silica-rich solutions to form cavity linings, veins and the cementing material for many sediments; and it may replace, partially or entirely, fossils, wood and other minerals. The most familiar examples of chalcedony are chert and flint nodules formed in chalk and limestones by deposition of silica on the sea floor.

A large number of semiprecious and decorative materials are subvarieties of chalcedony. These include sard and cornelian (translucent red), *jasper (opaque red, brown or yellow), chrysoprase (translucent green), prase and plasma (opaque green), bloodstone or heliotrope (green with red spots), *agate and onyx (banded), moss agate (whitish with dark moss-like patterns), and tiger-eye (replacing blue *asbestos).
Formula: SiO_2.

Chalcopyrite
Chalcopyrite is a brittle, brass-yellow metallic-looking mineral somewhat similar in appearance to *pyrite and *gold. It is easily scratched to produce a greenish-black powder. The mineral is tetragonal, although well-shaped tetrahedral crystals are rare: it commonly forms as irregular masses, often with a slight iridescent tarnish.

Chalcopyrite crystallizes in *igneous rocks and in hydrothermal veins with other metallic sulfides. Although at least six other ore minerals contain greater amounts of *copper, chalcopyrite is so abundant that it is one of the major sources of the metal.
Formula: $CuFeS_2$.

Chamosite
Chamosite is closely related in structure and composition to *chlorite. It is the most important primary iron silicate in *ironstones other than those of Precambrian age. It occurs as small green spherical aggregates (ooliths) commonly with *siderite, *calcite, *kaolinite and *goethite, and is also a constituent of some laterite deposits (see *bauxites and laterites). In some cases chamosite is thought to be an original precipitate; in others it appears to have progressively replaced clay or fossil material. It is a major *iron ore.
Formula:
$[Mg,Fe'']_3Fe'''_3(AlSi_3)O_{10}(OH)_8$.

Chlorite
The characteristic green color of many slates and other fine-grained rocks metamorphosed in the greenschist facies is due largely to the presence of the mineral chlorite. The name derives from the Greek word for green, *chloros*.

Chlorite forms platy crystals, scaly aggregates and earthy masses. Crystals have a single perfect cleavage reminiscent of the *micas, but cleavage flakes are brittle and inelastic.

In addition to its principal occurrence in low-grade regionally metamorphosed *schists, chlorite also forms in igneous rocks as an alteration product of *pyroxenes, *amphiboles and micas, and is present in the clay fraction of many sediments.

Formula:
$[Mg,Fe'',Fe''',Mn]_6(AlSi_3)O_{10}OH_8$.

Chromite

*Chromium is present in small amounts (a fraction of a percent) in basic magmas. As the magma cools, the metal combines with iron and oxygen to form chromite, which can often be seen as scattered accessory grains in the resulting rocks. Fortunately, since it is the only ore of the metal, chromite occasionally becomes concentrated by the process of crystal settling: if the magma is solidifying slowly, chromite grains, being denser, are able to sink to the floor of the magma chamber where they form thick layers and lenses.

The mineral is black with a metallic luster and forms equant cubic grains somewhat resembling those of *magnetite. The grains are durable and, when released from their parent rock by erosion, may become concentrated in alluvial sands and gravels.

In addition to its importance as the ore of chromium, chromite is made into refractory bricks used for lining blast furnaces.

Formula: $FeCr_2O_4$.

Cinnabar

Because of its bright vermilion-red color, cinnabar attracted attention in early times, and was powdered for use as a pigment before it was known to contain mercury – a dangerous poison. It is the commonest *mercury mineral and is the only important mercury ore. Cinnabar forms around hot springs and in fractures in areas of recent volcanic activity.

Formula: HgS.

Clay Minerals

To the mineralogist, "clay" is a generic term for a group of related minerals. They are related chemically (being all essentially hydrous aluminum silicates); structurally (being all sheet silicates similar to the *micas); and in their modes of occurrence (being aggregates of extremely small particles usually produced by the breakdown of aluminosilicates such as the *feldspars). The most important are *kaolinite, *halloysite, *illite, *montmorillonite and *vermiculite. They are not readily distinguishable from one another, and sophisticated techniques such as X-ray analysis or electron microscopy are usually necessary to identify individual species.

Collophane

Collophane is the name given to fine-grained phosphatic material occurring as a constituent of fossil bones and other organic matter. Mineralogically, it is a variety of *apatite. Extensive bedded deposits of collophane supply the market for crude phosphate required in the manufacture of agricultural fertilizers (see *phosphorus).

Formula: $Ca_5[F,Cl]_3(PO_4)_3$.

Cordierite

Cordierite usually crystallizes as irregular quartz-like masses or grains which may be colorless, blue or violet-blue. The trans-

Diamond mining employs a sophisticated technology in order to extract the precious stones – but not always, as shown by this diamond mine in Borneo.

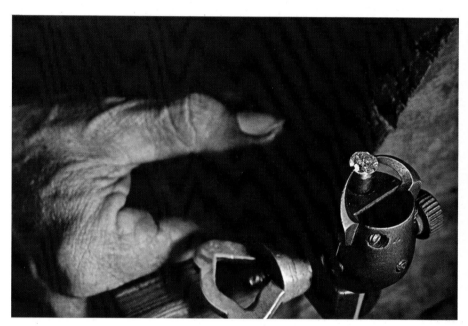

The faces of a gem diamond are not natural crystal faces: skilled craftsmanship must be used so that the "fire" of the stone is best enhanced. Here is a diamond in the final stages of cutting.

parent violet-blue variety, iolite, is used in jewelry.

Cordierite is formed by the medium- or high-grade metamorphism of aluminum-rich rocks, and is found in *schists, *gneisses and *hornfelses, as well as in alluvial gravels derived from these rocks.

Formula: $[Mg,Fe'']_2Al_4Si_5O_{18}$.

Corundum

Corundum is important for two main reasons. Firstly, it is second in hardness only to diamond among natural substances. The mineral and its synthetic equivalent (alundum) are widely used as industrial abrasives: emery, a fine-grained natural mixture of corundum and *magnetite, has been mined on the Greek Island of Naxos for thousands of years. Secondly, the vari-

eties *ruby and *sapphire combine beauty with durability, and so have been used as precious stones since earliest times.

Common corundum is typically gray or weakly tinged in any of several colors, and forms hexagonal crystals tapered at their extremities. It is of widespread occurrence, forming during metamorphism in crystalline limestones and dolomites, gneisses and schists: in some nepheline *syenites it has formed directly from a magmatic melt.

Formula: Al_2O_3.

Cristobalite

Silica occurs naturally in several different structural states (polymorphs). Of these *quartz, with its variations, is by far the most abundant, while others form only under enormously high pressures and are known only from large *meteorite impact craters.

Cristobalite lies between these extremes, being of fairly widespread occurrence but seldom abundant. It forms as small white or gray crystals in some lavas (e.g., *rhyolite, *obsidian) at temperatures higher than those appropriate for the crystallization of quartz. *Opal is essentially a variety of cristobalite, but where temperatures of formation have been relatively low. Formula: SiO_2.

Crocidolite

Crocidolite, also called "blue asbestos", is a variety of the amphibole mineral *riebeckite (see also *asbestos). Formula: $Na_2Fe''_3Fe'''_2Si_8O_{22}[OH,F]_2$.

Cryolite

Although an uncommon mineral, cryolite is important as a flux in the electrolytic process of refining bauxite ore to obtain *aluminum. It occurs in large amounts in only one location: Ivigtut, at the head of Arksukfjord in southwest Greenland. Here the cryolite is found in a unique pegmatite, rich also in *siderite, *quartz, *fluorite, *galena and other minerals. Nowadays much of the cryolite used in the production of aluminum is made artificially from *fluorite. Formula: Na_3AlF_6.

Cuprite

Cuprite is an important secondary ore of *copper, forming in the oxidized zone of copper deposits together with the copper carbonates *malachite and *azurite, and other less common oxides and silicates of this valuable metal.

Cuprite crystals belong to the *cubic system and are usually well-shaped octahedra or cubes, although the variety chalcotrichite (or "plush copper") consists of fine, hair-like fibers. Fine-grained earthy masses of cuprite are called "tile ore". Its color, usually a fine dark red, contrasts splendidly with the vivid greens and blues of associated copper carbonates. Formula: Cu_2O.

Diamond

No mineral excites our imagination more than diamond. Rare and beautiful, it holds pride of place among gemstones. In the modern industrial world, diamond achieves a strategic importance through its unique durability. As the hardest known substance, and quite impervious to attack by acids and alkalis, large quantities are used for grinding, cutting and polishing hard materials. Industrial diamonds are today in increasing amounts prepared synthetically.

In early times diamonds were obtained only from river deposits which, together with certain beach and off-shore gravels, are still important sources. The richest diamond workings, however, and notably those of South Africa, are within pipe-like bodies of *kimberlite. These kimberlite pipes represent magma squeezed up from great depths: from them the secondary deposits are derived by weathering and erosion.

Chemically, diamond is pure *carbon crystallized under great pressure and at high temperatures within kimberlite. Carbon crystallizing under less extreme conditions forms *graphite which has entirely different properties.

Crystals are usually octahedra or cubes, sometimes with curved faces. They may be colorless and transparent, or yellow, brown, reddish or even black. Uncut crystals have a distinctive, rather greasy, appearance.

Gem diamonds are cut so that white light entering the top of the stone is reflected internally and returned, being split into the spectral colors during its passage through the stone. The flashes of delicate colors seen in a well-cut stone are referred to as the "fire" of the diamond. Formula: C.

Diopside

Diopside is a calcium magnesium *pyroxene occurring chiefly in limestones and dolomites which have been thermally metamorphosed. The calcium of the limestone and the calcium and magnesium of the dolomite combine with silica – either supplied by the magma or originally present in the rock as sand grains – to form white or pale-green crystals of diopside that are occasionally large enough to be cut as gemstones. Less commonly, diopside is present in some ultrabasic rocks (where it may be bright green due to a small amount of chromium); and in some *meteorites. Substitution of iron for some of the calcium and magnesium of diopside changes it to the commonest pyroxene, *augite. Formula: $Ca[Mg,Fe'']Si_2O_6$.

Dolomite (Pearl-Spar)

Dolomite occurs widely as a rock-forming mineral. It may be mistaken for *calcite, especially when it forms white rhombohedral crystals with calcite-like cleavages, but it dissolves only slowly in cold dilute acid. It is more readily identified when its crystals develop curved composite faces to produce saddle-shaped aggregates often having a pink tinge and a pearly luster (whence its alternative name "pearl-spar").

Dolomite is formed in a variety of ways. As massive sedimentary deposits (*dolomite is also a rock name), it is probably largely of secondary origin, the result of magnesium-bearing solutions acting on calcite limestone. It occurs as a primary mineral in lead-zinc hydrothermal veins, and is found in cavities and geodes.

The mineral is used as a source of magnesium and in the production of cements and refractory bricks for furnace linings. Formula: $CaMg(CO_3)_2$.

Emerald

Emerald, the rare green variety of *beryl, is weight for weight more costly than *diamond. In contrast with other varieties of beryl, which form in granites and pegmatites, emerald is found in mica *schists and in *calcite veins.

Its green color is due to traces of chromium. Material of the finest deep green color is often badly flawed, and large stones of good quality are rare and extremely costly. Almost indistinguishable synthetic

Emerald's bright green is due to the presence of small quantities of chromium. This rare variety of beryl is weight for weight the most valuable gemstone of all, surpassing even diamond.

Epidote, also known as pistacite, crystallizes in the monoclinic system. Related minerals include clinozoite, piemontite and zoisite (orthorhombic).

emeralds are now made by a secret process: they arouse the suspicions of the expert only because they tend to be too free from flaws to be natural stones. Formula: $Be_3Al_2Si_6O_{18}$.

Enstatite

Enstatite's chief occurrence is in *meteorites (enstatite chondrites): although rare in the Earth's crustal rocks, it may be a major constituent of the upper mantle. It is an end member of the important series of orthorhombic magnesium-iron *pyroxenes. The minerals *bronzite and *hypersthene, which contain increasing amounts of iron substituting for magnesium, are more abundant members of this series. Formula: $MgSiO_3$.

Epidote

Epidote is formed mainly by low- to medium-grade metamorphism of calcium-rich igneous and sedimentary rocks. Individual crystals are green to black striated prisms which may be mistaken for *tourmaline unless the perfect epidote cleavage, parallel to the crystal's length, is noted. When the mineral occurs as disseminated grains in a metamorphic rock its yellowish-green color, similar to that of the pistachio nut, is unique among minerals and quite distinctive. Epidote is occasionally encountered as a gemstone. Formula: $Ca_2Fe'''Al_2O.Si_2O_7.SiO_4(OH)$.

Fluorite crystallizes in the cubic system, twinning (with one crystal interpenetrating the other) being common. The word "fluorescence" comes from fluorite's exhibition of that property, though the phenomenon is not especially pronounced. The most valued variety is Blue John (*above left*).

Feldspar Group

The feldspars are the most abundant minerals in the Earth's crust and are widely distributed in igneous, metamorphic and sedimentary rocks: indeed, the precise classification of many rocks depends upon the type and composition present.

They are aluminosilicates containing potassium, sodium and calcium, the group being subdivided into alkali feldspars (*microcline, orthoclase and *sanidine) in which potassium is dominant, sodium subordinate and calcium virtually absent; and the plagioclase feldspars, which vary continuously in composition from pure sodium feldspar to pure calcium feldspar, these having negligible potassium. (See also *feldspathoids.)

All the feldspars form colorless, white or pink (or rarely green) crystals of Mohs' hardness 6, with two cleavages at right angles. Crystals are blocky or, especially in the case of plagioclase, elongated and "lath"-shaped. The two groups of feldspars are distinguished firstly by the "company they keep" and secondly by the type of twinning they exhibit. (These differences are described under *plagioclase and *orthoclase.)

Feldspathoid Group

The feldspathoids are a group of silicate minerals with chemical compositions broadly similar to those of the *feldspars. However, they are relatively deficient in silica and richer in alkalis. The chemistry of the most common feldspathoids, *nepheline, *leucite and *sodalite, thus reflects the composition of the undersaturated magmas from which they have crystallized.

*Lazurite and *scapolite also belong to the feldspathoid group, but form under metamorphic conditions.

Fluorite (Fluorspar)

Fluorite is a common and widely distributed mineral. It crystallizes in veins, either alone or with metallic ore minerals, especially those of lead and zinc; and also forms as an accessory mineral in *igneous rocks. In addition, some of the finest crystals occur in solution cavities in *limestones. It commonly crystallizes as well-formed cubes with four perfect cleavages so disposed that a damaged cube will have one or more of its corners symmetrically broken off along a flat cleavage plane.

The color varies greatly. It may be blue, purple, green or yellow; less commonly colorless, pink, red or black. Although attractive, the mineral is too soft (4 on Mohs' scale) and too readily cleaved to find use as a gemstone. However, an interesting variety called "Blue John", found in Derbyshire, England, consists of fibrous flourite color-banded in shades of blue, purple and white, and this has been carved into ornamental vases and bowls since Roman times.

Fluorite gives its name to fluorescence. A variety of substances, including some varieties of fluorite and about a hundred or so other minerals, respond when bathed in ultraviolet light (which is invisible to the human eye) by glowing in bright colors that lie within the visible spectrum.

The name fluorite derives from the Latin *fluere*, to flow, and refers to its low melting point. It is this property which makes fluorite an important industrial mineral, used as a flux in the open-hearth smelting of iron. Other uses are in the production of hydrofluoric acid, refrigerant liquids and inert fluorocarbon resins such as those used to coat non-stick cooking vessels. Clear, colorless fluorite is made into lenses for use in special types of optical equipment.
Formula: CaF_2.

Galena

Galena, the most important ore of *lead, occurs chiefly in hydrothermal veins, often associated with the zinc sulfide *sphalerite. It forms also as a replacement mineral in *limestones and *dolomites.

Galena crystallizes as cubes or octahedra, or as a combination of these. It is soft ($2\frac{1}{2}$ on Mohs' scale), with a high density, a characteristic metallic lead-gray color, and three cleavages at right angles to one another and parallel to the cube faces. It is readily oxidized to a number of secondary lead minerals including *cerussite.

The extraction of lead from galena is one of the simplest metallurgical processes. The temperatures required are merely those of a coal fire, and indeed lead was smelted in this way by, among others, the early American settlers for lead bullets. Much galena contains significant quantities of silver: in extreme cases, galena is sufficiently rich in precious metal (up to 0.25%) to be mined specifically as a silver ore.

The abundance of the various isotopes of lead in galena specimens have been used by geochronologists for dating purposes (see *age of the Earth).
Formula: PbS.

Garnet Group

The garnets are a family of rock-forming silicate minerals which vary greatly in the metal atoms they contain. An individual can be regarded as an intimate mixture of two or more of the following end-members: pyrope (magnesium-aluminum garnet), almandine (iron-aluminum garnet), spessartine (manganese-aluminum garnet), grossularite (calcium-aluminum garnet), andradite (calcium-iron garnet), and uvarovite (calcium-chromium garnet).

All the garnets, whatever their composition, typically form hard, equidimensional 12-, 24- or 36-sided crystals, but in other respects they are extremely diverse. Garnets of all colors except blue are known, red garnets being the most commonly encountered.

The common garnet of *schists and

Galena crystallizes in the cubic system, octahedra being more common than cubes. In this photograph cubes of galena (dark) can be seen with minor calcite (white) and ankerite (buff).

*gneisses approximates to an almandine composition. Grossularite- and andradite-rich types are characteristic of metamorphosed impure limestones, and spessartine-rich garnets are found in metamorphosed manganese deposits. Garnet approximating to pyrope composition occurs in some ultrabasic *igneous rocks, and is probably an important constituent of the upper mantle. Uvarovite, the green garnet of some chromium deposits, is rare.

The hardness of garnet and its tendency when crushed to form sharp cutting-edges make it an important abrasive material. Some varieties, notably ruby-red pyrope, red almandine (carbuncle), orange grossularite (cinnamon stone) and green andradite (demantoid), are used as gemstones.

Glauconite

Glauconite is a member of the *mica group: however, it occurs not in typical mica-like "books" but rather as minute rounded aggregates of green platelets in sedimentary rocks of marine origin. It is the classic example of a mineral forming directly on the sea floor. Sediments rich in glauconite are distinctly green in color and are known as greensands. Since glauconite forms *in situ* in a sediment and contains potassium, it enables a greensand to be dated directly using the potassium-argon method of age determination (see *age of the Earth): as glauconite occurs in rocks of nearly all geological ages, its importance in establishing the time-scale for sedimentary rocks is obvious.
Formula: $K[Fe''', Mg, Al]_2 Si_4 O_{10}(OH)_2$.

Glaucophane

Glaucophane is an *amphibole. It occurs as slender bluish crystals or as massive or fibrous aggregates, typically in sodium-rich *schists which have undergone regional metamorphism at low temperatures and high pressures. These schists, often called blueschists because of their abundance of blue glaucophane, are often derived from geosynclinal sediments, and the necessary

metamorphic conditions for their formation are typical of destructive plate margin environments (see *plate tectonics).
Formula:
$Na_2[Mg, Fe'']_3 Al_2 Si_8 O_{22}(OH)_2$.

Goethite (Limonite)

Goethite, named after the German poet, Goethe, who collected minerals in his spare time, is produced by the oxidation and hydration of iron-bearing minerals such as *pyrite and *magnetite. Like *hematite, it forms black, rounded or stalactitic aggregates with a fibrous radial inner structure, sometimes showing beautiful internal color-banding in shades of brown and yellow.

Limonite is finely divided goethite with variable amounts of water of hydration, and is a distinctive ocherous yellow. Both goethite and limonite are natural pigments imparting yellow and brown hues to many rocks. With *quartz, they constitute the gossans or residual weathered cappings on deposits rich in iron-bearing sulfide minerals.

The greatest accumulations of goethite and limonite, those worked as ores of iron, have formed by direct precipitation from marine or fresh water in shallow seas, lagoons and bogs.
Formula (goethite): FeO.OH.

Graphite

Graphite is one of the natural forms of pure *carbon, the other being *diamond. It occurs typically in metamorphosed sedimentary rocks such as recrystallized limestones and coal beds, schists and quartzites, where it probably represents carbon of organic origin.

The contrasts in physical properties between carbon and diamond are extreme. Graphite is very soft, opaque, black and dull with a low density – diamond is more than 1.5 times as dense. The contrasts reflect grossly different atomic (and hence crystalline) structures, diamond requiring very high pressures and tempera-

tures for its formation and graphite being the stable form of carbon under normal conditions.

Graphite is used, in bonded form, in pencils (its soft black flakes cleave away and adhere to paper), as well as in the manufacture of high temperature alloys, lubricants and electrodes.
Formula: C.

Gypsum

Gypsum is the most common sulfate mineral. Its main occurrences are in sedimentary deposits, particularly *evaporite sequences. Having a low solubility, it is one of the first minerals to crystallize from evaporating seawater.

It is unusually soft and can be scratched by the fingernail, a property which makes the compact, fine-grained variety alabaster suitable for ornamental carvings. Large crystals have characteristic parallelogram or lozenge shapes, and are sometimes intergrown to form twin crystals having the shape of arrowheads or fishtails. Transparent varieties are known as selenite, and fibrous types, which may form curved or twisted aggregates, are called satin-spar.

Gypsum transforms to and from *anhydrite by the loss and gain (respectively) of water. Partial loss of water, induced by carefully heating powdered gypsum, produces plaster of Paris: when mixed with water this reverts to gypsum, setting as a rigid mass. Such plasters are used widely in the building industry and in the making of surgical casts and molds for ceramics.
Formula: $CaSO_4 . 2H_2O$.

Halite (Rock Salt)

Halite is common *salt, most familiar as a small but essential part of our diet. The sea owes its taste chiefly to dissolved sodium chloride, and the mineral crystallizes when sea or salt-lake water evaporates to 10% or less of its original volume (see *evaporites).

Most is colorless or white: gray, pink, red or brown material owes its color to impurities, while a striking blue-and-purple type from Stassfurt, Germany, is chemically pure but has structural imperfections. Most halite forms as massive aggregates of interlocking crystals; individual crystals are in the shape of cubes.

Halite, like ice, is able to flow; but unlike ice, which moves downward as glaciers, salt deposits buried in the Earth's crust are lighter than the enclosing rocks and so tend to flow upward to produce structures called salt domes. Valuable concentrations of *petroleum and *natural gas are often trapped by such structures.

The human consumption of salt and its role as a food preservative originally provided its prime uses; and in ancient times it was an important form of currency. Nowadays the chemical industry consumes three-quarters of the world's salt pro-

duction, and it is also used in large quantities to melt winter ice on roads.
Formula: NaCl.

Halloysite

A *clay mineral very closely related structurally and chemically to *kaolinite, halloysite is, like kaolinite, of widespread occurrence; and forms by the weathering or hydrothermal alteration of *feldspar and other aluminum silicate minerals.
Formula: $Al_4Si_4(OH)_8O_{10}.4H_2O$.

Hematite

Hematite is the principal ore of *iron and for this reason can be regarded as perhaps the single mineral of greatest importance to industrial civilization. Its name, derived from the Greek word for blood, refers to the red color of finely divided or earthy hematite, and most red rocks owe their color to this mineral. The largest deposits, those of economic value, are of sedimentary origin, the iron having been originally deposited on the floors of shallow seas. Many of these bedded ironstone formations are of Precambrian age: they are found on all continents.

Well-crystallized hematite, formed at high temperatures in igneous and metamorphic rocks and in hydrothermal veins, occurs as platey hexagonal steel-gray to black crystals with glittering mirror-like surfaces, quite unlike the red material of sediments.

In addition to being the chief source of iron, the metal on which modern civilization is founded, powdered hematite is employed as a fine polishing agent (jeweler's rouge), and has been used continuously as a pigment since earliest times: its stable red color is seen in the Paleolithic paintings in the caves of the Pyrenees, and in the hardy red oxide paints of the present day.
Formula: Fe_2O_3.

Hornblende

Hornblende is the most abundant and widely distributed *amphibole, occurring as a major component of many *igneous rocks, especially those of intermediate composition. It is also the dominant amphibole mineral in many medium-grade regionally metamorphosed rocks, its importance being reflected in the rock names hornblende-schist and amphibolite.

Hornblende forms more or less elongated, even fibrous, monoclinic, dark-green to black crystals, sometimes with a brownish tint due to the presence of titanium. It is most easily mistaken for *augite, but tends to form more elongated, six- rather than eight-sided crystals. Broken grains should be examined for the cleavage angle of 120°, characteristic of the amphiboles.
Formula: $[Ca,Na]_{2-3}[Mg,Fe'',Fe''',Al]_5$
$[Si,Al]_8O_{22}(OH)_2$.

Hypersthene

Hypersthene is the most abundant orthorhombic *pyroxene, containing more iron and less magnesium than does *bronzite. It occurs in somewhat more iron-rich (and less basic) rocks than does bronzite: thus the hypersthene-chondrites are a class of stony *meteorites more iron-rich than the bronzite-chondrites. The presence of hypersthene in a gabbro (or the closely related pyroxene, pigeonite, in a basalt) characterizes the rock as tholeiitic. Hypersthene is also an important constituent of many charnockites and granulites.
Formula: $[Mg,Fe'']SiO_3$.

Ice

Naturally formed ice can be classed as a mineral – and, indeed, is the most abundant mineral on the surface of the Earth! In areas where annual snowfall exceeds annual melting, ice caps and glaciers develop. These are of great importance as agents of erosion, as superimposed loads capable of depressing continental crust, and even as modifiers of worldwide sea levels. Frost too is significant. The splitting and shattering of rock caused by the expansion of water as it freezes in cracks and joints is an important weathering phenomenon. (For further dis-

Kidney iron ore is the name given to hematite in mammillated form. Hematite's distribution is wide, and large concentrations are found in many parts of the world: it is the most important ore of iron.

cussions, see *glaciation, *glacial landscapes, *erosion and *weathering.)
Formula: H_2O.

Idocrase (Vesuvianite)

The alternative name for idocrase, vesuvianite, derives from the occurrence of the mineral in dolomitic limestone brought up from depth by the lavas of Mount Vesuvius, Italy. Reactions between igneous magmas and impure limestones produce a variety of new minerals of which idocrase is one. It forms well-shaped tetragonal crystals with square cross-sections in various colors, usually dark green or brown, occasionally blue, yellow or red. The brown transparent crystals from Vesuvius are cut as gemstones. A bright green massive variety, californite, is made into carvings and ornaments, and has been fraudulently marketed as jade.
Formula:
$Ca_{10}Al_4[Mg,Fe'']_2(Si_2O_7)_2(SiO_4)_5(OH)_4$.

Illite

Illite, one of the *clay minerals, is structurally very similar to the *micas: it is the dominant mineral in shales and mudstones. Although some sedimentary illite may have been deposited as such after its formation by surface weathering of *feldspars, much of it is formed in place from other clay minerals during the subsequent compaction and lithification of the sediment (*diagenesis). It is extremely fine-grained, dull, and white or pale in color. Less commonly, illite is formed in certain hydrothermal ore deposits, and in alteration zones around hot springs.
Formula (simplified):
$KAl_4[Si,Al]_8O_{18}.2H_2O$.

Ilmenite

Ilmenite is a common accessory mineral present as scattered grains in many *basalts and *andesites and their coarser-grained equivalents, *gabbros and *diorites. Occasionally it forms segregations of size sufficient to be ranked as ore bodies, and these are worked for their *titanium. Ilmenite crystals are tabular but rare, the mineral more commonly occurring as irregular grains and masses.

Black and with metallic luster, it resembles *magnetite, with which it often coexists. Unlike magnetite, however, it is non-magnetic and this is used to distinguish the two and to separate the ores. Ilmenite is resistant to weathering and so survives as a major constituent of some black beachsand deposits.
Formula: $FeTiO_3$.

Jadeite

The rarer of the two minerals popularly known as jade (see also *nephrite), jadeite belongs to the *pyroxene group of minerals. White or gray when pure, the green variety regarded by the Chinese as the choicest of all gemstones owes its color to traces of chromium.

Crystals are rare, the mineral usually

Two varieties of chalcedony, a cryptocrystalline form of quartz. On the left is jasper, in this case red though brown and yellow colorations are also known. On the right is chrysoprase.

forming tough, compact aggregates of microscopic grains. Such material, normally found as stream-worn boulders, has been used from early times for the fashioning of implements and ornamental objects of all kinds.

Jadeite is a metamorphic mineral, requiring conditions of high pressure and relatively low temperature. For this reason it forms typically at destructive plate margins, where underthrusting lithospheric plates generate high pressures but where geothermal gradients are low (see *plate tectonics).
Formula: $NaAlSi_2O_6$.

Jasper
Jasper is hard, opaque *chalcedony colored red, brown or yellow by finely divided particles of iron oxides (*hematite, *goethite and *limonite). It forms at moderate to low temperatures, sometimes as thick beds of considerable area.

Jasper is the most common form of silica found in petrified wood. Under certain conditions, buried wood may become saturated with water, rich in silica and iron oxides, and the cellular structure may be replaced and perfectly mimicked by jasper to the extent that even the species of tree can be identified.
Formula: SiO_2.

Kaolinite
Kaolinite has a sheet structure, and is one of the most common of the *clay minerals. It occurs as snowy white earthy masses and loose aggregates of submicroscopic hexagonal plates. It forms secondarily by the breakdown and alteration of aluminous silicates, especially potassic feldspars such as *orthoclase.

The most famous deposits are in Cornwall, England. Here the feldspars of the granites have been severely attacked by hot vapors rising through the rock. The kaolinite (china clay) thus produced is quarried

with high-pressure water jets. The pure white clay is used in the manufacture of high-grade porcelain, and as a filler in paper.
Formula: $Al_4Si_4O_{10}(OH)_8$.

Kyanite
The minerals kyanite, *andalusite and *sillimanite have identical chemical composition. Each, however, has its own individual structure and related physical properties. This is an example of polymorphism. All three form in aluminum-rich rocks, typically pelites (sediments in which clay minerals are abundant) during metamorphism, the pressure and temperature conditions of metamorphism controlling which is formed.

The formation of kyanite is favored by high pressures, and it occurs in some *eclogites and in pelitic *schists formed at considerable depth in the Earth's crust. Crystals are long and blade-like and usually of a patchy blue color (the name derives from a Greek word meaning blue). They have the unusual property of being considerably softer parallel to the crystal length than at right-angles to the length: thus a knife will scratch a crystal in the former direction but will itself be blunted by the crystal in the latter. Transparent varieties are occasionally cut as gemstones.

As a commercial refractory mineral, kyanite is the most important of the aluminum silicate polymorphs.
Formula: Al_2SiO_5.

Lapis Lazuli (Lazurite)
The chief interest in the mineral lazurite, a member of the *feldspathoid family, lies in the attraction of its color (a deep azure-blue) when it occurs in the composite substance called lapis lazuli. Lapis, the commonly abbreviated name, is lazurite embedded in a matrix of white *calcite and almost always embellished with small golden specks of *pyrite. Prized since very early times, lapis lazuli occurs in only a few places, and only as a contact metamorphic mineral in limestones close to igneous intrusions. The most famous source is in the

Kotcha Valley in Afghanistan. Here the lapis-rich marble mines were already ancient when visited by Marco Polo in 1271, and are still worked today. Lapis of fine quality is also obtained by the Russians from a dolomite limestone near Lake Baikal in Siberia. The artist's pigment ultramarine, responsible for the glorious blue colors in the Old Masters, was made from lapis lazuli until late in the 18th century: in more recent times synthetic lazurite has been used for this purpose.
Formula (lazurite):
$[Na,Ca]_8[Al,Si]_{12}O_{24}[S,SO_4]$.

Leucite
Conspicuous in some of the fine-grained lavas of Vesuvius, Italy, are relatively large, dull, white equidimensional crystals with 24 more-or-less equal faces. These are crystals of leucite, a member of the *feldspathoid group. It crystallizes in place of *feldspar from magmas relatively deficient in silica and rich in potassium; but, being unstable at high pressures, is not found in igneous rocks formed at depth, being virtually restricted to lavas of appropriate composition (e.g., certain trachytes). Moreover, since leucite is easily altered, it is rarely found in lavas older than the Tertiary.
Formula: $KAlSi_2O_6$.

Magnesite
Magnesite is found in compact porcelain-like or coarser marble-like masses or, rarely, as rhombohedral crystals which may be colorless, gray or yellowish. Although similar in appearance to *calcite, it is much less common, and is hardly affected by dilute hydrochloric acid unless this is first heated. It usually forms as a replacement mineral in one of two ways: by the action of carbonate-bearing solutions on magnesium-rich rocks (serpentinite, dunite, peridotite); or by the complementary process involving magnesium-rich solutions interacting with carbonate-rich rocks.

Magnesite mine in Austria. Magnesite is mined both for itself and as an ore of magnesium.

Magnetite (also known as magnetic iron ore), one of the spinel group of minerals, is an important ore of iron found in placer deposits, contact metamorphic aureoles, replacement deposits and intrusive igneous rocks. Its name derives from its property of being attracted by a magnet.

Magnesite, an ore of *magnesium, is used in the manufacture of certain cements and in the production of magnesium oxide.

Formula: $MgCO_3$.

Magnetite

The outstanding property of magnetite, one of the major ores of *iron, is its strongly magnetic character: it is attracted by a magnet, and some rare specimens called lodestones are themselves natural magnets. The fact that grains of magnetite forming in an igneous rock adopt an orientation and polarity determined by the Earth's prevailing magnetic field has been of crucial value in the development of modern geological concepts of sea-floor spreading.

Magnetite crystallizes in the cubic system, usually as opaque black octahedra, and is very widely distributed – as an accessory mineral in almost all igneous and many metamorphic rocks, it is well-nigh ubiquitous. Its high density sometimes results in its sinking in slowly cooling magmas to form accumulations of economic value. New deposits are discovered at depth using magnetometers. To obtain the iron, the ore is reduced at high temperatures in a blast furnace, where oxygen is liberated, impurities combining with a flux such as limestone to be removed as slag.

Formula: Fe_3O_4.

Malachite

The vivid green color of malachite makes it one of the more spectacular minerals, especially when it occurs – as it often does – with bright blue *azurite. Both form secondarily in the upper zone of copper ore deposits. Malachite is the more abundant of the two, sometimes completely replacing crystals of azurite with perfect preservation of their original shapes. Otherwise it usu-

Mammillated malachite lining a cavity and cementing limonitic gossan. When masses of malachite are cut across they show concentric bands of different shades of green: for centuries such material has been polished for decorative use.

ally occurs in aggregates of fibers forming encrusting masses with curved surfaces. When these are cut across, they show concentric color bands of different intensities of green.

Malachite is sufficiently abundant to be mined as an ore of *copper. It is often seen as a green patina or coating on copper roofs which have been attacked by carbon dioxide and moisture in the atmosphere.

Formula: $Cu_2CO_3(OH)_2$.

Marcasite

When a piece of domestic coal is split, a golden-colored film is occasionally seen on the split surface. This is marcasite. More spectacular forms of marcasite – ball-, spear- or arrow-shaped aggregates found in chalk and clay – often attract attention and are brought to museums in the mistaken belief that they are *meteorites.

Marcasite is chemically identical to *pyrite, but crystallizes in the *orthorhombic system under conditions of lower temperature and higher alkalinity. If well crystallized the two minerals can be readily identified from their shapes, but otherwise simple identification techniques are inadequate to distinguish them.

Formula: FeS_2.

Mica Group

The micas are a small but important group of silicates characterized by their atomic structure. Silicon and oxygen form continuous, well-defined layers or sheets bound only weakly to adjacent layers by other elements, so that the minerals have a perfect cleavage yielding thin, generally flexible flakes. Mica "books" are single crystals (often six-sided), the "pages" of which are incipient flakes defined by the cleavage. Cleavage flakes can be easily detached from a mica crystal with the blade of a pocket knife.

The most important micas are *muscovite, *biotite and *phlogopite.

Microcline

Microcline, a member of the *feldspar family, is chemically identical to *sanidine and *orthoclase but has a more highly ordered structure, the aluminum and silicon atoms being arranged in a regular and predictable fashion. Microcline crystallizes at somewhat lower temperatures than do the other alkali feldspars, and it occurs typically in pegmatites and hydrothermal veins. Like orthoclase it is found as grains in sedimentary rocks.

Microcline forms stubby triclinic crystals very similar in their physical properties to orthoclase – indeed it is difficult to distinguish these two feldspars unless the crystals are green, since the only green feldspar is a variety of microcline called amazonite, or amazon stone, which is sometimes used as a gemstone. Microcline may also be white, pink, or gray.

The mineral may be intimately intergrown with *albite (this mixture is called perthite) or with *quartz, producing a texture reminiscent of ancient cuneiform writing – hence the name "graphic granite".

Formula: $KAlSi_3O_8$.

Monazite

Monazite is a phosphate of *thorium and the *rare earth elements and is exploited as a source of thorium. Although monazite is formed as yellow-brown crystals in granites, pegmatites and gneisses as an accessory mineral only, it is resistant to weathering and becomes concentrated in heavy beach sands and stream placers where it attains the status of an exploitable ore.

Formula: $[Th,Ce,La,Y]PO_4$.

Montmorillonite

Montmorillonite is a *clay mineral occurring only in gray or greenish gray earthy masses of such fine grain-size that crystals cannot normally be distinguished, even under the electron microscope. It owes its origin chiefly to the alteration of fine volcanic ash; and entire beds of volcanic debris may be converted to a montmorillonite rock called bentonite. When placed in water, montmorillonite absorbs water, swelling to

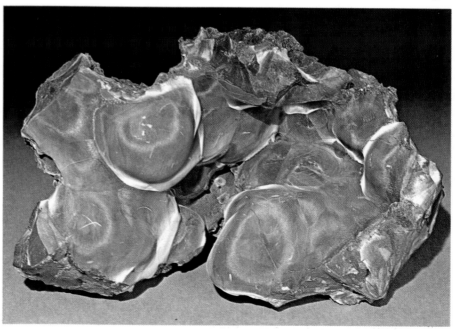

a gel-like mass, and this makes it an important industrial material. It is used as a plasticizer in drilling muds and as a catalyst.
Formula: $[Na,Ca]_{0.33}[Al,Mg]_2 Si_4 O_{10}(OH)_2 . nH_2O.$

Muscovite

Muscovite is one of the most important of the *mica group. Chemically complex, it shares with the other micas a sheet-like crystal structure which confers upon them a perfect cleavage, so that individual crystals can be split and opened up like the pages of a book. These cleavage flakes are flexible and extremely smooth and shiny. Muscovite is readily distinguished from *biotite mica by its color, which is silvery-gray, sometimes tinged with green, brown or pink.

It is a common rock-forming mineral, widely distributed in igneous, metamorphic and sedimentary rocks. In granites and pegmatites it is associated with *quartz, feldspars (especially *orthoclase and *microcline) and biotite. It is a common constituent of many low- to medium-grade *metamorphic rocks, especially mica-schists, in which muscovite grains are aligned parallel due to growth under directed pressure. Muscovite is relatively stable during weathering and transport, and survives as a common constituent of clastic sedimentary rocks such as sandstones and siltstones.

Muscovite is an essential industrial material, due to its unique combination of properties: perfect cleavage, flexibility, low thermal and electrical conductivity, infusibility and transparency. Large muscovite sheets obtained from pegmatites are used in the electrical industry for capacitors and high-temperature insulators. Before the manufacture of glass, it was used for window panes (Muscovy glass), and it remains the best material for furnace windows. Finely ground muscovite is used as a filler in roofing materials, wallpapers and paint.
Formula: $KAl_2(Si_3Al)O_{10}(OH)_2.$

Nepheline

Nepheline is the most important member of the *feldspathoid group. It crystallizes as hexagonal crystals or irregular grains with a distinctive greasy luster in silica-poor alkaline-rich *igneous rocks in place of *feldspar: it is found in both volcanic and plutonic rocks of appropriate composition (e.g., nepheline *syenites and *phonolites). Nepheline is mined for use in the manufacture of glass and ceramics.
Formula: $NaAlSiO_4.$

Nephrite

Nephrite is the compact, fine-grained fibrous variety of *tremolite and *actinolite. One of the two substances popularly known as jade (see also *jadeite), it is highly prized as a gem and ornamental stone. From early times, Chinese craftsmen have worked the stone, and it has long been used by the Maoris for weapons and decorative objects.

The color of nephrite is variable. White or gray material is relatively free from iron (tremolite); spinach-green material is iron-bearing (actinolite); and other colors due to

Adamite is a zinc olivenite. The olivenites, which crystallize in the orthorhombic system, are hydrous copper arsenates, and all of them are rare. They are most commonly found in copper ore deposits, though even here their occurrence is only very occasional.

various impurities are known. The interlocking microscopic fibers impart to the material great cohesive strength, so that it is extremely difficult to break a specimen, even with a geologists' hammer.
Formula: $Ca_2[Mg,Fe]_5(Si_8O_{22})(OH)_2.$

Olivine

Olivine is one of the most important rock-forming minerals. Its composition varies continuously from pure magnesium silicate (forsterite) to pure iron silicate (fayalite), most natural olivines being mixtures of these two end-members. Well-formed crystals are rare, the mineral usually occurring as rounded or irregular grains or as granular masses in igneous rocks. The color is usually a characteristic olive-green (hence the name), but iron-rich types incline toward yellow and brown.

Olivine is a common constituent of many ultrabasic and basic *igneous rocks, such as peridotites, gabbros, dolerites and basalts. Dunite, a rock originally described from the Dun Mountains of New Zealand, consists almost exclusively of olivine. Some dunites have formed by the sinking of olivine crystals and their accumulation on the floor of a magma chamber. Basalt lavas forming oceanic islands often contain rounded fragments of coarse-grained olivine-rich rocks which are believed to have originated in the upper mantle, where olivine is an important – perhaps even the dominant – mineral, as it is in many stony and stony-iron *meteorites. At depths of about 250mi (400km) within the Earth, the orthorhombic crystal structure of olivine is changed by pressure to a denser, cubic arrangement of atoms.

Gem-quality olivine is called *peridot.
Formula: $[Mg,Fe'']_2SiO_4.$

Opal

Opal is a variety of *cristobalite which, unlike *quartz and other forms of silica, contains varying amounts of water. It forms at low temperatures from circulating ground waters or hydrothermal hot spring solutions in cavities and cracks, occasionally even impregnating unconsolidated sediments. Pure opal is usually colorless or milky white, but the mineral may be colored by impurities. These types are, however, of only limited interest compared with gem opal, the variety which shows the brilliant flashing play of colors unique among gemstones.

It has long been known that the colors are due to interference effects on light penetrating the surface layers, but the cause of the interference was discovered only in 1964, when the electron microscope revealed that

Massive green orthoclase feldspar from Australia. Orthoclase has two cleavages at right-angles to each other, one of these cleavages being visible in this photograph. Orthoclase is the most important of the alkali feldspars.

opal consists of minute spheres of cristobalite packed together in an orderly fashion. If the spheres are of appropriate size, the play of interference colors results.

Precious opal has been esteemed as one of the noblest of gems since early times, although it suffered a temporary decline during the Victorian era. The discovery in 1872 of Australian opals of surpassing beauty reestablished the former eminence of the stone.

Formula: $SiO_2 \cdot nH_2O$.

Orthoclase

Orthoclase is chemically identical to *microcline and *sanidine but has a crystal structure intermediate between the other potassium feldspars. In microcline the aluminum and silicon atoms are well-ordered and regular; in sanidine they are disposed more-or-less randomly; whereas in orthoclase they are partially ordered. These differences reflect the temperatures at which the three polymorphs have crystallized – the lower this temperature, the more highly ordered the structure.

Orthoclase is the most important and abundant alkali *feldspar. It is a major constituent of granites and syenites and is the most common potassium feldspar in metamorphic and sedimentary rocks. It forms blocky or somewhat elongated monoclinic crystals, which may have square cross-sections, are white or pink in color, are slightly softer than *quartz, and show two cleavages at right-angles. Crystals are often twinned, this phenomenon being best seen on the freshly broken surface of a coarse-grained rock, such as granite, where twinned crystals show a flat cleavage surface extending over only approximately half the width of the grain. This so-called "simple twinning" is very distinctive and quite unlike the "multiple twinning" striations of *plagioclase.

Orthoclase is used as a raw material for the manufacture of porcelain, enamel and glass. A variety called moonstone shows a bluish *opal-like play of colors and is fashioned into gemstones. Perthite is an intimate mixture of orthoclase with *albite.

Formula: $KAlSi_3O_8$.

Peridot

Peridot is simply gem-quality *olivine. It has a bottle-green color and a somewhat oily luster, and makes handsome, if rather soft, cut stones.

Although olivine is a common mineral, large, clear inclusion-free crystals of suitable color are rare. The most famous source is the small island of St John in the Red Sea. St John's Island peridots were known in Biblical times and used by the ancient Egyptians, but no record of their source survived. This led to the speculation that ancient peridots were extraterrestrial, extracted from the *meteorites known as pallasites. The true source was rediscovered in the late 19th century, and new pits have yielded superb specimens.

Formula: $[Mg, Fe'']_2SiO_4$.

Plagioclase

The plagioclases, abundant and widely distributed rock-forming minerals, belong to the *feldspar group, and vary in chemical composition from pure sodium feldspar (albite) to pure calcium feldspar (anorthite), different names being assigned as the sodium content decreases and the calcium content increases: albite, oligoclase, andesine, labradorite, bytownite, anorthite. Individual members are not normally distinguishable without chemical analysis or use of a special microscope.

The triclinic crystals are often somewhat elongated and "lath"-like, colorless, white or off-white, and show two cleavages at right-angles to one another. Their most distinctive feature is the appearance on cleavage surfaces of numerous parallel striations of different reflectivity due to multiple twinning. This property distinguishes plagioclase from the alkali feldspar *orthoclase.

Plagioclases occur in most igneous rocks: indeed, their precise composition is used as a mineralogical basis for *igneous rock classification. Albite is characteristic of granites, granite pegmatites and spilites; andesine of diorites and andesites; and labradorite of gabbros, dolerites and basalts. Very calcium-rich plagioclase is found in some ultrabasic and lunar rocks. Anorthosites are large bodies of oligoclase-andesine rock found in ancient shield areas of the Earth's crust. Plagioclase is also common in *metamorphic rocks.

Cut and polished labradorite shows an iridescent play of colors and so is used as an ornamental stone.

Formula: $Na(AlSi_3O_8)$ to $Ca(Al_2Si_2O_8)$.

Polyhalite

Polyhalite usually forms as pink or red masses (due to iron oxide inclusions) which may be fibrous or foliated. It occurs in bedded *evaporite deposits formed by the evaporation of sea or salt-lake water, and is one of the last minerals to be formed in this way owing to its high solubility. Polyhalite and similar potassium and magnesium salts crystallize only when evaporating seawater has been reduced to 1.5% of its original volume.

Formula: $K_2Ca_2Mg(SO_4)_4 \cdot 2H_2O$.

Pyrite (Fool's Gold)

Pyrite, fool's gold, is a yellow metallic mineral which superficially resembles gold and hence may deceive the foolish or inexperienced prospector. Criteria for distinguishing the two are in fact quite simple: pyrite is brass-yellow, paler than *gold; is brittle and cannot be scratched by a knife, whereas gold can be cut like lead. Pyrite often forms regular crystals, the most common form being a cube with grooved or striated faces: other shapes are the eight-sided octahedron and the twelve-sided pyritohedron.

Pyrite is one of the most widely distributed of the sulfide minerals, forming in a wide range of environments and over a temperature range of 32–1800°F (0–1000°C). It occurs in igneous rocks as an accessory mineral; in metamorphic rocks; and as nodules on the sea floor or as grains in black shales formed in stagnant, oxygen-deficient water. It is the most widespread and common metallic mineral in ore veins, being especially abundant with the sulfides of copper, lead and zinc. Pyrite is mined for its *sulfur.

Pyrite in mineral collections requires care since it is attacked by sulfur bacteria: specimens left untreated may be rapidly reduced to piles of white powder.

The mineral *marcasite has the same chemical composition as pyrite but a different crystal structure.

Formula: FeS_2.

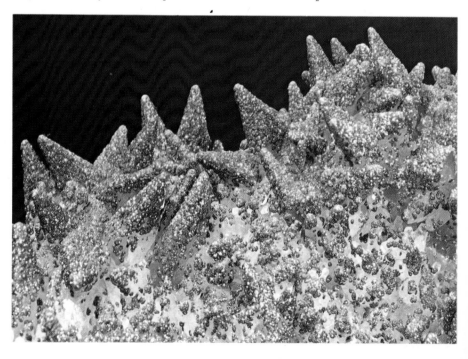

Beads of pyrite seen here against a background of white calcite. Pyrite (iron pyrites) is the most widespread sulfide mineral, occurring in igneous, sedimentary and metamorphic rocks. It can be distinguished from chalcopyrite (copper pyrites) by its lesser hardness and paler color.

Quartz is one of the most widespread minerals on the surface of the Earth, and is found in a wide variety of forms. It crystallizes in the trigonal system. *Below*, well formed crystals of colorless quartz, rock crystal. As rock crystal is piezoelectric (when pressure is applied to a crystal, positive and negative electric charges appear on opposite crystal faces) it is finding use in oscillators for clocks, radio and radar. *Bottom*, a crystal of smoky quartz.

A mountain of quartz waste from kaolin workings in Devon, UK. Quartz is the most common gangue material in mineral veins.

Pyroxene Group

The pyroxenes are a very important group of rock-forming silicates, found widely distributed in igneous and metamorphic rocks. They consist of single chains of silicon and oxygen atoms, the chains being linked by a variety of other elements. They form stubby or somewhat elongated orthorhombic and monoclinic crystals, having two cleavages at right-angles. This important property distinguishes pyroxenes from *amphiboles. Pyroxenes further differ from amphiboles in that they are anhydrous and thus occur in the water-free rocks of the *Moon and in *meteorites.

The most common rock-forming pyroxenes, *diopside, *augite, *enstatite, *hypersthene, *bronzite and *wollastonite, are silicates with differing amounts of magnesium, iron and calcium. The less com-mon members of the group, *jadeite, *spodumene and *rhodonite include additional elements.

Pyrrhotite

Pyrrhotite, a distinctive metallic, pinkish-bronze colored mineral, is an iron sulfide approximating to the formula FeS but showing a variable (up to 20%) deficiency in the amount of iron indicated by the formula.

Apart from *magnetite, pyrrhotite is the only appreciably magnetic mineral. It oc-curs principally as disseminated grains in some basic igneous rocks and in contact metamorphic deposits and pegmatites. Troilite, the sulfide found in *meteorites, is a variety with a negligible iron deficiency.

In recent years, pyrrhotite has been ex-ploited as an ore of iron and sulfur.

Formula: $Fe_{1-x}S$ $(x \leqslant 0.2)$.

Quartz

Quartz, one of the most abundant minerals in the surface layers of the Earth, is enor-mously diverse in origin, occurrence, varieties and uses. It is chemically ex-tremely simple, consisting only of *silicon and *oxygen in the ratio 1:2. Impurities are never present in more than minute amounts. Well-formed crystals are six-sided prisms terminating in six-sided pyr-amids. Quartz is hard (value 7 on Mohs' scale) and capable of scratching steel, is usually colorless or white, has a glass-like luster, and lacks a cleavage, forming curved fracture surfaces when broken.

Quartz forms over a wide range of tem-peratures, being an essential constituent of granites and granite pegmatites. It is the most abundant gangue mineral in ore-bearing veins; is common in a variety of metamorphic rocks, especially *gneisses; and is ubiquitous as a clastic sedimentary mineral. Common sand consists chiefly or entirely of rounded, water-worn grains of quartz. Consolidated *sandstones are ex-tremely rich in quartz and it is virtually the sole constituent of the rock quartzite. In addition, quartz in the form of flint and chert is precipitated in sediments and on the sea floor.

There are many named varieties of quartz, of which *amethyst and *chalcedony, and the subvarieties *agate and *jasper, are the most important. Rock crystal is clear, colorless quartz, and is of great technological importance as the mater-

ial for oscillator plates; milk quartz, smoky quartz, rose quartz and citrine are respectively white, gray-brown, pink and yellow. Rutilated quartz contains orientated needles of *rutile. Petrified wood and tiger-eye are respectively wood and fibrous *asbestos entirely replaced by submicroscopic quartz.
Formula: SiO_2.

Realgar
Realgar is a monoclinic mineral forming short, striated crystals or granular, compact masses. Its color, dark red to orange-red, attracted attention in early times, and it was used for centuries as a pigment until the poisonous nature of arsenic was discovered. It normally forms in hydrothermal veins with *stibnite and other arsenic minerals, around hot springs and in some limestones: it is a minor ore of arsenic. Fine specimens should be kept enclosed, since prolonged exposure to light reduces the mineral to a yellow powder.
Formula: AsS.

Rhodochrosite
Rhodochrosite has an attractive pink to rose-red color and would almost certainly be used as a gemstone if it were not far too soft. Crystals are rare, the mineral usually forming coarse cleavable masses or fine-grained color-banded aggregates in hydrothermal silver ore veins. In this association, rhodochrosite is believed to be a primary mineral, but it also forms secondarily in some high-temperature *metamorphic rocks and in residual manganese oxide deposits. Massive rhodochrosite is mined as a manganese ore.
Formula: $MnCO_3$.

Rhodonite
Rhodonite is closely similar in structure to the *pyroxene group (for this reason it is sometimes called a pyroxenoid). It occurs usually as pink masses or crystal aggregates in manganese-rich rocks. Its superior hardness, which allows a fine polish, and attractive pink color account for its use as an ornamental stone.
Formula: $MnSiO_3$.

Riebeckite
Riebeckite is a member of the *amphibole group. It occurs as discrete blue or blue-black crystals in some granites, syenites, rhyolites and trachytes, especially if these are rich in alkalis. It also forms veins in metamorphosed ironstones and sandstones, where it consists of fibers and is called *crocidolite.
Formula: $Na_2Fe''_3Fe'''_2Si_8O_{22}(OH)_2$.

Ruby
Ruby is the red, transparent variety of *corundum, highly prized since earliest times as a gemstone. It owes its color – ideally a dramatic deep red tinged with purple and described as "pigeon's blood" – to trace amounts of chromium. Although common corundum is abundant, ruby is rare, especially in the form of large un-flawed crystals, and this doubtless influences the prices which quality stones command, weight for weight surpassing *diamond. Corundum and its varieties, ruby and *sapphire, are exceedingly hard, inferior in hardness only to diamond, and for this reason small rubies are used for durable bearings in watches and other instruments.

Large quantities of ruby are now produced synthetically by the Verneuil process (see *sapphire). Except to the expert, these are identical in all respects to natural stones, even surpassing many of them in quality of color and freedom from flaws. Market forces, nevertheless, impose much higher prices on the natural gems.
Formula: Al_2O_3.

Rutile
Rutile occurs as an accessory mineral in a wide variety of igneous and metamorphic rocks. When well-crystallized it forms elongated tetragonal crystals with square or octagonal cross-sections and pyramidal terminations. Needle-like crystals of rutile sometimes occur entirely enclosed within transparent grains of *quartz. Rutile concentrated in beach sands is exploited as an ore of *titanium.

Although the mineral is invariably dark red to black (due to iron impurities), chemically pure, colorless rutile is synthesized in the Verneuil process (see *sapphire) for use as a gemstone. This synthetic substance has refractive indices and "fire" much superior to those of diamond, and makes dazzling, if somewhat soft, gems.
Formula: TiO_2.

Sanidine
Sanidine is a *feldspar, chemically identical to *orthoclase and *microcline but having a less well-ordered structure, the aluminum and silicon atoms being arranged in a more random fashion. Sanidine forms at higher temperatures and is less common than orthoclase, occurring as flat, tabular, glassy crystals in some rhyolite and trachyte lavas.
Formula: $KAlSi_3O_8$.

Sapphire
Sapphire is the name given to all colored varieties of *corundum (except red, which is *ruby), and of these blue is the most abundant and popular. Blue sapphire owes its color to traces of titanium, and yellow sapphire to traces of iron. Sapphires are among the five most prized gemstones, being extremely hard and durable, attractive and rare, though less rare and hence somewhat cheaper than are rubies. A variety known as star sapphire contains microscopic needle-like inclusions arranged in three directions at angles of 60° to one another. When such a stone is fashioned to a smooth rounded shape (cabochon), light is reflected from the inclusions in the form of a six-rayed star.

Large quantities of sapphire and ruby are now produced synthetically by the Verneuil process, invented by a French chemist in 1902. The process involves feeding finely powdered aluminum oxide into an oxy-hydrogen flame at 3600°F (2000°C), where it melts. The droplets fall onto a support beneath, crystallizing there as a pear-shaped mass called a boule. Addition to the alumina powder of small amounts of chromium oxide or titanium oxide produces the red and blue of ruby and sapphire.
Formula: Al_2O_3.

Scapolite
Scapolite refers strictly to a series of *feldspathoid minerals, mixtures of two complex aluminosilicates, one containing calcium and carbonate, the other sodium and chlorine. Members of the series crystallize in the *tetragonal system as normally white or bluish-gray prismatic crystals. A transparent yellow variety found in Brazil and Madagascar is cut as a gemstone. Often, however, scapolite is granular and massive with a splintery appearance. It occurs in *metamorphic rocks, particularly in metamorphosed impure limestones and as a replacement for *feldspars in altered *igneous rocks.
Formula:
$Na_4Al_3[Al,Si]_3Si_6O_{24}[Cl,CO_3,SO_4]$ *to*
$Ca_4Al_3[Al,Si]_3Si_6O_{24}[Cl,CO_3,SO_4]$.

Red crystals of realgar, which crystallizes in the monoclinic system. Realgar (AsS) is often found with another sulfide of arsenic, orpiment (As_2S_3).

Siderite crystallizes in the trigonal system. When its habit is massive (as shown here) it is generally described as clay ironstone.

Serpentines

The serpentines are: chrysotile, a fibrous mineral, the most important form of *asbestos; antigorite, which forms compact masses of small plates; and lizardite, extremely fine-grained matrix material usually associated with veins of chrysotile. Since the serpentines are sheet silicates like the *micas, it was not clear until recently how chrysotile could form fibers: X-ray and electron microscope studies have now shown that the fibers are sheets tightly rolled into concentric hollow cylinders and spirals.

The serpentines form secondarily from magnesium-rich silicates such as the *olivines and *pyroxenes of ultrabasic rocks: the alteration involves addition of water and a considerable volume increase. Serpentinites are rocks originally very rich in olivine that has been entirely converted to serpentine.

Chrysotile is the chief source of the asbestos used in the building industry. Massive varieties, especially those showing variegated colors, are carved as decorative or ornamental material.

Formula: $[Mg,Fe]_3Si_2O_5(OH)_4$.

Siderite (Chalybite)

Siderite is closely related to *calcite, its crystal shapes, three oblique cleavages and relative softness – those of its physical properties that depend on its trigonal crystal structure – being the same. The presence of iron rather than calcium, however, gives siderite a brown or yellow color, a higher density and a greater resistance to acid attack: hot, rather concentrated, hydrochloric acid is needed to make siderite effervesce. In addition, siderite becomes magnetic when strongly heated.

Massive siderite is common in sedimentary deposits of clay and shale, where it may form concretions called clay ironstones – it is extensively worked in these deposits as an ore of *iron. It also forms with sulfide minerals in metalliferous veins of hydrothermal origin.

Formula: $FeCO_3$.

Sillimanite

The minerals sillimanite, *andalusite and *kyanite all have identical chemical composition. Each, however, has its own individual structure and related physical properties. This is an example of polymorphism. All three form in aluminum-rich rocks, typically pelites (sediments in which clay minerals are abundant), during metamorphism, the pressure and temperature conditions determining which of the polymorphs is formed.

Sillimanite is relatively rare, but is of interest to geologists in that it denotes the highest temperature conditions in regionally metamorphosed pelites. It is usually distributed in *schists and *gneisses as long, slender – even fibrous – crystals, usually colorless. Pale blue transparent crystals, occasionally found in Burma and Ceylon, are cut as gemstones.

Formula: Al_2SiO_5.

Sodalite

Sodalite is a *feldspathoid. It occurs usually as blue masses with *feldspars and other feldspathoids in silica-poor igneous rocks, such as nepheline *syenites. It is similar in composition to, and often resembles, *lapis lazuli, but is distinguished by its mode of occurrence and lack of associated specks of *pyrite.

Formula: $Na_4Al_3Si_3O_{12}Cl$.

Sphalerite (Zinc Blende)

Sphalerite is the most important ore of *zinc. It occurs chiefly in hydrothermal veins, almost always with the lead sulfide, *galena. Apart from this, it also forms as a replacement mineral in limestones.

Until the discovery late in the 16th century of the means of extracting zinc from its ore, sphalerite in lead workings was a major inconvenience, since it was often mistaken for galena – but yielded no lead: the name sphalerite derives from a Greek word meaning treacherous.

It is not always easy to recognize. Its color varies, as the iron impurity content increases, from light amber with a resinous appearance to black with an almost metallic luster. Although it crystallizes in the *cubic system, crystals vary greatly in shape and may be complex and distorted with curved faces. An unusually large number of cleavages, six in all, is perhaps its most distinctive feature: cleavage and resinous luster together provide a reliable diagnosis.

While it is the chief ore of zinc, it often contains small amounts of the useful by-products gallium, cadmium, iridium and thallium.

Formula: ZnS.

Sphene (Titanite)

The secondary name for this mineral, titanite, is an allusion to its chemical composition: it is a minor ore of *titanium. The primary name derives from the Greek *sphenos*, an allusion to the mineral's typically flat wedge-shaped monoclinic crystals. Its color is usually yellow-green or brown, occasionally gray or black. Sphene crystallizes at high temperatures and is a common accessory mineral in many igneous and metamorphic rocks.

Although transparent sphene crystals from the St Gotthard district of Switzerland are cut as gems, having a brilliant luster and a "fire" surpassing that of diamond, they are too soft to be widely used.

Formula: $CaTiSiO_5$.

Spinel

The name spinel broadly refers to a group which includes the minerals *magnetite and *chromite. In a narrower sense, spinel is the magnesium aluminum oxide member of the group. It occurs as an accessory mineral in basic igneous rocks, in thermally metamorphosed limestones, and in very aluminum-rich schists.

Spinel crystals are hard and usually octahedral, and form in a variety of colors. Transparent crystals are used as gemstones, many of the historic "rubies" (such as the centerpiece of the British Imperial State Crown) proving to be in fact red spinels. Today synthetic spinels are produced in many colors by the Verneuil process (see *sapphire).

At depths between 25 and 43mi (40–70km), it seems probable that many peridotites of the mantle contain spinel; and at depths of about 250mi (400km), *olivine itself adopts a spinel-like structure.

Formula: $MgAl_2O_4$.

Spodumene

Spodumene is a somewhat rare *pyroxene. It usually occurs in long, flat, striated crystals of various colors in granite pegmatites associated with other lithium-bearing minerals. It is of importance both as an ore of *lithium and as a gem. The crystals are often very large, and the delicate lilac-pink variety kunzite and the rarer green variety hiddenite are especially prized as gems. Both display the interesting phenomenon called pleochroism, in which the color of the stone varies according to the crystallographic direction from which it is viewed.

Formula: $LiAlSi_2O_6$.

Staurolite

Staurolite is exclusively a metamorphic mineral, forming typically as large brown crystals (porphyroblasts) in medium-grade *schists and *gneisses. Crystals are well-formed and, although monoclinic, appear to have higher symmetry. Twins composed of two intergrown crystals are common: they take the form of a cross with the two components crossing either at right-angles or obliquely. These cruciform twins, especially the right-angle type, are known as "fairy stones" or "fairy crosses", and in certain Christian countries are mounted without cutting or polishing to be worn as pendants.

Formula: $Fe_2Al_9Si_4O_{22}(OH)_2$.

Stibnite

Stibnite is the major ore of *antimony. It forms with *quartz in hydrothermal veins, in hot-spring deposits and as a replacement mineral in some limestones. Stibnite can

form spectacular orthorhombic crystals: the finest are elongated, often gracefully bent, striated, and metallic steel-gray.
Formula: Sb_2S_3.

Strontianite

Strontianite usually forms white, gray or pale green needle-like crystals, which may be aggregated together into a fibrous mass. Typically, the mineral occurs in low-temperature veins in limestones together with *barite, *celestine and sulfide ore minerals. It is a minor source of *strontium but is less important commercially than the more abundant and usually purer celestine.
Formula: $SrCO_3$.

Sylvite

Sylvite is closely related to *halite. Not only are the two minerals chemically similar and structurally identical, crystallizing as colorless or white cubic crystals with cubic cleavages, but they also both form when a body of seawater or a salt-lake is evaporated (see *evaporites). Sylvite is less abundant and, being even more soluble, does not crystallize until almost all the water has evaporated. It may be identified by its unpleasantly bitter salt taste.

Millions of tons of sylvite are mined annually – for use almost entirely in the manufacture of potash fertilizers.
Formula: KCl.

Talc

Talc forms as a secondary mineral by alteration of magnesium-rich *olivines, *pyroxenes and *amphiboles of ultrabasic rocks: it is often associated with other secondary minerals such as *chlorite and *serpentine. It also occurs in schists produced by metamorphism of magnesium-rich rocks.

Commonly in white or pale-green foliated masses with a pearly luster, soap-like to the touch, talc is easily identified. Its extreme softness accounts for its soapy feel. Massive fine-grained talc is called soapstone or steatite and is carved into ornaments and images.

Powdered talc is used as a lubricant, in plasters and as a filler in paper, and is most familiar in the form of domestic talcum powder and French chalk.
Formula: $Mg_3Si_4O_{10}(OH)_2$.

Topaz

Topaz is found in granites, in cavities in rhyolites, in high-temperature veins and, most abundantly, in granite pegmatites. Well-shaped orthorhombic crystals which are elongated, blunt-ended and striated are particularly well developed in pegmatites, and these may be very large: a single transparent crystal weighing 596lb (270kg) may be seen at the American Museum of Natural History.

The transparent quality of topaz, together with its very wide range of attractive colors and its great hardness (8 on Mohs' scale), make it an important gem material. The most highly valued are sherry-brown: the lovely rose-pink topazes, much in demand, are obtained by heating these brownish stones, the color change resulting from a rearrangement within the topaz structure of trace impurities. The finest blue stones are found in the Ural Mountains.

Topaz is resistant to chemical *weathering and mechanical abrasion and thus also occurs as pebbles and grains in river gravels.
Formula: $Al_2SiO_4[OH,F]_2$.

Tourmaline

When a granite crystallizes, residual liquids may become enriched in a wide variety of elements which are not incorporated in the ordinary silicate minerals of the granite. Tourmaline forms at these later stages, either in the granite itself or in associated pegmatites and veins, and plays a major part in accommodating some of these residual elements, notably boron, lithium and fluorine.

Tourmaline crystals are trigonal, elongated and striated, often with curved triangular cross-sections. The two ends of a crystal are often different, and almost any color is possible. Particularly attractive are crystals that change in color from pink to green along their length.

Tourmaline belongs to a class of crystal structures which lack a center of symmetry. When such crystals are subjected to pressure, they develop an electrical charge; and tourmaline is used in this way in some pressure gauges. It is also used as a gemstone and, in view of its variety of colors, may superficially resemble a number of other gems. A hemispherical tourmaline stone in the Ashmolean Museum at Oxford is carved with the profile of Alexander the Great, and there is some reason to suppose that this may be a rare portrait from life.
Formula:
$Na[Mg,Fe'']_3Al_6(BO_3)_3(Si_6O_{18})[OH,F]_4$.

Tremolite

Tremolite is a member of the *amphibole group. Iron may replace some of its magnesium, the mineral then changing in color from white to green. With increasing amounts of iron the color changes to dark green, and the mineral is then known as *actinolite. Crystals are long and blade-like, but more commonly the mineral occurs as masses of parallel or radiating fibers. In this form it is exploited as an *asbestos. Very fine-grained and compact fibrous tremolite is called *nephrite. Tremolite is formed when impure dolomites or magnesium limestones are invaded, heated and metamorphosed by *igneous intrusions.
Formula: $Ca_2[Mg,Fe'']_5(Si_8O_{22})(OH)_2$.

Turquoise

Turquoise owes its "robin's egg" blue color to the presence, in varying amounts, of *copper. Turquoise usually occurs in veins as massive fine-grained material formed by the action of surface waters on aluminum-rich rocks. It is opaque and is valued for its color alone.

As a gem and ornamental material it has an ancient history. The world's oldest known examples of jewelry may be the carved turquoise bracelets of Egypt's Queen Zer (First Dynasty).
Formula:
$Cu[Al,Fe''']_6(PO_4)_4(OH)_8 \cdot 4H_2O$.

Uraninite (Pitchblende)

Uraninite is uranium oxide, a hard, heavy, black radioactive mineral which often has a pitch-like luster (hence the alternative name, pitchblende). The element *uranium was discovered in the mineral in 1789, but it was not until 1898, when the Curies isolated from it minute amounts of a further new element, *radium, that it attracted interest. Since WWII the search for uranium, the chief fuel of the atomic energy industry, has been thorough and at times frenetic. In the 1950s hundreds of prospectors, working independently, scoured the Colorado Plateau, USA, where brightly-colored secondary uranium minerals and portable Geiger counters aided them to locate deposits.
Formula: UO_2.

Vermiculite

Vermiculite is a *clay mineral. Although it occurs as minute particles in soils, it can

Wavellite, a common member of the phosphate group of minerals, crystallizes in the orthorhombic system: however, crystals are uncommon, the habit of the mineral being more usually as globular (or hemispherical) aggregates displaying a fibrous, radiating structure.

also form large yellow and brown platy crystals as an alteration product of *biotite – such large grain-size is unusual for a clay mineral. A unique property is the rapid and large (up to thirty times original volume) expansion when it is heated quickly to 480–570°F (250–300°C). Large quantities are mined and expanded in this way for use as an insulating material.
Formula: $[Mg,Fe,Al]_3$
$[Al,Si]_4O_{10}(OH)_2 . 4H_2O$.

Witherite
Witherite is much less abundant and widespread than *barite, but both sometimes occur in association together, especially in hydrothermal lead-bearing veins. Crystals are usually white or yellowish and, although orthorhombic, are often twinned to give a hexagonal (six-sided) appearance.
Formula: $BaCO_3$.

Wolframite
Wolframite, the principal ore of *tungsten, occurs as blackish, tabular crystal groups in *quartz veins and pegmatites close to certain granites, and is often associated with other ore minerals, particularly *cassiterite. It is heavy and has a single, good cleavage.
Formula: $[Fe'',Mn]WO_4$.

Wollastonite
Wollastonite is closely similar in structure to the *pyroxenes. It usually occurs as white, fibrous and splintery masses in siliceous *limestones which have been thermally metamorphosed.
Formula: $CaSiO_3$.

Zeolite Group
When lavas are erupted at the Earth's surface, gases are released from the fluid magma to form holes, called vesicles, in the solidified rock. If such lavas are subsequently buried at shallow depths, heated between 212°F and 932°F (100–500°C), and leached by alkaline waters, the vesicles

may become filled by a variety of minerals, the rounded white fillings being called collectively amygdales. The common minerals of amygdales are *chalcedony (agate), *calcite and a related group of closely similar hydrated aluminosilicates called zeolites.

These are white or colorless (when pure), soft, low-density minerals, often forming as delicate well-shaped crystals or crystal aggregates. Individual species can be identified often on the basis of crystal shape (zeolites are variously blade-like, equant, fibrous, etc.), but X-ray methods may be necessary to distinguish rarer or irregularly formed material. Altogether some thirty different zeolite minerals are known, the most common being stilbite, natrolite, heulandite, analcite and chabazite.

They all have open, sieve-like crystal structures and this accounts for their curious capacity for base exchange: if a sodium zeolite such as natrolite is soaked in water containing calcium ions, the calcium and sodium will change places; it is this property which is employed in water softeners. In addition to their base exchange capacity, zeolites, when dehydrated, are able to absorb a range of substances preferentially, and they are used as "molecular sieves" in many industrial processes.

Zircon
Zircon is one of the most widely distributed accessory minerals, and is found in acid and intermediate *igneous rocks; in metamorphic schists and gneisses; and, owing to its density, hardness ($7\frac{1}{2}$ on Mohs' scale) and resistance to *weathering, as detrital grains concentrated in river and beach sands and gravels.

Zircon forms distinctive brown prisms with square cross-sections and pyramid-shaped ends. Greenish zircons usually owe their color to radiation damage from small amounts of radioactive uranium and thor-

ium present in the structure. In addition to being the major source of *zirconium, zircons are in demand as gems. Cut stones have a brilliance similar to diamond, the most popular color being blue, produced by heating brown stones in the absence of air.
Formula: $ZrSiO_4$.   FBA

Elements
The Periodic Table of the Elements was first published in 1869 by the Russian chemist Dmitri Mendeléev. He found that, if he set down the elements in order of increasing atomic weight, there was a periodic variation in their properties: for example, starting with lithium, the valences of it and the succeeding seven elements read 1,2,3,4,3,2,1,0 (the valence of an element is a measure of the "combining power" of its atoms: e.g., the valence of hydrogen is 1, that of oxygen 2, and so the formula of water is H_2O). When Mendeléev had tabulated the known elements in this way he found gaps in his table: he correctly deduced that these represented elements, whose properties he predicted with remarkable accuracy, that had not yet been discovered.

More recently it was realized that it was an element's atomic number – the number of protons in its nucleus – that determined its position in the table. As the number of protons determines the (equal) number of electrons associated with the atom when it is not ionized, and as it is these electrons which determine the element's chemical properties, the reason for the periodic variation in properties becomes clear.

All of the elements treated below are of economic importance in one way or

A metalware shop in the bazaar at Shīrāz, Iran. Roughly 75% of the chemical elements are metals and, more than any others, they have played a major role in shaping our civilization.

The Periodic Table of the Elements. Elements marked with a triangle ($\triangle$) are treated in this section, those with a diamond ($\diamond$) being grouped together under the heading "Platinum Group" and those with a rectangle ($\square$) under the heading "Rare Earth Elements". Recently discovered element 107 is named Unnilseptium. Elements 104 and 105 are also known as Unnilquadium and Unnilpentium, respectively.

another. Most are metals, some are metalloids and some, like oxygen, are neither. They are arranged in order of their appearance in the Periodic Table (i.e., in order of increasing atomic number). AI

Lithium

The main occurrence of lithium is in the mineral *spodumene, a member of the pyroxene group. It also occurs in the lithium *micas lepidolite and zinnwaldite, and in the mineral petalite ($LiAlSi_4O_{10}$). It is produced either from pegmatites of magmatic origin (see *igneous rocks) which contain spodumene or petalite, or from natural subsurface brines which contain high lithium concentrations (of the order of 300 parts per million).

Nearly all the world's lithium is supplied by the USA and USSR, though that obtained from the USSR is depleted in the ^6Li isotope, which has been extracted for its applications in processes based on nuclear fission and fusion.

Lithium hydroxide is used in the production of greases for motor vehicles and aircraft – in the USA about 50% of all grease currently produced is lithium based. Lithium carbonate is increasingly being used as an additive in the electrical furnaces used for producing aluminum metal. Organo-lithium compounds are used as catalysts in the production of certain synthetic rubbers; and lithium salts are finding a medical application in the treatment of schizophrenia.

Lithium has atomic number 3, atomic weight 6.94, and chemical symbol Li. ETCS

Beryllium

The most common occurrence of beryllium is in combination in the mineral *beryl. Workable concentrations occur only in pegmatites associated with granitic intrusive rocks.

Over half the total world supply of beryllium is consumed in the production of copper-beryllium alloys, used in the manufacture of non-magnetic tools, springs, clips, connectors and wire. Beryllium oxide is used extensively in the electronics industry, and also in nuclear reactors to moderate (i.e., slow down) neutrons.

It has atomic number 4, atomic weight 9.01, and chemical symbol Be. ETCS

Boron

In nature, boron occurs principally in borates such as borax ($Na_2B_4O_7 . 10H_2O$), colemanite ($Ca_2B_6O_{11} . 5H_2O$) and ulexite ($NaCaB_5O_9 . 8H_2O$). It is also found combined in silicates such as *tourmaline.

Workable borate deposits are of sedimentary origin, formed by the persistent evaporation of lakes whose waters held an unusual combination of substances in solution (see *evaporites).

Boron compounds are used as fluxes to reduce the melting points of glasses and ceramics; and their use in the manufacture of fiberglass for insulation and reinforcement is particularly important. Boron nitride and boron carbide are the hardest substances known, after *diamond.

Boron has atomic number 5, atomic weight 10.82, and chemical symbol B. ETCS

Carbon

Of all the elements, carbon is the most important to us – and in the most basic of ways: were it not for the ability of carbon to combine with other elements in molecules that are either rings or long, complex chains, then life as we know it could not exist.

We find the element in uncombined form as the native element minerals *graphite and *diamond; in combined form in carbonate minerals such as *calcite, *siderite and *aragonite; and as a constituent of *coals and natural hydrocarbons (*natural gases and crude oils, as well as solids such as *amber).

Carbon has atomic number 6, atomic weight 12.01, and chemical symbol C. ETCS

Oxygen

This element constitutes almost 50% by weight of the Earth's crust, oceans and atmosphere. Gaseous elementary oxygen, which now makes up 21% by volume of the atmosphere, is essential to respiration and so to all animal life (see *origin of life). It is used up in combustion and oxidization processes: highly reactive, it forms oxides with almost every other element. Atmospheric oxygen is replenished by plant photosynthesis and by the decomposition of water vapor in the upper atmosphere. In combined form, oxygen occurs as water, in the oceans and in rocks, as carbon dioxide in the atmosphere, and as a major constituent of most minerals. The oxide minerals themselves are also of great importance, especially silica (SiO_2). The metal oxides, generally containing the oxide ion (O^{2-}), include alumina (Al_2O_3) and the various iron oxides. Many mixed oxides containing several metal ions are known.

Elementary oxygen normally occurs as molecules of two oxygen atoms (O_2), but forms also an allotrope with three atoms per molecule, ozone (O_3). Ozone is formed by

the action of ultraviolet radiation on oxygen in the upper atmosphere, where it occurs as a layer that protects the Earth from the Sun's ultraviolet rays.

Oxygen is used chiefly to support respiration or combustion, as in oxyacetylene torches for cutting and welding. In metallurgy vast amounts are used in smelting and refining to burn away impurities, especially in iron and steel production.

Oxygen has atomic number 8, atomic weight 16.00, and chemical symbol O. PCG

Sodium

A major element of the Earth's crust, sodium occurs combined in a variety of minerals, including silicates, such as the *feldspar albite ($NaAlSi_3O_8$); halides, such as *halite (NaCl); and hydrated carbonates, such as trona ($Na_2CO_3 . NaHCO_3 . 2H_2O$).

The principal minerals which are mined for sodium and sodium chemicals are halite and trona, and both occur as evaporitic deposits (see *evaporites). Sodium chemicals are also obtained from natural saline solutions, such as seawater (salt, NaCl), saline lakes (crude salt cake, Na_2SO_4), oil-well brines (salt and crude salt cake) and dry-lake brines (crude salt cake and soda ash, Na_2CO_3).

Sodium is of minor industrial importance compared with its compounds. It is, however, used in the manufacture of tetraethyl *lead, the anti-knock additive for gasoline, and as a core for electric cables. It bursts into flame on contact with water, and so must be stored carefully.

Sodium has atomic number 11, atomic weight 22.99 and chemical symbol Na. ETCS

Magnesium

An abundant element in the Earth's crust, magnesium is found combined in a large variety of silicates, such as *olivine; in oxides, such as periclase (MgO) and *spinel; in carbonates, such as *magnesite and *dolomite; and as the hydroxide, brucite ($Mg(OH)_2$).

The chief magnesium ore mineral is magnesite, but it is principally used for the production of magnesia (MgO). Magnesium metal is mainly produced from natural magnesium-rich solutions such as seawater, saline lake waters and oil-well brines.

40% of the world's magnesium metal is used in making light *aluminum alloys, though magnesium alloys themselves are also used extensively where weight is at a

Three stages in the obtaining of aluminum from its oxide, alumina (Al_2O_3). The metal is usually extracted by means of the Hall-Héroult Process: alumina is dissolved in a smelter filled with a molten electrolyte, usually the aluminum mineral cryolite. Direct current is passed to the bottom of the smelter by means of carbon electrodes, and a crust forms on top of the liquid. Alumina is piled on top of the crust, which is periodically broken to allow the alumina into the mixture beneath. The metal accumulates on the bottom of the smelter, from where it is siphoned off into crucibles (*top*) to be poured into molds (*top left*). The final product may be in the form of ingots or "logs" (*above*).

premium. In the USA the principal consumer is the aerospace industry; in Europe magnesium alloys are used extensively in the manufacture of transmissions and crank-case housings for motor vehicles. Magnesia is much used in the manufacture of refractory bricks for lining the basic oxygen furnaces required to purify steels.

Magnesium has atomic number 12, atomic weight 24.32, and chemical symbol Mg. ETCS

Aluminum

Aluminum always occurs in combination with other elements, and is one of the major constituents of the predominant group of rock-forming minerals, the silicates. It is also contained in the minerals diaspore (AlO . OH), boehmite (AlO . OH), gibbsite ($Al(OH)_3$) and *corundum (Al_2O_3).

The principal sources of aluminum ore are *bauxites. These contain aluminum hydroxides and hydroxyoxides, and form as surface residua left from the leaching effects of groundwater in tropical climates.

The major uses of aluminum take advantage of its lightness, resistance to corrosion and good electrical conductivity. It is a major component of light alloys.

It has atomic number 13, atomic weight 26.98, and chemical symbol Al. ETCS

Silicon

Silicon is the second most abundant element of the Earth's crust (27.72% by weight), the most abundant being *oxygen (46.60%). The compounds in which silicon occurs constitute the principal group of rock-forming minerals, the silicates and aluminosilicates. Most abundant of these is the simple oxide, *quartz (SiO_2).

High-purity silica sand is required for the manufacture of glass, and is used also as an abrasive. Moderate-purity silica sand is used for metallurgical molds and furnace linings; while impure sands are used as aggregate in cement and concrete. Silicon itself is used in ferrosilicon alloys, and for the manufacture of silicones, which are used as resins, adhesives and lubricants.

It has atomic number 14, atomic weight 28.09, and chemical symbol Si.   ETCS

Phosphorus

A reactive nonmetallic element, phosphorus is present in very many compounds – probably as many as is carbon – and is of great biological importance, phosphates playing a vital role in all energy-transfer processes. Nucleic acids, of which chromosomes consist, are phosphates.

Phosphorus is found in the phosphate minerals, a large group with over 150 members, all of which contain the orthophosphate ion (PO_4^{3-}). They fall into three classes. Primary phosphates are those which have crystallized from aqueous solution or from a melt. They include *apatite, by far the commonest and most important phosphate. Secondary phosphates are formed by low-temperature reaction of other minerals with phosphatic waters. Often beautifully colored, good specimens are much prized. Rock phosphates are formed by the action of water on phosphatic organic debris such as bones, shells and guano. They also include altered corals and phosphatic oolites.

Phosphate rock (impure fluorapatite) is mined from vast deposits found in the USA, the USSR, north Africa and elsewhere. Much is treated with sulfuric acid to give "superphosphate" (CaH_2PO_4), the main phosphate fertilizer. Another process is to heat the rock with silica and coke in a furnace, producing elementary phosphorus used in matches and incendiary bombs and in metallurgy. Most phosphorus thus made is converted to phosphoric acid. Phosphates are added to detergents as water softeners.

Phosphorus has atomic number 15, atomic weight 30.97, and chemical symbol P.   PCG

Sulfur

It is quite common for sulfur to occur in the native uncombined state. It is also a fairly common constituent of minerals, primarily sulfides such as *pyrite, *chalcopyrite, *galena, and *sphalerite; and sulfates, such as *anhydrite, *barite, and *gypsum. Large quantities also occur as the bad-egg-smelling hydrogen sulfide gas (H_2S) in "sour" *natural gas and crude oil.

Native sulfur is found principally in bedded deposits which formed by reduction of gypsum and anhydrite in *evaporites. It is worked by pumping hot water under pressure through the outer casing of a drill pipe into the sulfur-bearing formation (the Frasch process): this melts the sulfur (melting point, 235°F, 113°C) and forces it back up to the surface through an inner tube in the pipe. Sulfide *ore deposits are usually of hydrothermal origin.

Sulfur, as sulfuric acid (H_2SO_4), is mostly used in the manufacture of phosphatic fertilizers. Sulfuric acid is also used in the bleaching of fibers, in the vulcanization of rubber for motor vehicle tires, and in many other industrial and chemical applications.

Sulfur has atomic number 16, atomic weight 32.07, and chemical symbol S.   ETCS

Potassium

This is a common element in the major groups of rock-forming minerals, the silicates and aluminosilicates. It is found principally in *micas, *feldspars and the feldspathoid *leucite. The major ore minerals of potassium are, however, *sylvite and carnallite ($KCl.MgCl_2.6H_2O$). The potassium ore minerals occur in *evaporite deposits.

About 95% of the world's potassium is used in fertilizers, usually as potassium chloride, but also as the sulfate and in combination with nitrogen and phosphorus.

Potassium has atomic number 19, atomic weight 39.10, and chemical symbol K. ETCS

Calcium

A major element of the Earth's crust, calcium occurs combined in silicates, such as anorthite *feldspar; carbonates, such as *calcite, *aragonite and *dolomite; sulfates, such as *anhydrite and *gypsum; phosphates, such as *apatite; and the fluoride, *fluorite.

The principal calcium-containing materials of industrial importance are *limestone, dolomite, gypsum, anhydrite and fluorite. Limestone and dolomite occur as the major component of sedimentary carbonate rocks; gypsum and anhydrite occur in sedimentary rocks formed by the evaporation of seawater (see *evaporites); and fluorite occurs in hydrothermal/replacement deposits of carbonate rocks (see *ore deposits). Calcium metal is also obtained from calcium chloride produced from oil-well brines.

Calcium is used mainly as an additive to molten metals to remove oxygen, halogens, sulfur and phosphorus; and also as a reducing or dehydrating agent in organic chemistry. The calcium-containing materials have widespread use.

Calcium has atomic number 20, atomic weight 40.08 and chemical symbol Ca. ETCS

Rare Earth Elements

These elements are normally grouped together because they are produced from the same minerals and have similar chemical properties. They occur chiefly in *monazite, bastnaesite (($Ce,La)CO_3F$, which accounts for 60% of rare-earth-element production) and xenotime (YPO_4).

Bastnaesite is chiefly obtained from pegmatites, whereas monazite is produced from sedimentary concentrates in beach sands and as by-products of *tin placer working and processing *uranium ores.

Scandium is used principally as a radio-isotope and in high-intensity lamps, yttrium in color TV phosphors, neodymium in lasers, and the rare earth elements in general in special steels, ceramics, glasses and catalysts.

They have atomic numbers, atomic weights and chemical symbols as follows:

Scandium:	21;	44.96;	Sc
Yttrium:	39;	88.91;	Y
Lanthanum:	57;	138.91;	La
Cerium:	58;	140.12;	Ce
Praseodymium:	59;	140.91;	Pr
Neodymium:	60;	144.24;	Nd
Promethium:	61;	~147;	Pm
Samarium:	62;	150.40;	Sm
Europium:	63;	151.96;	Eu
Gadolinium:	64;	157.25;	Gd

Although it is a rare mineral, vanadinite is exploited as an ore of the technologically important metal, vanadium. Color is frequently red, but may also be yellow, orange or brown. Vanadinite forms a solid-solution series with mimetite by replacement of the vanadium by arsenic.

Terbium:	65;	158.93;	Tb
Dysprosium:	66;	162.50;	Dy
Holmium:	67;	164.93;	Ho
Erbium:	68;	167.26;	Er
Thulium:	69;	168.93;	Tm
Ytterbium:	70;	173.04;	Yb
Lutetium:	71;	174.97;	Lu
			ETCS

Titanium

The principal occurrence of titanium is in the oxide minerals *ilmenite and *rutile. It is also found in the silicate mineral *sphene and as an accessory element in many other silicates. Workable titanium mineral deposits occur mainly as sedimentary concentrates in beach sands: such accumulations have been derived from the *erosion of plutonic *igneous rocks, in which ilmenite and rutile occur as accessories. In the case of ilmenite, occurrence in igneous rocks may provide workable magmatic concentrations (see *ore deposits).

Titanium metal has a higher strength-to-weight ratio than steel, is highly resistant to corrosion and can withstand high temperatures. Its dioxide (TiO_2) is the major source of the white pigment used in paints and plastics.

It has atomic number 22, atomic weight 47.90, and chemical symbol Ti.   ETCS

Vanadium

The minerals in which vanadium is a principal element are uncommon. They include patronite (VS_4), carnotite (K_2O . $2U_2O_3$. V_2O_5 . $2H_2O$) and vanadinite ($Pb_5Cl(VO_4)_3$).

About 80% of the world's vanadium is used in the manufacture of high-strength steels which are widely used for gas and oil pipelines. A further 10% is used in non-ferrous alloys (i.e., alloys which do not contain iron), in particular as an additive to *titanium. Of the remaining uses, the most important is as vanadium pentoxide (V_2O_5), a catalyst used in the manufacture of sulfuric acid.

Vanadium has atomic number 23, atomic weight 50.95, and chemical symbol V. ETCS

Chromium

In only one mineral does chromium occur in significant amounts, *chromite. Chromite occurs in layers formed by selective crystallization and settling in *igneous intrusions of basic composition. It is also found in large pod-shaped bodies in ophiolitic ultrabasic rocks.

There are two types, metallurgical chromite and refractory chromite. The former is used as a source of chromium metal for the manufacture of hard and stainless steels. Refractory chromite is used in combination with magnesia (MgO) and a binder to make bricks used in blast-furnace linings. Chromite is used also as a raw material for the manufacture of chromate and dichromate, from which other chromium chemicals may be derived.

Chromium has atomic number 24, atomic weight 52.01, and chemical symbol Cr.   ETCS

Manganese

The principal minerals of manganese, which occurs only in combined form, are oxides such as pyrolusite (MnO_2) and braunite (Mn_2O_3); and hydroxyoxides, such as manganite (MnO.OH) and psilomelane (an amorphous hydrated oxide, $[Ba,H_2O]_2$ Mn_5O_{10}). Manganese nodules, which occur on the deep *ocean floor, consist of two complex hydroxyoxides. Other minerals include *rhodocrosite and *rhodonite.

The three types of manganese *ore deposits are all of sedimentary origin: shallow marine chemical precipitates associated with *sandstones and *siltstones; residual deposits, similar to *bauxites and laterites, left as surface accumulations by deep *weathering in tropical climates; and the manganese nodules we've mentioned (see *ore deposits).

About 95% of manganese output is used in making a variety of hard steels. Other uses include that of pyrolusite as a catalyst in the manufacture of chlorine, bromine and iodine; and of sodium and potassium permanganates ($NaMnO_4$ and $KMnO_4$) as disinfectants.

It has atomic number 25, atomic weight 54.94, and chemical symbol Mn.   ETCS

Iron

5% by weight of the Earth's crust is iron. Native iron occurs, though rarely, in basaltic *igneous rocks which have been contaminated by coal or wood, the additional *carbon having acted as a reducing agent (i.e., having removed the *oxygen from previously existing iron oxides); and is also found alloyed with *nickel in iron *meteorites. Iron forms a large variety of minerals: silicates, such as *olivine; oxides, such as *magnetite and *hematite; hydroxyoxides, such as *goethite; carbonates, such as *siderite; and sulfides, such as *pyrite and *pyrrhotite.

Most iron ore is produced from sedimentary banded *ironstones of *Precambrian age, which are rich in hematite, magnetite and siderite. In France there are ores of *Jurassic age, consisting primarily of goethite, and these are also sedimentary in origin.

As the essential component of every variety of steel, iron is obviously the most important of all industrial metals. Also, of course, it has played a large part in the development of our modern civilization – one thinks of the Iron Age. But from a scientific point of view, iron's most important property is that it becomes magnetized: paleomagnetic studies have been vital in establishing the theory of *plate tectonics.

Iron has atomic number 26, atomic weight 55.85 and chemical symbol Fe. ETCS

Cobalt

The principal occurrences of cobalt are in the minerals smaltite ($CoAs_2$), cobaltite (CoAsS), linnaeite (Co_3S_4) and cobaltiferous *pyrrhotite. *Ore deposits can occur in hydrothermal veins, magmatic cobaltiferous pyrrhotite deposits, or nickeliferous laterites (see *bauxites and laterites).

Cobalt has three major uses: it is employed in a variety of alloys; in cobalt-molybdenum catalysts, which have been employed in the desulfurization of high-sulfur *coals and in hydrocracking crude oil shale; and for pigments, particularly blue, in the glass, enamel and pottery industries.

It has atomic number 27, atomic weight 58.94, and chemical symbol Co.   ETCS

Nickel

Nickel never occurs as a native metal, but it is a subsidiary component of the *iron alloys present in iron *meteorites. Most commonly, it is found combined in sulfides such as millerite (NiS) and pentlandite ($[Fe,Ni]_9S_8$). In addition, *pyrrhotite may contain up to about 5% nickel. The metal is also found in the arsenide, niccolite (NiAs), and in a silicate, garnierite, similar to the mineral *serpentine.

There are two very different kinds of nickel *ore deposit: pyrrhotite-pentlandite deposits in both intrusive and extrusive basic and ultrabasic *igneous rocks; and

sedimentary residual deposits, similar to
*bauxites and laterites.

Nickel is used primarily to produce hard
steels of high tensile strength. It is also
employed in *NiFe* (nickel-iron) batteries
used in the mining industry to power cap
lamps.

Nickel has atomic number 28, atomic
weight 58.71 and chemical symbol Ni. ETCS

Copper

Copper occurs quite commonly as the uncombined native metal; and also in a large
variety of minerals, including sulfides, such
as *chalcopyrite and *bornite; oxides, such
as cuprite; and hydrated carbonates, such
as malachite and azurite.

Porphyry copper deposits of hydrothermal origin are the main sources of
copper ore. These are large, low-grade
disseminations of copper minerals in altered rocks centered on high-level, normal
porphyritic igneous stocks.

Copper is one of the most important
industrial metals. Metallic copper is malle-
able and an excellent conductor of electricity. Copper alloys – such as bronze (copper
with tin) and brass (copper with zinc) – are
also important. Copper chemicals, too, find
many applications: the sulfate is of particular use as a fungicide.

Copper has atomic number 29, atomic
weight 63.54 and chemical symbol Cu. ETCS

Zinc

The element zinc does not occur in the
uncombined state, but is found principally
as the sulfide, *sphalerite, and the carbonate smithsonite ($ZnCO_3$). Zinc *ore
deposits are of hydrothermal origin.

Zinc is resistant to corrosion since, on
exposure to air, a thin surface coating of
zinc oxide (ZnO) forms, and this protects
the metal from further attack. For this
reason, its major use is in galvanizing, the
process whereby steel is coated with a thin
layer of zinc to prevent rusting. It is also
used for the manufacture of die castings,
especially in the motor-vehicle industry.

Zinc has atomic number 30, atomic
weight 65.38 and chemical symbol Zn. ETCS

Gallium

Although gallium is as common in the
Earth's crust as, for example, *lead, it forms
no important minerals. It does, however,
occur as a trace element dispersed at low
concentrations in other minerals. It is produced entirely as a by-product of processing aluminum (90%), zinc and phosphate
(together 10%) ores – total world production is about 15 tons a year.

When alloyed with *arsenic and
*phosphorus, gallium can be used in the
manufacture of light-emitting diodes,
whose main application is in the construction of colored numeric displays for
electronic calculators.

Gallium has atomic number 31, atomic
weight 69.72 and chemical symbol Ga. ETCS

Germanium

Like gallium, germanium is not found as a
major constituent of any reasonably abundant minerals, but occurs as a trace element,
at low concentrations, in many minerals.

Five stages in the processing of copper from the raw ore to the pure metal. *Above far left*, the arrival of the untreated ore. Larger pieces are separated from smaller in this case by the simplest of methods. The ore is then pulverized and concentrated, the latter being usually by use of water to "wash out" some of the unwanted material (*below far left*). Smelting commences with the production of "matte", a mixture of copper and iron sulfides: it is this matte that is smelted by addition of air to achieve iron oxide (which may be removed as a slag with silica) and copper sulfide. Further addition of air provides sulfur dioxide (gaseous) and metallic copper (*above left*). Refining removes trace impurities, the result being metallic copper that is more than 99.9% pure (*below left*). *Above*, the final product: copper whisky stills at Convalmore Distillery, Dufftown, Scotland.

The bulk of germanium supply is obtained from *zinc smelter residues.

Together with gallium, indium and silicon, germanium is one of the principal materials used for semiconductors in solid-state transistors, diodes and rectifiers.

It has atomic number 32, atomic weight 72.60, and chemical symbol Ge.　　　ETCS

Arsenic

Though it does occur as a native metalloid (metalloids are so named because they have some metallic and some non-metallic properties), arsenic is principally found in the mineral *arsenopyrite. It is also found in sulfides, such as *realgar and orpiment (As_2S_3); arsenides, such as smaltite $(CoAs_2)$ and chloanthite $(NiAs_2)$; and sulfo-salts, such as tennantite $([Cu,Fe]_{12}As_4S_{13})$.

Arsenic minerals are frequently found in connection with hydrothermal sulfide deposits of many types (see *ore deposits). It is hardly surprising, then, that its production is almost entirely as a by-product of the smelting of arsenical sulfide ores.

Arsenic compounds are extremely toxic and are used principally in pesticides and insecticides (and detective stories).

Arsenic has atomic number 33, atomic weight 74.91 and chemical symbol As. ETCS

Strontium

The two minerals in which strontium occurs significantly are the sulfate *celestine and the carbonate *strontianite.

Strontium chemicals are used mainly in pyrotechnics – for fireworks, distress flares and tracer ammunition. They burn with a strong maroon-colored flame. Strontium chloride is used to produce the phosphors in the activated coating of fluorescent lights and color television screens. Strontium is also added to the glass used to manufacture the face-plates of color television sets in order to absorb the small quantities of X-radiation which would otherwise bombard the viewer.

It has atomic number 38, atomic weight 87.63, and chemical symbol Sr.   ETCS

Zirconium

The principal occurrence of zirconium is in the silicate *zircon: it is also found as the oxide, baddelyite (ZrO_2). Zircon is worked mainly from sedimentary placer concentrates in beach sands (see *ore deposits). It is found in association with *rutile, *ilmenite and *monazite.

Zircon's uses are, in order of decreasing importance, in foundry sands, in the manufacture of corrosion-resistant alloys, in refractories for metallurgical furnaces, and in ceramics.

It has atomic number 40, atomic weight 91.22 and chemical symbol Zr.   ETCS

Molybdenum

The two main minerals of molybdenum are the sulfide, molybdenite (MoS_2), and a molybdate, wulfenite ($PbMoO_4$). It is produced from large low-grade hydrothermal *ore deposits associated with calc-alkaline intrusive *igneous rocks; and is supplied partly as a by-product of some porphyry *copper deposits, but mainly from geologically comparable porphyry molybdenum deposits.

About 75% of the world's supply is used in the manufacture of high-strength corrosion-resistant steels employed in construction and for tools. Paint manufacturers are today turning toward non-toxic molybdate pigments to replace toxic *lead and *chromium compounds. Molybdenum disulfide (MoS_2), which has properties similar to those of *graphite, is used as an additive to greases and lubricating oils.

Molybdenum has atomic number 42, atomic weight 95.95, and chemical symbol Mo.   ETCS

Silver

Quite commonly, silver occurs as a native uncombined metal. In addition, it is found in the sulfide, argentite (Ag_2S); in a variety of sulfo-salts which include the "ruby silvers" pyrargyrite (Ag_3SbS_3) and proustite (Ag_3AsS_3); and in the chloride, cerargyrite or "horn silver" (AgCl).

Apart from a small amount of silver found alloyed with *gold in sedimentary placer deposits, the major silver *ore deposits are of hydrothermal origin. These include vein deposits and disseminated deposits in *sedimentary rocks.

The principal applications of silver and silver compounds are industrial: they are mainly used in monochrome photography, in the electrical industry and for the manufacture of silverware. Silver is also used significantly in coinage, commemorative medals, and jewelry.

Silver has atomic number 47, atomic weight 107.88, and chemical symbol Ag.
   ETCS

Cadmium

The sole significant occurrence of natural cadmium is in the form of the sulfide, greenockite (CdS). The metal is produced entirely as a by-product of the processing of *zinc sulfide ores, in which small grains of greenockite occur: such ores rarely contain more than 0.4% cadmium.

Around 40% of the world supply of cadmium is used in electroplating, to protect parts of automobiles, household app-

One of the principal uses of the metal strontium is to provide the reddish-maroon coloration in flares and fireworks – as in this catherine wheel.

A silver mine at Guanajuato, Mexico. While the best known use of silver is as a decorative metal, it has several more important uses: where better electrical conduction than even that of copper is required; in photography; and for silverware.

liances, electronic equipment and numerous fastening devices such as nuts and bolts. The second largest user of cadmium is the pigment industry: cadmium salts give strong red and yellow colors. The metal is also used in stabilizers for vinyl plastics, and for electrodes in nickel-cadmium batteries.

It has atomic number 48, atomic weight 112.41, and chemical symbol Cd.   ETCS

Tin

In nature, tin is found mainly in the form of its oxide, *cassiterite, though it is also found, less commonly, in the sulfide stannite (Cu_2FeSnS_4). Cassiterite occurs in hydrothermal vein deposits associated with intrusive granitic *igneous rocks, commonly in proximity to other minerals such as *tourmaline and *topaz. The most important concentrations from an economic point of view are, however, secondary sedimentary placer deposits derived from the *erosion of primary ore.

The main uses of tin are, in decreasing order of importance, for tinplate, solders, bearing alloys, bronze chemicals, and the manufacture of float glass. Molten tin is very fluid and runs over a surface easily, and has therefore been used to coat steel, forming a corrosion-resistant covering. The main use of tinplate is for tin cans.

Tin has atomic number 50, atomic weight 118.70, and chemical symbol Sn.   ETCS

Antimony

Only rarely does antimony occur in the uncombined state as a native metal. Its commonest mineral is *stibnite, though it is also found as a constituent of pyrargyrite (Ag_3SbS_3), bournonite ($CuPbSbS_3$), tetrahedrite ($[Cu,Fe]_{12}Sb_4S_{13}$) and other less common minerals.

Antimony oxide is used to flame-proof cable coverings and plastic upholstery in automobiles – in the USA it is now a legal requirement for seating in automobiles to be treated in this way. Antimonial lead is used for electrodes in batteries.

Antimony has atomic number 51, atomic weight 121.76, and chemical symbol Sb.
     ETCS

Iodine

The heaviest naturally-occurring member of the halogen family of elements (the others being fluorine, chlorine and bromine), iodine is found worldwide but usually in very low concentrations. In trace quantities it is vital to animals, and it is also found in many plants, notably seaweeds. Elementary iodine is a volatile violet-black solid, too reactive to occur as such in nature. Most is produced from calcium iodate ($Ca(IO_3)_2$) found in Chile saltpeter; it is also extracted from oil-well brines containing sodium iodide (NaI).

The main uses of iodine and its compounds are as antiseptics and in pharmaceuticals. Several major dyes contain iodine. Silver iodide (AgI), being light-sensitive, is used in photographic film emulsions.

Iodine has atomic number 53, atomic weight 126.90, and chemical symbol I (J, for *jod*, in Germany).   PCG

Caesium

Caesium (or cesium) is not an abundant metal, and its normal occurrence is as a minor constituent of lithium- and potassium-rich minerals. It is, however, a major component of the rare mineral pollucite. Economic concentrations of caesium occur only in pollucite-bearing pegmatites.

Because light falling on its surface causes the emission of electrons, caesium is used in photoelectric cells, spectrophotometers, infrared radiation detectors, etc.

Caesium has atomic number 55, atomic weight 132.91, and chemical symbol Cs.
     ETCS

Barium

Barium occurs combined in two principal minerals – *barite and *witherite. It is also found in an uncommon *feldspar, celsian ($BaAl_2Si_2O_8$).

The major ore mineral, barite, occurs in hydrothermal veins and in disseminated deposits which form strata-bound replacements of carbonate *sedimentary rocks.

Small amounts of barium chemicals are used in the glass industry, but this is insignificant compared with barite's use as an unmodified industrial mineral. It has a high density – 290lb/ft³ (4.5g/cm³) – and this explains why 75% of the world's production is used as a weighting agent in drilling muds, to prevent gas or oil blowouts. It is also a strong absorber of X- and γ-radiation, and thus is used as an additive in concrete used to construct nuclear power plants. "Barium meals" are used for obtain-

Above, tin ore in slate. *Right*, panning for tin at Taraouadji, Niger. In the processing of cassiterite, tin's principal ore, smelting is initially performed using coke or coal as a reducing agent. The smelting is performed twice, the resulting crude tin being partially remelted to extract further impurities.

ing medical X-ray photographs, in which the additive shows up, so revealing details of the structures of internal organs.

Barium has atomic number 56, atomic weight 137.36, and chemical symbol Ba.

ETCS

Tungsten

There are two principal tungstate minerals, *wolframite and scheelite ($CaWO_4$). These two minerals are found mainly in hydro-thermal vein deposits spatially as-sociated with plutonic *igneous rocks of granitic composition. An association with *tin minerals is quite common.

Tungsten steels and tungsten carbide (WC) are extremely hard materials, and both are used in the manufacture of cutting and machining tools. Tungsten metal is used to make the filaments in electric light bulbs.

It has atomic number 74, atomic weight 183.86, and chemical symbol W (from its little-used alternative name, wolfram). ETCS

Platinum Group

The platinum group of metals contains, aside from platinum itself, palladium, rhod-ium, iridium, osmium and ruthenium. They are found largely in the uncombined native state; as platinum alloys; as separate native elements; and as alloys with each other. Platinum is also found combined as the arsenide, sperylite ($PtAs_2$).

Their main occurrence is in magmatic *ore deposits in seams in layered basic intrusions, though sperylite also occurs associated with iron-nickel sulfide deposits. Sedimentary placer deposits may also con-tain the platinoid elements.

Platinum is used principally as a catalyst in oil refining and in catalytic converters designed to reduce emissions of carbon monoxide and nitrogen oxides from motor vehicle exhausts. It is also used in jewelry and to manufacture crucibles used in chemical laboratories and for handling mol-

ten glass. Palladium is used to coat electrical contacts; and rhodium is used in the glass-fiber industry and, with platinum, for manufacturing thermocouples. Iridium is used as a catalyst in the petroleum industry. Osmium and ruthenium have few industrial applications.

The metals have atomic numbers, atomic weights and chemical symbols as follows:

Platinum:	78;	195.09;	Pt
Palladium:	46;	106.40;	Pd
Rhodium:	45;	102.41;	Rh
Iridium:	77;	192.20;	Ir
Osmium:	76;	190.20;	Os
Ruthenium:	44;	101.10;	Ru

ETCS

Gold

The main occurrence of gold is as an uncombined native metal alloy with *silver (white gold) or *copper (red gold): usually about 85–95% of the alloy is gold. It can also occur in combined form in tellurides such as sylvanite ([Au,Ag]Te_2).

Gold can be found either in hydro-thermal gold-quartz veins or in placer deposits formed by mechanical sorting dur-ing sedimentation, particularly associated with rivers (see *ore deposits): such placers may be of either recent or ancient origin. The bulk of the world's gold is obtained

from a *conglomerate of *Precambrian age in the Rand of South Africa.

Investment demand for newly mined gold and gold coins accounts for, re-spectively, 45% and 20% of gold output. Industrial uses in dentistry and electronics, and of course its use in jewelry, account for most of the remainder.

Gold has atomic number 79, atomic weight 197.0 and chemical symbol Au. ETCS

Mercury

At ordinary temperatures, mercury is a liquid, its freezing point being −38 F (−39 C). It occurs naturally as small fluid globules in the principal mercury mineral, *cinnabar. Both cinnabar and native mer-cury occur in shallow hydrothermal veins associated with volcanic rocks (see *ore deposits).

Mercury's major use is as a liquid elec-trode in the electrolytic production of chlorine and caustic soda (sodium hydrox-ide, NaOH). It is also employed in the elec-trical industry for automatic switches and blue mercury-vapor lamps. Its more familiar uses are in thermometers and barometers, and as a component of the amalgam used in filling dental cavities.

It has atomic number 80, atomic weight 200.61, and chemical symbol Hg. ETCS

Lead

It is exceptionally uncommon for uncombined lead to be found in nature, its most usual occurrences being as the sulfide *galena, the carbonate *cerussite and the sulfate *andesite. All lead *ore deposits are of hydrothermal origin.

40% of the world's lead output is used in the making of antimonial lead electrodes for batteries, used mainly for motor vehicles (see *antimony). Tetraethyl lead is used in large quantities as an additive in gasoline (petrol) to reduce "knocking". Lead has many other minor uses: for example, in low-melting-point alloys used for soldering, and in combination as fluxes in glass and glaze manufacture.

Lead has atomic number 82, atomic weight 207.21, and chemical symbol Pb.
ETCS

Bismuth.

The uncombined native metal bismuth, which is silver-white with a faint tinge of red, occurs quite commonly. The most important naturally occurring bismuth compound is its sulfide, bismuthinite (Bi_2S_3). Both occur associated with other elements in hydrothermal vein deposits (see *ore deposits).

Bismuth is produced only as a by-product of the smelting and refining of lead and copper ores. In the USA, 38% of the supply is consumed by the pharmaceutical industry. In combination with metals such as *tin, *lead and *mercury, bismuth forms a series of "fusible alloys", which have low melting points and are used in casting; and it is used as an additive in various alloys.

Bismuth has atomic number 83, atomic weight 209.00 and chemical symbol Bi. ETCS

Radium

Radium occurs as a natural disintegration product of unstable *uranium isotopes: it is itself radioactive. It forms no minerals in its own right, but occurs as an accessory in the principal uranium minerals *uraninite and carnotite ($K_2O.2U_2O_3.V_2O_5.2H_2O$). Radium is thus found in the same ore deposits as is uranium, and processed solely as a by-product of the processing of uranium.

Radium produces X-rays, and therefore has applications in any technique that requires a source of X-radiation – for example, in the treatment of cancer. Small quantities are used in luminous paints.

It has atomic number 88, atomic weight 226.05, and chemical symbol Ra. ETCS

Thorium

A radioactive metal in the actinide series, thorium occurs in the minerals thorianite (ThO_2) and thorite ($ThSiO_4$), found chiefly in pegmatites. The major source, however, is *monazite sand, a phosphate of cerium and other rare earths containing up to 10% thorium.

Because of its occurrence, and the analogy between the actinides and the lanthanides, thorium is sometimes treated with the *rare earth elements. Its chemistry differs radically, however, as thorium always has a valence of four, and most

resembles *zirconium and hafnium. Thorium oxide is used to make incandescent gas-lamp mantles, and is added to the *tungsten filaments in electric light bulbs. Thorium metal gives strength to *magnesium alloys. Of great potential importance is the conversion of thorium in nuclear reactors to uranium-233, a nuclear fuel.

Thorium has atomic number 90, atomic weight 232.04 and chemical symbol Th. PCG

Uranium

The main occurrence of the radioactive metal uranium is in *uraninite and carnotite ($K_2O . 2U_2O_3 . V_2O_5 . 2H_2O$). In zones where water has percolated down through uraniferous deposits, torbernite ($Cu(UO_2)_2P_2O_8 . 12H_2O$) may occur.

Uranium minerals occur principally in strata-bound deposits in sandstones and conglomerates (see *ore deposits). The former were deposited hydrothermally at low temperatures, whereas the origin of the latter is not clear. Uranium minerals can also occur in hydrothermal vein deposits.

By far the most important of the world's producers of uranium is the USA. In the near future, however, the large new ore deposits which have recently been found in Australia may make that country a major producer.

The principal uses of uranium are in

A billet of refined uranium ore. Processing of uranium depends on the mineral concerned: often there is conversion to uranium (IV) fluoride, from which the metal is isolated by electrolysis or reduction with calcium or magnesium.

nuclear fission reactors to produce electrical power, and in military weapons.

It has atomic number 92, atomic weight 238.07, and chemical symbol U. ETCS

Petroleum

Man's quest for petroleum began when God told Noah to coat the ark with pitch. In prehistoric and early historic times, petroleum from natural seepages on the surface of the Earth was used for many purposes, military and medical as well as nautical. But

The first production platform for the giant Brent oilfield in the North Sea on tow down Stavanger Fjord, Norway, to its destination some 250mi (400km) away. This platform, launched on August 4 1975 and to date the biggest, heaviest and most expensive offshore oil production unit ever built, towers some 420ft (130m) above the waterline – the height of a thirty-storey building – and has a towing draft of 260ft (80m).

An oil tank "farm" on Kharg Island in the Persian Gulf: the flames are from the burning off of unwanted natural gas. The yellow rectangle over toward the coast is a sulfur plant. Petroleum products from the Middle East have in recent years ensured the dominance of the Arab states in the world's economy.

it was only when petroleum products were required in large quantities, first paraffin for lamps, then petrol for cars, that Man's search became scientific instead of haphazard.

We now know that a petroleum accumulation requires five conditions: an organic-rich source rock, generally a fine-grained shale, from which the oil was generated; a porous reservoir rock to contain the accumulation; an impermeable cap rock above the reservoir to prevent its escape; and a configuration of the rocks such that the oil is trapped in the reservoir beneath the seal. Given a source, a reservoir, a seal and a trap, the fifth condition is that the source rock must have been heated sufficiently to expel the oil.

Types of Petroleum. Petroleum is the name given to solid, plastic (i.e., pliable) and liquid hydrocarbons which occur naturally within the Earth. Solid and plastic forms go under a variety of names, including elaterite, ozokerite and bitumen. With increasing fluidity these grade through tar into what is variously termed crude oil, rock oil, natural oil – or simply oil or "crude".

Crude oils are oily liquids whose color varies from dark brown to tan and yellow-green. Again, they are very variable in density and viscosity, ranging from thin, colorless, translucent light oil to heavy, dark, viscous asphalt. They consist of varying proportions of four main groups of organic compounds: the aromatics, the paraffins, the naphthenes and the asphalts.

The Origin of Petroleum. Petroleum is found in rocks of all types, igneous, metamorphic and sedimentary, of all ages ranging from the Precambrian to sands less than a million years old. The majority of petroleum geologists believe, however, that regardless of where it now occurs most oil was generated from marine muds of Cambrian or younger age. (Natural gas is generally believed to have formed either from land-derived plant material or from the breakdown of crude oil at high temperatures.)

Criteria cited in favour of an organic origin for petroleum include the fact that it commonly contains microscopic particles of identifiable matter and that it shows the property of levorotation, the ability to rotate polarized light leftward, a phenomenon peculiar to organic substances.

Facts which confirm the formation of petroleum from sedimentary rocks include that it occurs within basins of sedimentary rocks, and not within the shield areas of continents which are composed of igneous granites and metamorphic gneisses. Moreover, it is sometimes found within porous sand beds that are entirely surrounded by impermeable shales, demonstrating the improbability of migration from a distant igneous source. Where it does occur in igneous rocks these are generally found to be adjacent to organic-rich sediments from which it is reasonable to suppose it came.

The most favorable conditions for the extensive preservation of organic matter are underwater environments where current circulation is minimal and where the bot-

Name	Properties	Composition (weight %)		
		Carbon	Hydrogen	Sulfur, Nitrogen, Oxygen, etc.
Kerogen	Solid at normal temperatures and pressures. Insoluble in petroleum solvents.	75	10	15
Asphalt	Solid at normal temperatures and pressures. Soluble in petroleum solvents.	83	10	7
Crude Oil	Liquid at normal temperatures and pressures.	85	13	2
Natural Gas	Gaseous at normal temperatures and pressures.	70	20	10

...om is stagnant and anaerobic (without oxygen). Thus the most likely places for petroleum source beds to form are in fine-grained clays in shallow sheltered embayments and deep waters of restricted bottom circulation: these conditions are most commonly found in marine environments. In fact, most ancient identified petroleum source rocks are of marine origin, though there are several notable exceptions.

Rapid burial by continuous sedimentation is a further factor favoring the preservation of organic matter. This is typically found where the crust of the Earth is unstable and rapidly subsiding. As a mud is buried, it is compacted, due to the weight of overlying sediment, it loses porosity, and water is expelled. With increasing depth of burial, pressure and temperature reach the point at which petroleum forms. The physical conditions at which this occurs are a matter for debate, and probably vary considerably depending on the chemistry of the organic material and on the catalytic effect of the clays and pore fluids. $150°F$ ($65°C$) is generally accepted as a temperature requirement for the formation of significant quantities of petroleum.

For the incipient petroleum to emigrate from the source rocks they must be interstratified with permeable carrier beds – sands are ideal. Petroleum may migrate for considerable distances through such carrier beds in response to hydrodynamic pressure gradients within a sedimentary basin. There is debate as to whether these fluids are already free oil, or whether the hydrocarbons migrate as an emulsion in water.

In the ordinary course of events, oil will migrate up through permeable rocks to the surface of the Earth, where it is dissipated, oxidized and destroyed. But, in certain favorable circumstances, upward-migrating oil may be trapped beneath impermeable strata, through which no fluid can flow. In this way is a petroleum reservoir formed.

Petroleum Traps and Reservoirs. A situation in which oil is retained within porous rocks beneath an impermeable seal is termed a trap. Four main types are generally recognized, though variations are countless.

Commonest are *structural traps*. These are due to bending or upward arching of porous strata into domes or linear folds, termed anticlines. A second type of structural trap is caused by rocks moving along faults in such a way that a porous reservoir formation is juxtaposed with impermeable strata.

The second type of petroleum trap is a *stratigraphic trap*. In this variety the trapping situation is due to lateral variations of permeability in stratified sequences. Examples include channel and beach sands and porous reef limestones enclosed in impermeable shale.

The third group of traps are called *combination traps* because they contain elements of both structural and stratigraphic control. An example would be petroleum

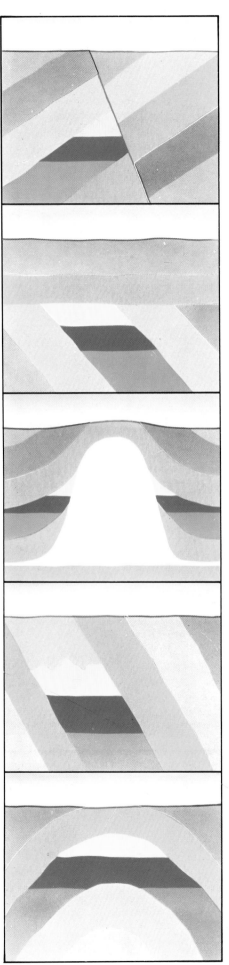

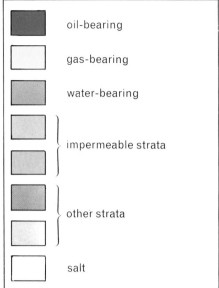

■	oil-bearing
□	gas-bearing
▨	water-bearing
□	impermeable strata
▨	other strata
□	salt

Various types of petroleum trap: from top to bottom, faulting, unconformity, salt dome, facies change and anticline.

accumulated within a sand which was erosionally truncated (an unconformity) on the crest of a faulted block.

The fourth type of trap is a *hydrodynamic trap*: these are very rare and are seldom specifically sought. They occur where the upward flow of oil due to buoyancy is offset by a fluid potential gradient such that pore water is moving downdip. In these rare instances petroleum may accumulate in uniformly dipping strata with no structural or stratigraphic trapping elements.

Another group of traps, sometimes classified on their own, are those due to *salt domes. Beds of salt often occur interbedded with other sedimentary rocks. Because of their low density and plastic properties, these salt beds often deform, creating domes and vertical pillars which, in moving upward, intrude into, fracture and dome the overlying sedimentary layers. When this occurs in petroleum-rich strata, many traps may be formed in folded and faulted porous beds adjacent to the salt dome.

Global Distribution of Petroleum. World petroleum reserves at the end of 1985 were as follows:

Area	Thousand Million Tonnes	%
Middle East	54	56.3
Sino-Soviet area	11	11.5
Africa	7.4	8.1
North America	5.6	6.0
Latin America	11.9	11.9
Western Europe	3.4	3.7
Western Far East & Australasia	2.5	2.5
Total:	95.8	100.0

These figures can in no way be regarded as indicating the true distribution of petroleum. The search for oil is governed by many factors, economic, geographic and political, and this means that the reserves discovered to date may give a false picture of the resources of different regions. In particular, only in recent years has it been technically possible to explore and exploit petroleum deposits beneath the deeper seas.

Methods of Exploration and Production. As we have seen, the first step in petroleum exploration is to find a basin of sedimentary rocks – more specifically, a sedimentary basin in which marine shales (potential source rocks) are interbedded with porous sandstones and limestones (potential reservoirs), and in which these have been so deposited and deformed as to form traps. Furthermore, the sediments must have been at some time sufficiently heated to generate oil.

Exploration methods range from surface geological mapping to subsurface geophysical techniques (such as seismic, gravitational and magnetic studies). Present exploration techniques can locate only *potential* traps. Each trap must be tested in turn by drilling bore holes.

This is done by means of a drilling rig or derrick. In modern rotary drilling a multi-toothed bit is rotated on the end of a length of drill pipe. Drilling mud is pumped down the drill pipe and flows upward between the outside of the drillpipe and the side of the borehole. On reaching the surface the rock chips are collected so that the geologist can identify the rocks and so detect any signs of petroleum.

Petroleum is generally drawn from the reservoir through perforations in the steel casing lining the sides of the borehole. Where the reservoir pressure is sufficiently high, petroleum flows naturally to the surface, where it is fed through a system of valves (termed a Christmas Tree) to a pipeline. In low-pressure reservoirs it may be necessary to pump the oil to the surface.

Conclusion. Probably more geologists are currently employed in the hunt for petroleum than in all the other professional branches of the science put together. Conversely, the petroleum geologist is only one of many specialists, ranging from economists to engineers, who are involved in the exploration and production of petroleum.

RS

Natural Gas

Natural gases include the inorganic compounds of carbon and sulfur, the inert gases, and the gaseous hydrocarbons. They emanate from volcanoes – oxides of carbon and sulfur, water vapor, and other gases in minor quantities – but the natural gases we are most concerned with are those that are to be found in the pore spaces of many

different types of rock, of various ages, and in many different parts of the world.

Inert gases, including nitrogen and helium, are rare but can occur locally in significant quantities. The reasons for their origin are little understood. It is known that helium forms from the decay of radioactive minerals, and there is therefore a strong presumption that its presence in porous rocks indicates the existence of radioactive minerals, such as uranium, at greater depth. But very little is known of the origin of concentrations of nitrogen.

The most important gases from an economic point of view are the gaseous hydrocarbons. Of major importance are: methane (CH_4), ethane (C_2H_6), propane (C_3H_8), pentane (C_5H_{12}) and hexane (C_6H_{14}). The origin of gaseous hydrocarbons is intimately associated with that of liquid *petroleum. It is generally accepted that these gases are organic in origin, and can form in three ways:

(*i*) Biogenic gas is the name given to gaseous hydrocarbons, principally methane, formed by bacterial degradation of organic matter. To be within the environmental tolerance of the bacteria, this can occur only at or near the Earth's surface. For example, methane is extensively produced from rotting vegetation in swamps, where it is termed "marsh gas".

(*ii*) The second main origin of natural gas is from organic matter disseminated in sedimentary rocks. It is generally believed that oil (liquid hydrocarbon) forms from organic matter contained within muds of marine origin which have been buried and heated to over about 150°F (65°C). Conversely, it is thought that natural gas tends to be generated within continental sediments from plant-derived organic matter, which may be dispersed throughout sands and muds, or coal.

(*iii*) The third origin is from the breakdown of liquid hydrocarbons. This is believed to take place when temperatures exceed about 300–350°F (150–175°C). If the temperature becomes much greater than this, gaseous hydrocarbons are themselves destroyed to leave a residue of carbon.

The origin, migration and entrapment of hydrocarbon liquids and gases are intimately associated. Nevertheless, within a single sedimentary basin they often show some degree of positional segregation. Gas tends to be present in the deep traps in the center of the basin, oil in a peripheral ring around the gas zone, and water in the shallow traps of the basin margin.

An explanation for this arrangement is termed for its proposer Gussow's Principle. The idea is that, within a porous trap, gas will tend to rise to the roof above the oil, and the oil to float above the water. Fluids surplus to the capacity of each trap will flow out below the spill-point and migrate up into the next trap where the process is repeated. Thus gas fills the deepest traps, oil those of intermediate depth, and water the shallowest.

An alternative explanation for the observed zonation in a basin is that gas occurs in the center below the gas/oil maturation boundary, and oil occurs in the peripheral zone within the optimum thermal window for oil generation and preservation (between about 150°F and 300°F (65–175°C)). Traps around the basin margin are barren of hydrocarbons because they have been flushed out by meteoric water.

Whether these hypotheses are correct or not, it is clear that there is a close relationship between the origins of oil and natural gas.

Commercially, natural gas is not as valuable as oil. Gas deposits are generally worth developing only if they occur close to major centers of population or industry. Natural gas is often produced with oil – where this has happened far from any potential market, the gas has often been burned as a waste product or reinjected into the reservoir to maintain pressure and so productivity.

But, while our resources of geologic natural gas are limited and often unexploitable for economic reasons, biogenic gas manufactured on the surface of the Earth could be one of Man's most important energy sources in the centuries to come.   RS

Coal

Coals are organic rocks consisting mainly of altered accumulations of terrestrially derived plant materials, originally deposited as peats, with varying but generally small amounts of mineral matter. Ever since a land flora established itself on the Earth's surface some 400 million years ago, the potential for the formation of substantial coal deposits has existed. The development of a coal-forming peat, however, particularly its subsequent preservation, depends on a number of factors, understanding of which permits full exploitation.

The Origin of Coal and the Formation of Coalfields. Many of the world's coal seams originated from peats deposited in extensive coastal swamps that were probably in many ways similar to those forming on the coasts of Florida and New Guinea at the present time. These swamps are vast low-lying regions with virtually no relief and containing extensive deltaic spreads; and over them numerous wide, sluggish rivers flow, carrying large quantities of muds, silts and finely degraded organic matter.

The peats in the swamps accumulate in a wide belt so close to sea level that any slight change in the relative levels of land and sea will either cause flooding of extensive areas by the sea or, alternatively, expose previously submerged areas of the shallow sea bed that before had fringed the swamp. Thus the swamp belt, which may be tens of miles wide, does not usually maintain a stable position with the passage of time, but shifts backwards and forwards broadly parallel to the margins of the associated landmass. These movements allow all forms of lateral and vertical transition of sediments and peats to take place, but, at any point in time, a series of peat types can be expected to develop perpendicular to the coast.

Among the more important factors

Connecting detonator tapes to the firing line preparatory to blasting the coalface in the Mount Isa coalmines, Queensland, Australia. Because of the inherent dangers, alternative techniques to underground working are now increasingly being used.

An example of the type of swamp in which coal deposits are laid down: the Everglades in southern Florida. In swamps such as these dead and decaying vegetation accumulates in the form of peat which, on burial, becomes subject to compaction and a certain degree of heating. The degree of coalification depends upon the amount of heating, and represents a progressive increase in carbon content and decrease in volatile content.

governing the development of a coal-forming peat and its subsequent preservation are: the climate, which is probably most favorable when warm and oceanic with a high rainfall; the plant types present, their abundance and their degree of evolutionary development; and the rate of subsidence of the region in which the peat is accumulating – to ensure continuous peat formation: if subsidence is too slow, rapid destruction of the dead organic matter will occur by atmospheric oxidation; if it is too rapid, a premature submergence will occur under sediments transported by streams and rivers draining the land surrounding the swamps. The balance between these factors is critical and, if a major coalfield is to form, then the same sequence of inter-related conditions must be repeated time and time again over periods of many millions of years, the periods between peat accumulations being occupied by the deposition of muds, silts, sands and even limestone when increased subsidence carries the region below water level. This repetition of sedimentary environments in the vertical sense is described as "rhythmic" or "cyclothemic" deposition.

The seams formed from peats in coastal-swamp environments (paralic coals) are characteristically relatively thin after compaction – generally less than 10ft (3m) thick. The original peat may be compacted to as little as one twentieth of its original thick-

The world's major coalfields.

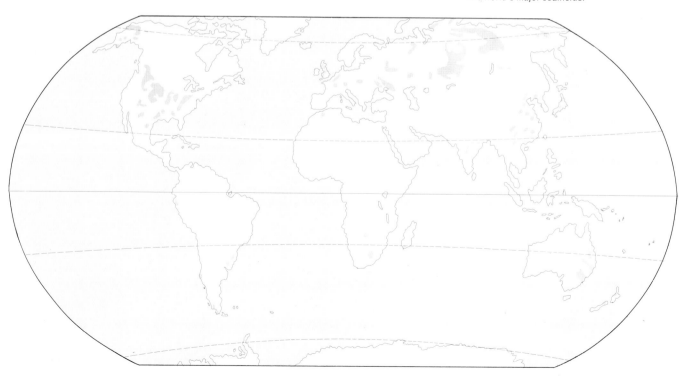

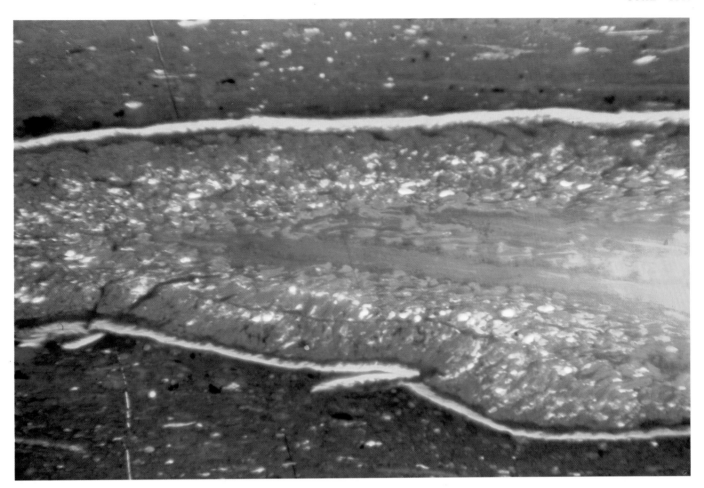

ness in the time bituminous coal takes to form. A major coalfield will contain many such seams.

In contrast to paralic coals, seams may develop within large inland continental basins (limnic coals). Typically, coal seams in these environments are extremely thick (up to 650ft (200m)) but few in number, and each results from subsidence that is just sufficient to allow continued growth of the peat: the *Carboniferous coal deposits of the French Massif Central are a good example of limnic development.

However, whether limnic or paralic, the vast majority of coal seams are regarded as forming *in situ*; the minority, in contrast, having developed from organic remains that were washed into, or drifted into, the position where the peat ultimately formed.

Coal Types. The plant remains in peats usually occur in two principal forms, still recognizable even in mature coals: as discrete and often sizeable parts of trees, bushes and smaller plants; and as a matrix composed of a wide size-range of tissue fragments, in varying stages of decay, from different plant organs and including seed and spore coats, leaf cuticles and highly resistant plant impregnations such as tannins and resins.

The different factors which control plant growth and the deposition and accumulation of coal-forming peats must also influence the chemical and physical compositions of the coals produced: the coal developed will reflect the plant components

from which it originated. Thus, a coal formed from a forest peat will be rich in modified wood and bark tissues, whereas a coal developed from a rich organic mud may be almost wholly composed of resistant spores, some heavily degraded organic matter and finely pulverized minerals; or, alternatively, have algae as its major organic component.

Peats which have contrasting plant compositions, having formed in different parts of the coal-forming swamp, lead to the concept of "type" in coals. Fundamental differences in coal type are obviously introduced very early in the history of the coals. Biochemical changes resulting from extensive fungal and bacterial degradation of the massive input of cellulose, lignin and proteins from the plants, with a consequent enrichment of the peat in more resistant waxy constituents, contribute further to these type differences. The depositional environment, however, may become sterile due to microbial overactivity, in which case further decay can occur. The particular depositional environment will govern the relative proportions of different plant constituents remaining in the peat: oxygen-bearing waters are important in modifying the proportions of organic constituents in peats – and so must influence type.

The technological implications of type variation may be considerable. For example, a coal rich in waxy spores will yield much greater amounts of gas and tar than a coal predominantly derived from the mass-

Cuticularized leaf in bituminous coal of Jurassic age. Due to the processes that act upon peat during its transformation into coal, such well-preserved remains are not altogether common: however, plant debris when found in or overlying coal seams can be of considerable value in studies of coal formation.

ive structural parts of trees. Similarly, differences in flora can produce type – and hence technological – variation in coals which in every other way have suffered the same histories.

Coal Rank. Later changes which modify peats into coal are purely physical and chemical in character and are mainly related to the length of time that the organic accumulations are exposed to high temperatures in the Earth's crust. Pressure from overlying rocks and stresses caused by Earth movements also influence the progress of these changes. In this way coals of different rank or "degree of coalification" are produced, these terms referring to the particular level of physical and/or chemical development attained by a fuel. Using one or several of a wide range of different properties, all fuels can be placed at some point within a continuous rank series that extends from peat to anthracite and beyond, towards a graphite-like end-product. The well-known terms brown-coal, lignite, bituminous coal and anthracite refer to specific subdivisions of increasing rank within this series.

Many coal properties display a systematic variation with rank increase and can be used to estimate rank level. The changes that occur are related to the composition of the original material, primarily carbon, hydrogen and oxygen, with smaller amounts of nitrogen, sulfur and other elements. As rank increases, the proportion of carbon relative to oxygen rises, nitrogen and sulfur remain approximately the same – as does hydrogen until, at higher rank levels, it too begins to fall with the development of highly aromatic products. These changes in the elementary composition of coals with rising rank are accompanied by the release of a variety of gases during the coalification process, predominantly a loss of differing proportions of water, carbon dioxide and methane.

All the organic constituents display changes, to a greater or lesser degree and depending on the original compositions, with rank increase. If possible, the principal coal constituent, vitrite (forming on average perhaps 70% of all coals), is used for rank estimation, first because the properties of vitrite vary in a relatively linear manner with rank increase, and second because the properties of a single constituent will give a more precise estimate of rank than will the properties of a whole coal, which is a mixture of constituents of differing composition.

Rank changes, then, reflect the response of the organic matter of fuels to geological conditions: as a consequence systematic lateral and vertical variations of rank can be observed within all coalfields. If a borehole penetrates a vertical succession containing numerous coal seams, the rank would be expected to vary systematically from seam to seam down the borehole. The carbon content and the calorific value would rise, and volatile-matter yield would fall.

The rate at which changes in individual properties take place in a number of boreholes over a coalfield area will not necessarily be the same, because the downhole variation is closely related to the rate at which past temperatures have increased with depth in the crust of different parts of the coalfield. Geothermal gradients of approximately 0.02F/ft (1C/30m) would be usual and so a temperature of about 400°F (200°C), regarded as a maximum for anthracite formation in regional coalification processes, would be reached in seams which were originally at the considerable depth of about 20,000ft (6000m) below the surface. Variations in the geothermal gradient from this value may, however, be substantial and the gradient much higher.

Distribution and Age of Coals. There has been only one major coal-forming period that widely affected both hemispheres – during the Carboniferous and Permian periods, reaching its acme approximately 300 million years ago. There have been two more recent but less important periods of coal formation, in early Jurassic times and during the Tertiary era: this latter coal-forming period is probably still continuing in certain parts of the world, notably in the Far East. Many of the older coal occurrences today form isolated coalfields, but originally they were parts of much more extensive depositional areas that have become disrupted as a result of Earth movements and subsequent weathering and erosion.

Earlier discussion has shown that a number of factors control the development of coals of different type and rank. The same general types of coal can be recognized through the different eras, but clearly the opportunity for greater rank change exists the longer the coal has been in the crust. Consequently, the older a coal, the more valuable it usually will be as an energy source: thus, coals deposited during the Paleozoic and in the early part of the Mesozoic are generally of bituminous or higher rank, while late Mesozoic and Tertiary coals are predominantly brown coals, lignites and sub-bituminous coals.

World Coal Resources. The total amount of coal in the Earth's crust is acknowledged as being vastly greater than the total resources of *petroleum that may ultimately be discovered. The table gives a breakdown of world resources and reserves either by continent or by major country.

Universal acceptance of the precise definitions of "recoverable reserves", "total reserves" and "total resources" is probably not possible because of the different opinions that exist on how reserves and resources should be estimated. In general, however, "recoverable reserves" means those coals whose precise position in the crust is known through detailed prospecting and which could be removed economically by current mining methods. The re-

World Solid Fuel Resources (excluding Peats) in Megatonnes

Country or Continent	Recoverable Reserves	Total Reserves	Total Resources
USSR	136,000	273,200	5,713,600
China, Republic of	80,000	300,000	1,000,000
Asia, Remainder of	17,549	40,479	108,053
USA	181,781	363,562	2,924,503
Canada	5,537	9,034	108,777
Latin America	2,803	9,201	32,928
Europe	126,775	319,807	607,521
Africa	15,628	30,291	58,844
Oceania	24,518	74,699	199,654
World Total	591,191	1,402,274	10,753,880

mainder of the reserves comprise coal which has been proved to be there by prospecting, but which could not be removed economically by mining technology at the present time. Quantifying "total resources" is more speculative and uncertain, but the term can be considered to describe estimates of coal that might reasonably be expected to occur in areas which have not been adequately prospected. The uncertainty in such figures lies in deciding what constitutes "adequate

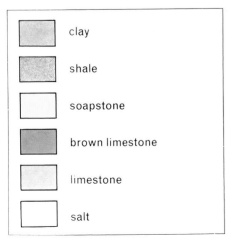

	clay
	shale
	soapstone
	brown limestone
	limestone
	salt

A typical salt well. Hot water is passed down the shaft to dissolve the salt: the resulting brine is then drawn up through the central pipe and the salt extracted from it by evaporation or otherwise.

prospecting". Clearly opinion on this point can range widely.   DGM

Salt

Salt has played a major part in the gastronomic and economic life of Man since the days of the Romans: our word "salary" is derived from the Latin *salarium*, the money given to Roman soldiers to buy salt, *sal*.

By "salt" we generally mean common salt, sodium chloride (NaCl), known to geologists as ★halite. It is one of a group of sedimentary rocks termed the ★evaporites.

The Origin of Salt. The classic theory for the origin of salt and other evaporites is the "evaporating-dish" model. This envisages an embayment of the sea in an arid climate, the mouth of the embayment being restricted by a shallow sill. Continuous evaporation in the embayment raises the concentration of the seawater so that dense brine flows to the embayment floor, but cannot escape to the sea because of the sill. When the brine is sufficiently concentrated, evaporite crystallization can take place. Once begun, this process may continue for some time as seawater intermittently flows over the sill to replace that which has been lost by evaporation and crystallization.

There is a second model for evaporite formation which explains those deposits which show evidence of a very shallow

Salt pans along the shore near Ruwenzori National Park, Uganda. Salt pans are small enclosed bodies of water which are permitted to evaporate so that concentrations of salts (evaporites) may build up. In some cases – as here – the salt pans are artificially created.

origin, perhaps not under water at all.

Many modern desert coasts are bordered by salt marshes, usually known as sabkhas. Here there are no rivers bringing sand and mud to the sea, and the shores consist largely of carbonate muds and skeletal debris sands. Seawater, already concentrated by evaporation in coastal lagoons, is drawn into the carbonate muds beyond the reach of the tides to replace pore water lost by evaporation at the surface. Thus a build-up of salinity occurs to the extent that evaporite minerals begin to form, not just by crystallization, but also by extensive replacement of the carbonate muds.

This process is well documented in modern sabkhas, which would suggest that the term "evaporite" may be inappropriate as a collective name for halite and its associated salts.

Economic Importance. There are three main reasons why salt is of economic importance. Apart from the fact that it is in itself a natural resource of great value, it is closely associated with the occurrence of petroleum, and there is strong evidence to indicate that it is connected with the occurrence of certain metallic ores.

Large salt deposits such as those of

Germany, England, and the Gulf Coast of North America are extensively mined – for more than just table salt. Halite and its associated salts are the basis for extensive chemical industrial complexes, the source for the world's requirements for rare earth elements, sodium and potassium, for the halogens, principally chlorine and bromine, and also for sulfur.

Salt deposits are closely related to *petroleum deposits for three reasons: structure, seal and source. Salt beds often deform plastically and domes of salt move up through denser sediments forming fold and fault traps in which *petroleum can be preserved. Secondly, because of its plasticity (pliability) and impermeability, salt makes an excellent seal to trap petroleum within porous reservoir beds. And, thirdly, salt is commonly interbedded with organic matter because they both require stagnant conditions for their preservation. For these reasons petroleum source beds are often found in intimate proximity to salt deposits.

The third important economic aspect of salt is the observed correlation between evaporites and metallic sulfide ores, such as those of lead, zinc and copper. These ores appear to be of low-temperature origin, and often replace reef limestones adjacent to evaporites. In this situation metallic ions, themselves concentrated from seawater, may have been carried in the residual brines and precipitated in carbonate reefs around the basin margin.

From all of this it can be seen that the common salt of our dinner table is, in terms of origin, occurrence and economic significance, a mineral whose importance is very, very far from common. RS

Building Stone

The raising of stone for building has been going on since time immemorial, and certainly for centuries before the science of geology evolved. The particular stone selected depended on many factors, not least the type of building envisaged. The main priorities were always durability, local availability and nearness to the Earth's surface. Difficulty of working a stone seems never to have been a major constraint.

The selection of stone for building was thus inextricably bound up with the local geology. One has only to look at the domestic and older ecclesiastical architecture of a country to see this. The building-accounts for an English almshouse, built 1439–44, show that for special stone fetched a distance of only about 12 mi (20km) the cost of haulage was almost double that of the stone itself. In this light, one can understand why local geology was, until relatively recently, crucial.

As a result many materials that are not very durable had to be used, especially in domestic situations – though ecclesiastical building, on the other hand, could often afford the cost of haulage, which explains the widespread use of French Caen Stone in Southern England in the Middle Ages.

The petrology of building stone is immensely variable, and so a meaningful classification on scientific principles is impossible – as well as unnecessary. All rock types of sufficient durability have been used. Each group has its own unique qualities and appearance: to appreciate this one need only contrast the cold granitic exteriors of Aberdeen or Rennes with New York's brownstones or the warm limestone facades of Oxford.

Basic requirements determining the choice of stone are equally difficult to quantify. If a harmony with previous buildings has to be achieved then color is the prime consideration: otherwise texture may be important, and a stone with grain-size sufficiently small to allow smooth surfaces to be generated will be preferred. Smooth surfaces are needed because only accurately shaped blocks will withstand stress well and so allow the architect full rein. The durability of particular types of stone in the face of *weathering has been investigated, but if this factor is as vital as has been claimed one can hardly explain the widespread and successful use of Bath Stone, which in this respect is at best about four times weaker than Portland Stone.

The best test to find out whether a particular stone stands up to a particular environmental attack is always the simple if irreversible one of time. Again, environments change: the sulfation of limestones in many industrial cities, with the consequent unsightly and damaging exfoliation, has been largely checked by recent legislation over use of fuels.

One vital property especially difficult to control is that the quality of each type of stone should be consistent. Even within a single quarry the stone can, and does, vary enormously. Much can be done at the time of quarrying by a skilled overseer, who can check quality as the stone is removed, and by marking the lie of the stone, if sedimentary, on the extracted blocks to allow this to be reproduced in the building.

The techniques of extraction of the stone were amazingly simple until very recently – the methods of the Egyptians of the Pharaonic era, who worked granitic rocks with extreme sophistication, remained essentially unchanged. Mechanical aid has come in more recent times. The few concessions to modern technology include large-scale wire and sand saws, compressed air tools and electric coal-cutting machines and scabbing hammers.

New techniques of building with stone have also helped the stone extraction industry. Precast reinforced concrete blocks have – for economic reasons – come to be used more and more in building. This has generated a need for crushed stone, enabling inferior material to be used up. Harmony with preexisting stone buildings has been achieved by use of new techniques of cladding thin slabs of the matching material to the outsides of the concrete structures: cladding can be similarly fixed to brickwork or steel.

A whole range of artificially created stone products have been made. Two examples are limestone chips set in a matrix, cut and polished, and used as interior marble flooring; and reconstituted stone, where the natural material is crushed and recast in blocks simulating the original in color and texture, with the advantage that the blocks are of uniform size.

Quarrying of stone has always brought benefits other than just the stone itself. The early development of paleontology was greatly aided by the fossils provided by quarrymen. The modern decline in the quarrying industry has frequently made new fossil material impossible to obtain from the original source. HST

Selection of rock for use as building stone depends as much on factors such as local availability as on the inherent suitabilities of the rock concerned. Where the rocks are relatively soft, wire saws (endless wires driven at speed and pulled through rock bodies) or even, as in this quarry in Menorca, circular saws may be used for extraction.

ILLUSTRATION CREDITS

Unless otherwise stated, all the illustrations on a given page are credited to the same source. Reference numbers denote page number followed by position on page (where relevant) and initials of source as listed below. (t = top, b = bottom, r = right, l = left, c = center)

Photographs by:

Allard Design Group Ltd. (ADG)
Andrews, M. (MA)
Associated Press Ltd. (AP)
Atkins, F. B. (FBA)
Bäcker, H. (HB)
Bell, J. D. (JDB)
Boulton, G. S. (GSB)
Brierley, P. (PB)
Brown, G. M. (GMB)
Collinson, J. D. (JDC)
Cox, K. G. (KGC)
Diagram Visual Information Ltd (DVI)
Equinox Archive (EQ)
Estall, R. (RE)
Fotolink (F)
Fraser, D. G. (DGF)
Gorringe, R. (RG)
Robert Harding Associates (RHA)
Heirtzler, J. R. (JRH)
Alan Hutchison Library (AHL)
Institute of Geological Sciences (IGS)
Institute of Oceanographic Sciences (IOS)
James, H. L. (HLJ)
Kennedy, W. J. (WJK)
Lawson, A. (AL)
Johns, L. (LJ)
Murchison, D. G. (DGM)
Mutch, T. A. (TAM)
NASA
Natural Science Photos (NSP)
Nicolls, O. W., by courtesy of the Selection

Exploration Trust, Canada (OWN)
Nimmo, M. (MN)
Oxford Illustrators (OI)
Picturepoint Ltd. (PP)
Price, N. J. (NJP)
Roedder, E. (ER)
Servizio Editoriale Fotografico (SEF)
Shell U. K. Ltd. (SUK)
Space Frontiers Ltd. (SF)
Spectrum Colour Library (SCL)
Waltham, A. C. (ACW)
Wilson, R. C. L. (RCLW)

970 (official Naval Observatory photograph) SF, 972 RG, 974-75 ADG, 976 SF, 978t SF, 978b (courtesy the G. P. Slide Co., Houston) GMB, 979 GMB, 980 SF, 981 SF, 982 AP, 983 NASA, 984 LJ, 985 TAM, 986 SF, 987t SF, 987b RG, 988 FBA, 989 LJ, 990t IGS, 990b LJ, 991 SF, 992 OI, 993t LJ, 993b OWN, 994 LJ, 995 LJ, 996-97 FBA, 998 DGF, 1000 EQ, 1001 LJ, 1004 RG, 1005t SF, 1005b LJ, 1006t LJ, 1006b SF, 1007t RG, 1008 RHA, 1009 RHA, 1010t RHA, 1010b AL, 1011 RHA, 1012t ACW, 1012b JDC, 1013t RHA, 1013b RG, 1014 RHA, 1015 NSP, 1016 RHA, 1017tr RCLW, 1017l RG, 1017cr WJK, 1017br JDC, 1018 RCLW, 1019 (by courtesy of the Greenland Geological Survey) JDC, 1020 OI, 1021t RCLW, 1021b JDC, 1022t b RG, 1022 NJP, 1023 MN, 1024t bl OI, 1024br LJ, 1025 PP, 1027 SCL, 1028 RG, 1029t NSP, 1029b RG, 1030 SCL, 1031 DVI, 1032t WJK, 1033b DVI, 1033t SCL, 1033bl LJ, 1033br JDB, 1034 RHA, 1035 RHA, 1036 RHA, 1037 RHA, 1038t ACW, 1038b RG, 1039t ACW, 1039b RHA, 1040 DVI, 1041 NSP, 1042 SCL, 1043l RG, 1043r WJK, 1044t

JDC, 1044b RG, 1045 ACW, 1046t LJ, 1046b RHA, 1047 RHA, 1048 RHA, 1049l tr cr RHA, 1049tcr RCLW, 1049lcr GSB, 1049br MN, 1051 GSB, 1052 RHA, 1053t (by courtesy of the Greenland Geological Survey) JDC, 1053c b RG, 1054 EQ, 1055 RHA, 1056 RG, 1057tr RG, 1057l JDB, 1057br RHA, 1058 KGC, 1059 IOS, 1060b JRH, 1061 RCLW, 1063 KGC, 1065 RHA, 1066 RHA, 1067 F, 1068 RG, 1069t SEF, 1069b RG, 1070 ACW, 1071 MA, 1072t RG, 1072b RHA, 1073 MA, 1074l ER, 1074r (courtesy of Economic Geology) HLJ, 1075tl PB, 1075tr HB, 1075b OI, 1076t FBA, 1076b DVI, 1077 OI, 1078 OI, 1079t br OI, 1079t bl PB, 1080 tl bl bc br OI, 1080tr PB, 1081 RHA, 1082 t cl cr br PB, 1082bl FBA, 1083tr PB, 1084 PB, 1085t RHA, 1085bl bc br PB, 1086t PB, 1086bl br IGS, 1087 PB, 1088 RHA, 1089t SCL, 1090l IGS, 1090r PB, 1092 IGS, 1093t PB, 1093b RHA, 1094t PB, 1094b IGS, 1095t PB, 1095b IGS, 1096 IGS, 1097tl PB, 1097r MN, 1098 PB, 1099 PB, 1100 PB, 1101t PB, 1101b RHA, 1102 LJ, 1103tl RHA, 1103tr AHL, 1103b PB, 1104 SCL, 1105 RHA, 1106t RHA, 1106b RE, 1107tl AHL, 1107tr RHA, 1107b MA, 1108 RHA, 1109 RHA, 1110l PB, 1110r AHL, 1111t PB, 1111b SUK, 1112 RHA, 1113 RG, 1114 RHA, 1115 RHA, 1116t DGM, 1116b LJ, 1117 DGM, 1118 RG, 1119 RHA, 1120 RHA.

The Publishers have attempted to observe the legal requirements with respect to the rights of the suppliers of photographic materials. Nevertheless, persons who have claims are invited to apply to the Publishers.